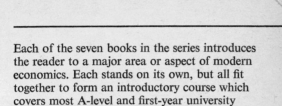

Fontana Introduction to Modern Economics
General Editor : **C. D. Harbury**

Each of the seven books in the series introduces
the reader to a major area or aspect of modern
economics. Each stands on its own, but all fit
together to form an introductory course which
covers most A-level and first-year university
syllabuses, and those of most professional bodies.

An Introduction to Economic Behaviour, by C. D.
Harbury, Professor of Economics, City University.

Private and Public Finance, by G. H. Peters,
Professor of Economics, University of Liverpool.

Income, Spending and the Price Level, by A. G.
Ford, Professor of Economics, University of
Warwick.

Economics of the Market, by G. Hewitt,
Lecturer in Economics, The Civil Service College.

International Trade and the Balance of Payments,
by H. Katrak, Lecturer in Economics, University
of Surrey.

Britain and the World Economy, 1919–1970, by
L. J. Williams, Senior Lecturer in Economics,
University College of Wales, Aberystwyth.

Mathematics for Modern Economics, by R.
Morley, Lecturer in Economics, University of
Durham.

Richard Morley

Lecturer in Economics, University of Durham

Mathematics for Modern Economics

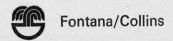

Fontana/Collins

First published in Fontana 1972

Printed in Great Britain
for the Publishers Wm. Collins Sons & Co Ltd,
14 St James's Place, London, S.W.11,
by Richard Clay (The Chaucer Press), Ltd,
Bungay, Suffolk

ACKNOWLEDGEMENTS
The book owes much to the suggestions of the staff and students of the
Department of Economics at the University of Durham. John D. Hey
gave much assistance with the final chapter. I am particularly grateful
to Dr Julian Bharier for his encouragement and constructive criticisms
throughout the many drafts of the book. Any errors or inelegancies
that remain will be in spite of their helpful comments.

Contents

Introduction

Intentions

This book introduces the reader to a number of abbreviations which are useful in economics. These abbreviations have the immediate advantage of saving time in writing. Once they are understood, after only a few hours of work, they also save time in thinking, because the concepts they represent can be immediately grasped by the mind.

The abbreviations used here are symbols which can look like mumbo-jumbo at first. However, these symbols have been developed by mathematicians for a particular reason. When problems are translated into symbolic form, the symbols are arranged into patterns which allow manipulation in a way that can simplify the hunt for a solution. Once a few different types of problem have been solved, new problems turn out surprisingly often to have patterns which the reader has already met, and this shows that the new problems are just variations of more familiar ones.

It is not possible to tell the reader exactly how to solve problems because the most difficult part of problem-solving is describing just what the problem is. Many of the examples are drawn from business because we assume (often wrongly) that the problem facing the businessman is how to maximise his profit. The techniques which we develop in these simplified examples can then be extended and adapted to cover a wider range of economic activity.

Some attention has been given to the units of measurement used in the examples. This allows us to tackle particular problems by replacing the symbols with numbers. The numerical approach has two advantages. First, if the techniques and the numbers are correct, a conclusion in numerical form is far more useful than one in symbolic form. Symbols can be used to suggest in which direction we ought to move if we want to achieve a certain objective; but numbers tell us how far in this direction we ought to move. The second advantage is more important: if the techniques are wrong, or if we have described our objective incorrectly, we shall find out our mistakes far more quickly by using numbers. Numerical results are easier to criticise and for that reason they are more valuable.

Some understanding of Ordinary Level mathematics will help the reader, but experience has shown that this is too much to expect from every student of economics. Those who were badly taught, or who were ill at a time when the opportunity arose to learn some of the foundations of a mathematics course, or who learnt their mathematics many years ago may find that they are not happy about some parts of the first few chapters.

For such people there is a selection of readily available reading given at the end of each of these chapters. The elementary foundations should be clearly understood. Since each chapter builds on the one before, each chapter should be understood before proceeding to the next.

Rapid manipulation of algebraic symbols is found difficult by many beginners in economics. The reader is recommended to work through the drills in manipulation when they appear in the text, as they will clarify the sections that follow. The exercises at the end of each of the earlier chapters are designed to develop ability in applying the techniques.

The use of symbols in economics is generally found to be easy by two types of student: those who instinctively see the power and elegance of the approach, and those who are prepared to take on trust anything they do not understand. This book is designed for the large number of students who do not fall into either of these categories.

Anecdotage

'*Anecdotage*: noun, the telling of anecdotes, especially as a sign of senility.' Despite this dictionary definition, here are three short stories.

First story: Once upon a time in a small English town there were two motor repair firms, Jones Ltd. and Cholmondeley Ltd., who competed with each other for business. Both firms earned reasonable profits, but it gradually became clear that each of them could provide better services for their customers and earn higher profits for themselves if they employed a greater number of skilled workers. Since there was a shortage of skilled labour in the area, Jones announced that he was going to invest in a scheme to train men in the required skills. Cholmondeley was asked if he was going to institute a similar scheme to improve his service and increase his profits. 'Certainly not', he replied. 'I shall wait until Jones has trained his men and then I shall induce them to come over and work for me. The money I pay them as an inducement will be far less than the costs of training, so I shall be better off.' However, Jones soon heard of Cholmondeley's plan, so cancelled his training programme. Thus in the end neither firm trained labour; neither was able to earn higher profits, and neither improved its service to its customers.

Second story: Once upon a time there were two firms, Multibubble and Unisuds, who made domestic detergents. Their products saved housewives a great amount of work compared with that involved in older methods of cleaning, and so the firms advertised how useful their products were. After several years the market stopped expanding, not because some people were still unaware of the products (indeed, everyone knew all about them) but simply because people were already buying all they could use. So Multibubble thought that a reduction in the amount of expensive advertising would be a good idea. If sales stayed the same and costs were reduced, profits would increase. But then Multibubble realised that if it stopped advertising and Unisuds continued to advertise, Multibubble's sales would not stay the same. Its share of the market would be reduced and its competitor's share would be increased. Its expensive manufacturing equipment and distribution network would be underutilised, and its profits would fall. Thus both firms continued to advertise.

Third story: Once upon a time two nations decided to engage in an arms race. At first they armed themselves with rockets. Then there arose the technical possibility of producing rockets which would intercept other rockets: anti-ballistic missiles (ABMs). Already the existing state of the two nations' armories was sufficient to make it impossible for either side to win a war. Nevertheless, and in spite of the expense of ABMs, it seemed worthwhile for each nation to ask itself whether it should adopt this innovation. The USA reasoned as follows: 'Suppose the USSR does not adopt ABMs. In this case we should equip ourselves with them because we will then be in a position in which most of the enemy's rockets will be intercepted but all our rockets will reach their targets. This will put us in a strong position in the diplomatic power game. Of course the chances of either of us starting a war are very small, but our diplomats will be in a stronger bargaining position if there is a small chance of only partial disaster to our own country compared with a small chance of total disaster to the USSR.'

'Next suppose that the USSR does adopt ABMs. In that case we should adopt ABMs in order to cancel out their advantage.'

'Finally, suppose that the above reasoning is wrong. It may be, but even if it is wrong it is the way in which the USSR thinks that we think, so they will adopt ABMs, and therefore we should adopt ABMs.' So they both adopted ABMs.

Concepts

Each of the three examples involves economics, decisions about the allocation of scarce resources among competing ends. In manpower, policy, advertising, and the arms race, economics has a contribution to make towards an understanding of the problems. Economists by themselves cannot solve any of these problems, but the techniques and ways of thinking used by economists can assist in finding solutions.

In each story, the actors were caught in a dilemma. When each actor behaved rationally as an individual, the resulting outcomes were not optimal for the group of actors. There is an underlying concept uniting the three examples, the concept which we understand by the word 'dilemma'. This concept does not depend for its existence upon descriptions of real situations. The concept of 'dilemma' exists whether an actual dilemma exists or not. However, it is the concept which allows us to draw analogies between one situation and another.

The examples are illustrations of the branch of mathematics known as Game Theory. The game is the same in the three cases because all are examples of the same type of dilemma. The game shows that under certain circumstances a group of people may be behaving in an apparently irrational way, yet the individual members of the group are behaving rationally and the individuals are the decision-makers not the group. Even if both actors in each story were to make an agreement that both would train labour, or reduce advertising, or not move on to the next stage of the arms race, such an agreement would be very unstable. Each actor would be tempted to break the agreement; each would know that the other was so tempted and this would further increase his own temptation. Anticipation of this instability makes it unlikely that an agreement will be made in the first place.

The significance of this type of dilemma was first appreciated by psychologists. The reader may be surprised to find a book on elementary economics discussing political problems in terms of mathematical concepts which were first appreciated by psychologists. This is because many concepts are widely applicable. However, the generality of concepts raises two difficulties. The first involves the imagination: it is often difficult to make the jump in understanding which allows an analogy to be seen between two apparently different situations. The second difficulty arises because we are tempted to see common concepts in situations where none arise, and we tend to ignore any facts which do not fit in with our preconceived views.

Each of the examples of the previous section is an example of conflict. Many students are puzzled by elementary courses in economics because these courses include little about conflict. The surprising thing, the thing that needs to be explained, is why so much of economic activity does go along fairly smoothly, why so many changes in economic variables are relatively small changes. Much of economics is about ways in which conflict is resolved by a continual process of small adjustments. Such resolution is possible because in so much of economic activity all the participants gain. Much of this book provides techniques to aid the understanding of the concepts involved.

Abbreviations

Economic activity is detailed and complex. In order to make some sense out of it we have to discover those concepts which are sufficiently general to enable us to apply them to most situations, and we have to know what to look for in order to spot those situations which are exceptions to the 'general' rule. Generality, abstraction, and theory allow us to leave out much of the detail. Theories always simplify. People often dismiss theory because it is simplification, but theories are valuable because they cut out unnecessary detail. Mathematics is particularly helpful in allowing a general approach to be taken to problems. It encourages the investigator to dismiss irrelevancies, but it allows detail to be incorporated into the analysis whenever the detail seems to be important. By Chapter 5 this will become clear.

Perhaps the easiest way to approach mathematics is to treat it simply as a list of abbreviations. 'a multiplied by b' takes up more space than the multiplication sign, '$a \times b$', or than a dot, '$a \cdot b$', or than brackets, '$a(b)$'. Multiplication is used so often that even these abbreviations are omitted: multiplication is understood by the juxtaposition of the two things that are being multiplied together, 'ab'. Other useful abbreviations of phrases are:

> $>$ 'is greater than'
> $<$ 'is less than'
> $=$ 'is equal to'
> $\approx$ 'is approximately equal to'

The symbols, abbreviations, and definitions have a consistency which allows logical statements to be made. Consider the statement: 'If $a > b$, then $-a < -b$.' Such a statement has no empirical content: it does not refer to an actual situation in the world. It is a 'valid' statement in the sense that it follows from the mathematicians' definitions of the symbols $>$, $<$, $-$, and the logicians' understanding of the words 'If . . ., then . . .' But it is not a 'true' statement in the sense that it corresponds with reality, because it does not say anything about the world. However, once we define a and b in terms of measures of some real phenomena, then the statement does have empirical content.

The use of symbols such as a and b instead of numbers allows for much more generality, as well as saving space. However, so many nouns will be used that confusion will be avoided if we define them just before we use them. There is a shortage of appropriate abbreviations which we can use. Sometimes the same symbol is in conventional use for widely different nouns. For example, 'C' is always used as an abbreviation for the goods and services which are consumed in an economy over a period of time, but 'C' is also used as a symbol for costs. This book is designed to be read alongside those introductory economic texts which take a more verbal approach to the subject, and most of the topics discussed in other introductory texts will also be discussed here, hence the large number of different nouns which will be used. Sometimes abbreviating nouns will involve us in writing more than would be the case in a verbal text. For example, the statement: 'In the United Kingdom, one-fifth of national income is spent on imports.' becomes: 'Let M be UK imports per annum in £s, and Y be UK national income per annum in £s. $M = \frac{1}{5}Y$.'

The reader is asked to bear with this for the first few chapters, after which the advantages will become clear.

The contents of the book

In Chapter 0, five different types of reasoning are used to solve a simple problem, and some snags in the traditional mathematical approaches are discovered. We label the starting chapter O, in the same way that we label a person's age, because this method of counting has advantages which will appear in Chapter 7.

In Chapter 1, the use of nouns is discussed with particular emphases on ways of avoiding ambiguities and nonsense. Several symbols are introduced which will appear occasionally in later chapters. Most readers will find it more relaxing if they refer back to Chapter 1 when the symbols occur later in the book, rather than try to remember everything as it appears. The concepts are more important than the notation. However, it is advisable to jot down on a piece of paper anything which appears strange. Chapter 1 is important also for those readers who intend to study the recent theories of Welfare Economics.

In Chapter 2, the types of relations between one variable and another are investigated. This chapter provides the foundations on which the rest of the book is built. Again, understanding is more important than memorising, particularly since Chapter 5 provides a number of short-cuts which enable many of the statements of Chapter 2 to be worked out in the head.

In Chapter 3, simple methods of performing apparently complicated calculations are given. This chapter has immediate practical applications and is also necessary for the understanding of Chapters 7 and 8.

Chapter 4 gives some reasons for the stability of economic variables. The traditional analysis of supply and demand is the main theme. Chapters 4, 5, and 6 should be read in conjunction with a good verbal text. Hopefully, a combination of the verbal and mathematical approach to problems should lead to a better appreciation of economics, mathematics, and the power of logical reasoning in English.

In Chapters 5 and 6 the importance of small changes is analysed. A man who makes decisions which affect economic variables is like a man who is taking a long walk: he is more immediately impressed by the steepness of the path than by the height of the hill.

Chapters 7 and 8 discuss the ways in which economic change can be measured and described. Chapter 8 provides some short-cuts for understanding the contents of Chapter 5, which in turn provided them for Chapter 2. Unfortunately, Chapter 8 requires Chapter 7 before it can be understood. (As the farmer said when he brought in the last load of hay, 'If we'd done that one first, we'd have been through a lot quicker.')

Chapters 9, 10, and 11 deal with a selection of important economic problems which are far easier to understand by using a mathematical approach than by using a verbal approach.

In the previous section, the formula '$M = \frac{1}{5}Y$' was given as if it were a law of economics. Chapters 12 and 13 show how such formulae are found and what sort of reliance can be placed on them.

Chapter 0

Five Ways to Solve a Problem

0.1 Introduction

We start by looking at traditional ways of solving problems and show how these are related to the contents of the following chapters. So in this chapter we examine five ways of solving a problem: verbal reasoning, arithmetic, graphs, algebraic formulae, and a pair of simultaneous equations. These are all different types of logical reasoning, but basically they are only different ways of saying the same thing. The fascination of mathematics is not that it supplies many different techniques for solving the same problem but rather that the same technique can be used for many different problems. This should become obvious as the reader moves further into the book, but at the moment it may be reassuring to find different methods producing the same answer.

0.2 A problem

Consider the following everyday problem. A man wishes to buy a car to use for one year. He is not worried about the car's appearance, nor its age. He just wants to know which car will give him the lowest cost motoring for a year. Such a choice is effectively between a new car which is expensive to buy but cheap to run, and an older car which is cheaper to buy but more expensive to run. Since the man is interested in the costs for one year only, the second-hand value of each car at the end of the year must be taken into account. For each car he needs three items of information: the purchase price, the second-hand value when he sells, and the running costs per thousand miles. His estimates are as follows:

	New car	Old car
Purchase price	£800	£600
Second-hand value	£600	£450
Running costs per thousand miles	£25	£35

0.3 Verbal reasoning

For each car there is a fixed cost which will have to be met no matter how many miles the car is driven. This is the difference between the purchase price and the second-hand value: £200 for the new car, £150 for the old. So the cost of owning the new car for a year is £50 greater than the cost of owning the old one. The question is: will the cheaper running costs of the new car compensate for the greater fixed costs? This depends on how many miles the car is expected to be driven. The new car costs £10 less per thousand miles to run, so if the man expects to drive less than 5000 miles the old car is the best buy; if more than 5000 miles the new car is the best buy.

0.4 Tables of numbers

In practice, verbal reasoning can be rather difficult to use. For important decisions, setting out the arithmetic provides a check that the common-sense answer is correct. In Table 0.1 the costs for each car are set out for each thousand miles that the car is driven. When

Table 0.1   Costs

Number of miles driven (in thousands)	Fixed		Variable		Total	
	New car	Old car	New car	Old car	New car	Old car
0	200	150	0	0	200	150
1	200	150	25	35	225	185
2	200	150	50	70	250	220
3	200	150	75	105	275	255
4	200	150	100	140	300	290
5	200	150	125	175	325	325
6	200	150	150	210	350	360
7	200	150	175	245	375	395
8	200	150	200	280	400	430

the car is driven for no miles, only the costs of ownership of the car for the year are relevant. The first row of the table shows this. The headings at the top of each column tell us how to form a statement by reading across the row. In this case the statement is: 'If driven for 0 miles, a new car has costs of £200 and an old car has costs of £150.'

After the cars have been run for 1000 miles, the running costs must be added to the fixed costs, as shown in the second row. Inspection of the table shows that fixed-plus-running costs are more for the new car up to 5000 miles and less after 5000 miles.

0.5 Graphs

It is possible to picture on a diagram the way in which the costs of running a car depend upon the distance which the car is driven. This has three advantages over the table in the preceding section. First, a picture helps in understanding the way costs change as distance changes. Second, we can quickly find out the costs corresponding to those distances which are not simple multiples of 1000. Third, for problems where the answer is not as simple as here, we can find an accurate solution by drawing an accurate diagram, whereas a table might not yield such a solution.

Suppose we want to draw the graph of the relationship between the total costs of a new car and the distance the car is driven. From the first two columns of Table 0.1 we can select an appropriate number of observations, say, eight. One observation in each pair is the distance in thousands of miles, which we abbreviate by calling 'x'; the other observation in each pair is the corresponding costs in £s, abbreviated to 'y'. These pairs are set out in the following two rows:

distance (x)	1	2	3	4	5	6	7	8
costs (y)	225	250	275	300	325	350	375	400

In this example, distance causes the costs to change. It is common to label 'the thing that does the causing' as x.

The next step is to draw a diagram. Figure 0.1 shows a suitable diagram for picturing the pairs of observations. It consists of a horizontal axis labelled x, and a vertical axis labelled y. Using the horizontal axis for x is the conventional method of drawing such a diagram. In this example, the spacing of the measurement of x is different from that for y. The choice of measurement scales depends on the visual result. Any scale which conveys a clear impression is a suitable scale.

When $x = 1$, $y = 225$. These two numbers are pictured as one point on the diagram. The point is positioned by moving one unit along the x-axis from 0, and 225 units up the y-axis from 0. The point at the bottom left-hand corner of the diagram is the point from which the measurements along the axes are made, so the point where $x = 0$ and $y = 0$ is called the **origin**.

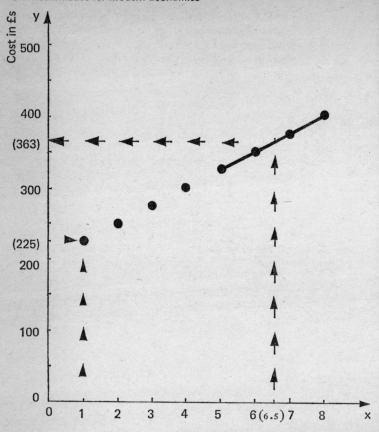

Figure 0.1 Locating the points which will form the curve; and using the curve to find *y* when *x* is known

Of course, a car does not have to be driven exact multiples of 1000 miles in a year. To find the cost for distances involving fractions of a thousand, the points of the graph are connected by a curve. (In this case the 'curve' is a straight line, but in mathematical language a straight line is just a particular type of curve.) Only a section of the curve is illustrated in Figure 0.1.

When the points are being plotted from the table of numbers, we find each point by moving vertically up from the appropriate number on the x-axis and horizontally across from the corresponding number on the y-axis. (Note the direction of the arrows pointing to the position of the point where $x = 1$ and $y = 225$.) Once sufficient points have been plotted to obtain the shape of the curve, the curve can be drawn to connect the points. It is then possible to find from

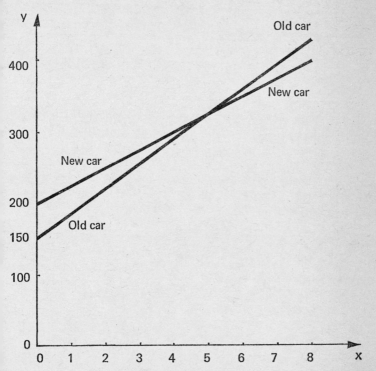

Figure 0.2 Which car is cheaper?

the graph of the curve the cost which corresponds to any distance. To do this, move vertically from the given point on the x-axis up to the curve, then move from the curve horizontally across to the y-axis and read off the number which gives the cost. For example, if x is 6·5, then y is about 363, so the cost of running a new car for 6500 miles is about £363. Note the direction of the arrows from $x = 6·5$ to the curve, and then from the curve to the y-axis at $y = 363$. In order to build the points which locate the curve, we move out from each axis. In order to use the graph to find y when x is known, we start at the known value of x, move up to the graph, then across to find the value of y.

As an exercise plot on a sheet of graph paper the graph of the points for the old car, as given by the first and third columns of Table 0.1. Check that these points lie on a straight line. Now enter on your diagram the curve for the new car and check that the two curves intersect at the point where $x = 5$ and $y = 325$. The two curves are illustrated in Figure 0.2. The old car is cheaper up to 5000 miles, and after 5000 miles the new car is cheaper. So the graph gives the same result as was found from the verbal reasoning and from Table 0.1.

0.6 Equations

Owning the old car for a year costs £50 less than owning the new car, and this can be looked upon as an advantage of £50 gained from the decision to purchase the old car rather than the new one, an advantage which does not depend on the distance that the car is driven. However, driving the old car for each thousand miles costs £10 more than driving the new car. If we let x stand for the number of thousands of miles that the old car is driven, the disadvantage of the decision to buy the old car is ten times the number of miles driven, which is $10x$. Hence the net advantage, measured in £s, from the decision for any annual mileage is $50 - 10x$. If we let y stand for these net advantages from owning the old car, we can derive a formula $y = 50 - 10x$, which can be used to calculate the money value of the advantage for any given mileage. These net advantages can be calculated in numerical terms by putting different values for x into the formula:

When x is 0, $y = 50 - 10(0) = 50 - 0 = 50$
When x is 1, $y = 50 - 10(1) = 50 - 10 = 40$
When x is 2, $y = 50 - 10(2) = 50 - 20 = 30$
. . .
When x is 8, $y = 50 - 10(8) = 50 - 80 = -30$

The following is a tabulation of the results:

Thousands of miles	x	0	1	2	3	4	5	6	7	8
Advantage of old car (in £)	y	50	40	30	20	10	0	-10	-20	-30

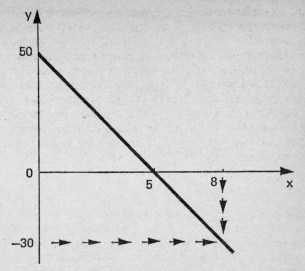

Figure 0.3 The net advantage of buying the old car

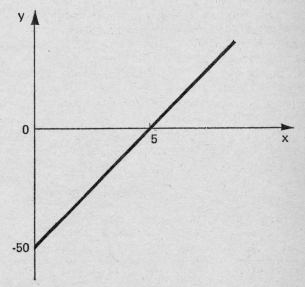

Figure 0.4 The net advantage of buying the new car

There is no net advantage in the decision when x is 5. When x is greater than 5 the net advantage becomes negative, a disadvantage. The graph of this equation is shown in Figure 0.3. For each value of x there is a corresponding value of y. For example, when x is 2, y is 30. These two values are plotted into one point by moving along the x axis to the x value of 2; then moving vertically upwards from the x axis until horizontally level with the y value of 30. This locates the single point where x is 2 and y is 30. This procedure is repeated for other points until the shape of the curve becomes clear. Note that the curve falls below the x-axis when x is greater than 5.

Now find the formula which gives the net advantages from the decision to buy the new car rather than the old one. Plot the curve on a diagram and check that it looks like Figure 0.4.

0.6 Simultaneous equations

We can think of the problem in a conceptually different way by asking the question: at what mileage will both cars cost the same amount? Once this question is answered, we can then decide which car is the best buy for mileages below this level and which is the best for any mileage greater than that where both cars are an equally good buy.

The two curves illustrated in Figure 0.2 can also be expressed as equations, using the information contained in section 0.3.

Total costs are fixed costs plus running costs

For the old car $y = 150 + 35x$
For the new car $y = 200 + 25x$

These two equations contain two unknowns, the particular value for x and the particular value for y which will make both equations true. We have to use both equations in order to find a solution. Both equations have to be manipulated at the same time, that is, simultaneously.

There is some value of x where the costs of the two cars are the same. This is when:

$$150 + 35x = 200 + 25x$$

Subtract 150 from both sides of the equals sign to obtain:

$$35x = 50 + 25x$$

Subtract $25x$ from both sides to obtain:

$$10x = 50$$

Divide both sides by 10 to obtain:

$x = 5$, as before.

The corresponding value of y can be found by substituting this value of x into either of the original equations:

$y = 150 + 35(5) = 150 + 175 = 325$
$y = 200 + 25(5) = 200 + 125 = 325$

Solving a pair of simultaneous equations gives the same answer as finding the point on a diagram where two curves intersect. The algebraic approach is more concise than verbal reasoning, tables of numbers, or graphs. Instead of writing 'number of thousands of miles that a car is driven', we write 'x'. Since x is something that can take different values it is known as a **variable**. The letter which we used as an abbreviation for another variable was y. Unfortunately we have managed to give y a variety of different meanings. Inspection of the five diagrams in this chapter shows that we have given the following meanings to x and y.

Figure	x	y
0.1	distance the new car is driven	total costs of new car
0.2	distance that either car is driven	total costs for either car
0.3	distance the old car is driven	net advantage from old car
0.4	distance the new car is driven	net advantage from new car
0.5	distance that either car is driven	total costs for either car

Although the axes have different meanings for the different approaches to the problem, there is a common meaning for x which applies to all the diagrams: distance in thousands of miles. Also the y axis always measures £s: all the different meanings of y are different types of measurement in £s. In the next two chapters we shall introduce an alternative way of using algebra which will eliminate the dangers of ambiguity.

In the present chapter the problem was stated in such a way that the answer was contained in the question. There is a clear relationship between costs and distances for each of two cars; find the two relationships, and find the point of decision. We are told that costs and distances are worth observing, that costs are so much and distances so much, and that the two variables are connected by a known relationship. The approach of the following chapters is easier to use in the analysis of complex situations, and it is also more widely applicable. It starts with a few rules about how to observe things.

READING

Sawyer, W. W., *Mathematician's Delight*, Penguin, 1943, pp. 78–87.

If this chapter proved to be particularly difficult, work through some of the examples in the next book until confidence comes:

P. Abbot, *Teach Yourself Algebra*, London English Universities Press, 1942, Chapters 1–12.

Chapter 1

Classification and Counting

1.1 Classification

Classification is the most important part of problem-solving. Many problems in economics involve classifying things in such a way that counting them is easy. Often classifying, counting, and comparing are enough to solve the problem. For example, we may wish to know which of two firms really is the more profitable. If we compare the profits they have reported over each of the last five years we shall not be much wiser because every firm has a different way of calculating its profit. But if we find that the annual percentage increase in profit for one firm is 3 per cent and for the other firm 23 per cent we are much more likely to be correct in saying that the second firm has the better profit record. Instead of measuring profit in £s per annum we measure the annual increase in profit as a percentage of the previous year's profit.

One of the advantages of starting the study of economics by studying the way markets behave is that the markets do much of the classifying for us. The set of prices and the set of quantities sold are of importance to buyers and sellers as well as to economists. The appropriate classification is not always so obvious, particularly in the public sector of the economy. How do we count the output of a public library, or a hospital, or a motorway? We may make many surprising discoveries by counting but first we have to decide what to count. This is the problem of classification.

Classes of things are known as sets and the part of mathematics which shows us how to handle sets is known as set theory. Sets are collections of things; they are rather like nouns in grammar. Relationships between sets are rather like verbs. Sets and relationships allow us to make statements, and a series of statements allows us to make deductions, getting more information out of the original statements than seems to be there.

1.2 Notation

Nine symbols which are used in this chapter and which may seem strange at first are given below. The rest of the chapter explains how they are used and why they are useful so that there is no need to memorise the phrases that they abbreviate. They are given at the beginning to familiarise the reader with them. Many of us are very suspicious about symbols, but they become easier to use if the way they are spoken is known and if they are written down on a piece of paper so that they become symbols which can be reproduced by the reader and are not just specialities of the printer. (A jotting pad is the main requirement for an understanding of this book. If in doubt, write it down.)

$a \in A$

'a is an element of the set A', or 'a is a member of the set A', or 'a belongs to the set A'. (For example, if a is Mr Smith and A is the set of students of economics at a particular university, then $a \in A$ means Mr Smith is one of the students of economics at a particular university.)

$A = \{a, b, c\}$

'A is the set whose members are a, b, and c.' (If a is Mr Smith, b is Mr Brown, and c is Mr Jones, then the students of economics consist only of Messrs Smith, Brown, and Jones.)

$|A|$

'modulus A.' The number of elements in A. (In our example, the number of students of economics is three.)

$A \cap B$

'A cap B.' The intersection of the set A and the set B. (If B is the set of students of politics in the particular university, then $a \in A \cap B$ means that Mr Smith is reading both economics and politics.)

$A \cup B$

'A cup B.' The union of the sets A and B. (The set $A \cup B$ is the set of all those students who are reading either economics or politics or both.)

$A \subseteq X$

'A is a sub-set of X', or the set A is contained in the set X. (If X is the set of all the students of a particular university, then $A \subseteq X$ means simply that the economics students of a particular university are students of that university.)

$x \leqslant y$

'x is less than or equal to y.' (3 is less than or equal to 4.)

$X \supseteq A$

'the set X contains the set A.'

$y \geqslant x$

'y is greater than or equal to x.'

1.3 Sets

The formal definition of a set is 'any collection of definite distinguishable objects of our intellect or of our intuition, to be conceived as a whole'. All sets are characterised by the following four qualities:

First, a set contains all the things which have a certain definite property. Examples of properties are: redness, volume, taste. (But we could also describe as a property anything which affects supply, and as another property anything which affects demand.) If we are worried about meeting a bull we may pay particular attention to the set of all red clothes.

Second, no thing not having this property belongs to the set. We need not worry about yellow clothes when meeting a bull.

Third, each thing has a permanently recognisable individuality. A red shirt is still a particular red shirt even though it belongs to the set of all red clothes.

Fourth, the set itself is to be grasped as a whole. We are thinking about red clothes in general.

Note that our examples are correct illustrations of the characteristics of sets but may be based on a false hypothesis about the world. Bulls are almost colour-blind; they can distinguish between bright and dull colours but not between red and yellow. Mathematics is an excellent tool for exposing illogical thinking about problems of the world: if the mathematics is wrong the process of reasoning must be wrong. But anyone who knows a 'pure' mathematician will appreciate that the reverse is not always true. Correct mathematics does not always lead to correct statements about the world. However, correct mathematics will lead to correct empirical conclusions if the basic postulates are correct. Applied mathematics is rather like a sausage machine: provided the machine is working correctly, the quality of what comes out depends on the quality of what goes in.

A set can be described either by listing all its members individually, or by giving some rule which describes the members. We could say '$A = \{1, 2, 3, 4\}$' or 'A is the set of the first four integers'. The members of a set are written between curly brackets. The order in which they are written does not matter: $A = \{1, 4, 3, 2\}$ is also the set A as we defined it above.

1.4 The intersection of sets

When we speak of a red shirt we are putting into words the idea of something belonging to two sets at the same time, the set of all things having the property of redness and the set of all shirts. Another example is given more formally in the next paragraph.

Let W be the set of all people who earn wages or salaries, and let K be the set of all people who get income from capital assets. There is a group of people who belong to both sets; they are both workers and capitalists in the sense that their income derives partly from payment for their labour and partly from their capital assets. These people belong in the intersection of the two sets W and K. The intersection of two sets is itself a set, and such a set contains all those things or people which are members of both sets. This set is written $W \cap K$ (spoken 'W cap K'). In symbols:

$W \cap K = \{x : x \in W \text{ and } x \in K\}$	
The intersection of W and K	$W \cap K$
is the set	$= \{ \qquad \}$
of any person	x
such that	$:$
the person is a member of W	$x \in W$
and the person is a member of K	and $x \in K$

In Figure 1.1, the circle represents the set of wage-earners and the triangle represents the set of those whose income is from capital assets. An income receiver might be anywhere in the two shapes, including the part where the two shapes overlap, in which case the income-receiver is a member of both W and K, so he is a member of $W \cap K$.

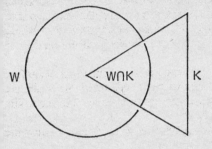

Figure 1.1 Some people can be classified as both wage-earners and capitalists

1.5 Disjoint sets

Suppose that N is the set of all numbers and B is the set of all British people. No British person is -4, or 0, or $\frac{1}{2}$, or 0.01 and no number is Smith or Jones or McTavish. N and B have no elements in common so they are called disjoint sets. The intersection of N and B is not really defined; it is not really a set at all. However, a common failing is to imply that there is a connection between sets where none exists in reality, so we invent a set with no elements and call it the empty set, written ø, just to remind ourselves that there is a set with nothing in it. In our example, $N \cap B = $ ø, the empty set.

1.6 The difference between two sets

If we wanted to know the names of all male sociology students, we could find the names of all sociology students and delete any of these who were also female students. If we wanted to know the names of all female students who were not studying sociology, we could find the names of all female students and subtract from these any who were also sociology students. Let S be the set of sociology students and F be the set of female students. In the first case we want to know $S - F$ and in the second case $F - S$. (Note that sets are not the same as numbers. Sets are labels or categories.)

The difference between two sets is also a set. The definition can be put most neatly in symbolic form because it depends on the order of writing. The symbol $\notin$ is used for 'is not a member of' or 'does not belong to'.

$$S - F = \{x : x \in S \text{ and } x \notin F\}$$

so '$x \in S - F$' is the same as '$x \in S$ and $x \notin F$'.

$$F - S = \{x : x \notin S \text{ and } x \in F\}$$

so '$x \in F - S$' is the same as '$x \notin S$ and $x \in F$'.

Differences and intersections are particularly important when dealing with sets of people. Often in casual conversation we assume that if two sets intersect there is no difference. For example, the set of arts students (A) and the set of innumerate students (I) certainly intersect, but $A - I$ need not be ø.

It is tempting to confuse sets with numbers, particularly when the word 'difference' is used. The difference between 12 and 9 is 3: either $12 - 9 = 3$, or $9 - 12 = -3$. However, sets are more like adjectives. If S is the set of students and T is the set of all people who receive an income of less than £1000 per annum, then $S - T$ is the set of all students who receive £1000 or more per annum. $S - T$ is not the number of students in the world (a few million) minus the number of people with less than a thousand pounds a year (most of the world's population of over 3000 million). We shall be discussing the number of elements in a set in a later section, but here it is worth pointing out that it cannot be negative.

1.7 The union of two sets

Suppose that a doctor is concerned about improved methods of repairing Eskimos' broken legs and that he asks the Medical Literature Analysis and Retrieval Service to supply him with any articles which seem relevant to his problem. Let B be the set of articles that refer to broken limbs and C the set of articles that refer to treatment in cold climates. If he asks for copies of those articles which refer to both broken limbs *and* cold climates, $B \cap C$, he will get what he wants. But if he asks for those articles that refer to either broken limbs *or* cold climates he will be inundated with thousands of articles, which will include the information that he requires but will also include a large amount of irrelevant information such as how to heal broken limbs in Malaya or how to cure influenza in Greenland.

If B and C are sets, the union of B and C is the set of all members of B together with all members of C. The union of two sets is written $B \cup C$ (spoken 'B cup C'):

$$B \cup C = \{x : x \in B \text{ or } x \in C\}$$

so '$x \in B \cup C$' is the same as '$x \in B$ or $x \in C$'.

Compare the union of two sets with their intersection:

$$B \cap C = \{x : x \in B \text{ and } x \in C\}.$$

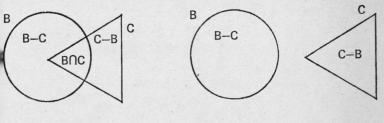

1.2a   1.2b

Figure 1.2 The difference between two sets depends upon the intersection of the two sets

Any of the medical articles can be represented by x, but suitably qualified:

$$B = \{x : x \in B\}$$
$$C = \{x : x \in C\}$$
$$B - C = \{x : x \in B \text{ and } x \notin C\}$$
$$= \{x : x \in B \text{ and } x \notin B \cap C\}$$

If there are no things in $B \cap C$, then $B \cap C = \emptyset$ and $B - C = B$, as pictured by the shapes in Figure 1.2(*b*). Figure 1.2(*a*) illustrates the case when, if an element is in $B \cup C$, then it may be in B but not C, in C but not B, or in both B and C. In Figure 1.2(*b*) an element may be in B or C, but it cannot be in both at the same time since there is no intersection.

1.8 Subsets

If B is the set of all British people and E is the set of all English people, then E is a subset of B, in symbols $E \subseteq B$. Alternatively we could say that B contains E, $B \supseteq E$. The notation is supposed to recall the symbol for 'is less than or equal to', as used for numbers. The number of English people $\leqslant$ the number of British people. The number of British people $\geqslant$ the number of English people.

If there are two sets, X and Y, such that both $X \subseteq Y$ and $Y \subseteq X$, then $X = Y$. Again there is an analogy between sets and numbers. If $a \leqslant b$ and $b \leqslant a$, then a must equal b, otherwise a would be both less than and greater than b at the same time. For example, it is true that $0 \cdot 5 \leqslant \frac{1}{2}$ and it is true that $\frac{1}{2} \leqslant 0 \cdot 5$, but this means that $0 \cdot 5 = \frac{1}{2}$. However, sets cannot always be handled in the same way as numbers, as was seen in the previous section where $B - C$ could equal B even when C was not the empty set.

1.9 Finite and infinite sets

If a set has a finite number of members it is called a finite set. Otherwise it is an infinite set. It is possible, at least in theory, to count the number of members of a finite set. The population of the world is finite, in spite of the large numbers involved and the difficulty of organising a count.

Let A be a finite set. The number of members of A is written $|A|$, spoken 'modulus A'. If $A = \{a, b, c\}$, then $|A| = 3$.

1.10 Counting

Although counting is something we all know how to do, we often forget that most counting is done after the classification problems have been solved. The skill of classifying what we want to count is worth developing.

In some cases counting is straightforward. If A is a finite set and B is a subset of A, then the number of elements in $A - B$ is the number of elements in A minus the number of elements in B:

$$|A - B| = |A| - |B|.$$

For example, if A is the set of students of economics and B is the set of students of econometrics, then B is a subset of A because all students of econometrics also study economics. However, if B were the set of all students of politics, and not all students of politics also study economics, then B would not be a subset of A. $A - B$ would be the set of those economics students who do not also study politics, and to count this set simply by subtracting $|B|$ from $|A|$

would result in a number that was too small. Under these circumstances we must use the formula:

$$|A - B| = |A| - |A \cap B|$$

This is a more general rule because it also applies to the case where B is a subset of A, in which case $A \cap B = B$ because the whole of B is contained in A. The rule applies too when A and B do not intersect, in which case $A \cap B = \emptyset$.

The three cases are illustrated in Figure 1.3, which pictures in part (a) the case where $A \cap B = B$, in (b) the case where $A \cap B$ is the only way of describing $A \cap B$, and in (c) the case where $A \cap B = \emptyset$.

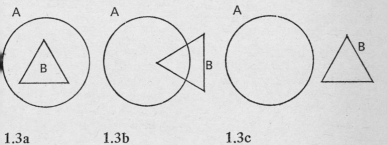

1.3a   1.3b   1.3c

Figure 1.3 The number of elements in the union of two sets depends both upon the number of elements in each set and upon the number of elements in the intersection of two sets

When counting the number of elements in the union of two sets care has to be taken to avoid obtaining numbers that are too large. The number of elements in $A \cup B$, for any finite sets A and B, is the number of elements in A plus the number of elements in B minus the number of elements in $A \cap B$. Without this last subtraction all those elements in $A \cap B$ would be double counted.

$$|A \cup B| = |A| + |B| - |A \cap B|$$

The problem of double counting frequently arises in social science. Suppose that each of a group of people are members of one or more clubs. There are three clubs, club A, club B and club C. The clubs may be considered to be the meeting places of an elite and we want to know the number of people involved, but the membership lists of the clubs are the only information we have. If we count the members of each of the three clubs we shall be double counting all those who are members of two or more clubs. Even if we subtract from the total membership of the clubs all those who are members of two clubs, we shall still be double counting those who are members of all three. The number of people we are trying to count is the number in the set $A \cup B \cup C$, and this number is given by the following formula:

$$|A \cup B \cup C| = |A| + |B| + |C| - |A \cap B| \\ - |B \cap C| - |C \cap A| \\ - |A \cap B \cap C|$$

If we were interested in the way political ideas develop into rigid attitudes among students, we might decide to investigate the problem by studying 100 students. Let L be the set of those students who discuss left-wing ideas and R the set of those students who discuss right-wing ideas. We observe the numbers as shown in Figure 1.4.

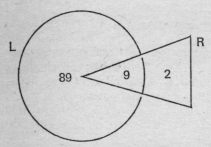

Figure 1.4 Who discusses what?

All students in the sample: $|L \cup R| = 100$
Those who discuss left-wing ideas: $|L| = 98$
Those who discuss right-wing ideas: $|R| = 11$
Those who discuss both: $|L \cap R| = 9$
Those who discuss only left-wing ideas:

$$|L - R| = |L| - |L \cap R| = 89$$

Those who discuss only right-wing ideas:

$$|R - L| = |R| - |L \cap R| = 2$$

The sociologist, Simmel, pointed out that beliefs are strongest when they are not challenged. If a group finds that its members' beliefs are weakening, it will try to withdraw from contact with others. Then the members will discuss their beliefs only with people whose beliefs are similar, and so their beliefs will be reinforced, provided they do not get bored. Which group is most successful at this withdrawal depends on the way the nine students in $L \cap R$ behave.

Drill

X, Y, and Z are three finite sets, and each has 100 members. W is a set with 2 members. Use diagrams to answer the following three questions. Then see what you make of question 4.

1. If $X \cap Y = \varnothing$, what is $X - Y$? What is the numerical value of $|X - Y|$? What is $Y - X$? What is the numerical value of $|Y - X|$?

2. If $|X \cap Z| = 20$, what is the numerical value of $|X - Z|$? of $|Z - X|$? of $|Z \cup X|$?

3. If $|W \cup X| = 100$, is it correct to write $W \subseteq X$?

4. P is the set of all people. C is a subset of P and is the set of all people who are capable of doing things. D is a subset of P and is the set of all people who actually do things. T is a subset of P and refers to those who teach. Put into words the statements '$C = D$; $P - C = T$'.

Answers

1. X; 100; Y; 100.
2. 80; 80; 180.
3. Yes.
4. 'Those who can, do; those who can't, teach.'

1.11 Probability introduced

Suppose that the chance of a house catching fire is 3 in a thousand, that is, if we observed any million houses over their lifetime, we would expect 3000 of them to suffer fire damage of some sort. We can use 'probability' to measure this chance in numerical terms. The probability of a house catching fire is $\frac{3}{1000}$ or 0·003. The probability that a house is a house does not really involve chance at all since it is a certainty. A certain event is an event with a probability of one. An impossible event is an event with a probability of zero.

Suppose that the chance of a house becoming flooded is only 1 in a thousand; the probability of a flood is 0·001. What is the probability of a house both catching fire *and* becoming flooded? (To keep the problem simple we assume that fires are always in roofs and floods are always in basements, and the one never affects the other. We are discussing the chance of particular types of events happening

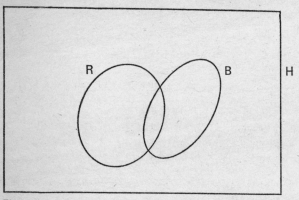

Figure 1.5 Some houses catch fire, some become flooded, and a few do both

to a house at some time during its lifetime, so both events need not happen at once.) Of any million houses, 3000 can be expected to have a fire of some sort. For these 3000 the chance of a flood is 0·001, so 3 are likely to be flooded. Therefore the chance of both events occurring to the same house is 3 in one million, or a probability of 0·000 003. In order to find the probability that both one type of event and another type of event will occur, we multiply together the probabilities of each event: $0·003 \times 0·001 = 0·000\ 003$.

What is the probability of a house either catching fire *or* becoming flooded? Is it the sum of the two probabilites, $0·003 + 0·001 = 0·004$? No, because here we are double-counting those houses which both become flooded and catch fire. The probabilities of a fire or a flood is $0·003 + 0·001 - 0·000\ 003$.

The language of sets is helpful in sorting out these various probabilities. Write H for the set of all houses, and R for the set of all houses that have a fire in the roof at some time in their life, and B for the set of all houses that have a flood in the basement at some time in their life. Let h be a particular house, so $h \in H$.

Figure 1.5 illustrates the three sets, the rectangle being the set of all houses. The probability that h lies in a particular set can be calculated from the information which we have already.

The probability that $h \in H$ is 1
The probability that $h \in R$ is 0·003
The probability that $h \in B$ is 0·001
The probability that $h \in R \cap B$ is 0·003 × 0·001 = 0·000 003
The probability that $h \in R \cup B$ is 0·003 + 0·001 − 0·000 003 = 0·003 997
The probability that $h \in R - B$ is 0·003 − 0·000 003
The probability that $h \in B - R$ is 0·001 − 0·000 003
The probability that $h \notin H$ is 0

If we write prob(A) for the probability that h belongs to the set A, we have:

$$\text{prob}(R \cup B) = \text{prob}(R) + \text{prob}(B) - \text{prob}(R \cap B)$$
$$\text{prob}(R - B) = \text{prob}(R) - \text{prob}(R \cap B)$$
$$\text{prob}(B - R) = \text{prob}(B) - \text{prob}(R \cap B)$$

Note how the notation for probabilities follows the same pattern as that for the number of elements in sets.

1.12 Sets of sets

Let $A = \{q, r, s, t\}$, $B = \{p, s, t\}$, and $C = \{r, p\}$. The members of A, B, and C are p, q, r, s, t. The number of elements in the three sets is five. Using the formula of the previous section:

$$|A \cup B \cup C| = 4 + 3 + 2 - 2 - 1 - 1 - 0 = 5$$

Now let S be the set of the sets A, B, and C, so $S = \{A, B, C\}$ and $|S| = 3$. The members of the set S are themselves sets, but the members of A, B, and C are not members of S.

A number is a set. 'Two' is the set of all things like 'a brace of pheasants', 'a pair of kippers', 'a couple of lads', 'two tractors'. Unfortunately the familiar concept of number turns out to be very difficult to put into words, but all we need do here is to point out that a set of numbers is also a set of sets. Those of philosophical bent may like to ponder this statement of Frege: 'The number of things in a given class is the class of all classes that are similar to the given class.'

1.13 Metalanguages

Consider the sentence: 'This statement is untrue.' If it is true, it is not; and if it is not true, it is. To find out how this paradox arises we have to study the structure of the sentence. Really it takes the form 'x is false' where x is the statement that 'x is false'. The trouble here is that we are trying to describe a concept in terms of the very concept that we are trying to describe. But we can only speak of

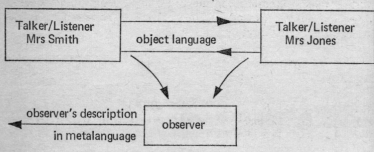

Figure 1.6 Language and metalanguage

something if we have the word or words to describe it. If we wish to tell someone that a cow can be exchanged for twenty spears, either we can show them the deal actually taking place, or we must use the concept of number to describe the deal.

If we wish to describe a language, we have to use a further language, a metalanguage, to do so. If a person interested in linguistics is trying to compare the way housewives talk to each other in different parts of the country, he will not get very far by only repeating the housewives' conversation. The object of the study is the housewives' language, but the description of the housewives' language is given in metalanguage. The object language is classified, and then discussed in terms of these classes. The classes form the nouns of the metalanguage. Figure 1.6 illustrates how the observer is detached from the observed.

Many words used in the social sciences appear to be jargon, new words invented to replace other words that are quite adequate for the task but do not give the same impression of being inside the mysteries of the subject. Sometimes this is the case, but often new words are used to convey new concepts or new ways of classifying people and things.

The appropriate classification always depends on the problem in hand. Classification relies upon similarity, but things are only similar from a particular point of view, and the point of view from which they are similar depends on the problem being tackled. In the days before railways were nationalised there was a very complicated classification scheme for pricing different types of freight. A small boy asked the ticket inspector whether a ticket was needed for his pet tortoise. The inspector knew the rule book by heart and replied with complete accuracy for the problem in hand: 'Son, dogs is dogs, and cats is dogs, and monkeys in cages is parrots, but tortoises is insects and they travels for nothing.'

Drill

1. $A = \{q, r, s, t\}$, $B = \{p, s, t\}$ and $C = \{r, p\}$.

 i. What are the members of the sets $A - B$, $B - A$, $A - C$, $C - A$, and $C - (A \cup B)$?

 ii. What are the values of $|B \cap A|$, $|C \cap B|$, and $|C \cap B \cap A|$?

2. A is the set of the first eight positive integers.

 i. What is $|B \cap C|$, when $B \subseteq A$, $C \subseteq A$,
$B = \{x : x \in A \text{ and } x < 6\}$,
$C = \{x : x \in A \text{ and } x > 3\}$?

The symbol $<$ means 'less than', and $>$ means 'greater than'.

 ii. What is $|D \cap E|$, when $D \subseteq A$, $E \subseteq A$, and
$D = \{x : x \in A \text{ and } x \leqslant 6\}$,
$E = \{x : x \in A \text{ and } x \geqslant 3\}$?

Answers

1. i. $\{q, r\}$, $\{p\}$, $\{q, s, t\}$, $\{p\}$, ø.
 ii. 2, 1, 0.
2. i. 2, ii. 4.

Exercise 1

1. Would you measure the output of the British coal industry in tons, in calories or in £s, if you were attempting to compare this output with:

   i. The total requirements of fuel for the British economy?

   ii. The proportion of this total requirement that should be met by coal (rather than gas, oil, or nuclear fuels) if the objective were to provide fuel as cheaply as possible?

   iii. The amount of rolling stock needed by British Railways?

2. Let S be the set of all statements about things which affect supply, and let D be the set of all statements about things which affect demand. Which of the following statements are members of the sets $D - S$, $S - D$, and $S \cap D$?

   i. The weather at harvest was sunny.

   ii. High-yielding strains of wheat are now in widespread use.

   iii. Housewives are worried about getting fat.

   iv. Wheat merchants have improved their marketing arrangements after a study of what consumers want.

3. Let X be the set of the following book titles which seem to you to be relevant to the problem 'Should an oil company expand its productive capacity?' Let Y be the set for the problem 'How can employment be found for redundant miners in North-east England?'

a. The Economics of Rural Industry.
b. Sources of Fuel for the British Economy in 1980.
c. The Sociology of Mining Villages.
d. The Construction of Oil Refineries in North-east England.
e. Tourism in North-east England.
f. The Demand for Petrol.
g. Recent Developments in Electric Cars.
h. The Arab–Israel Conflict.
i. Goethe's Use of the Comma.

   i. What are X, Y, $X \cap Y$, $X \cup Y$, $X - Y$, and $Y - X$?

   ii. What are the values of $|X|$, $|Y|$, $|X \cap Y|$, $|X \cup Y|$, $|X - Y|$, and $|Y - X|$?

   iii. If X and Y are to be housed in separate libraries, how many duplicate copies must be bought?

READING

Land, Frank, *The Language of Mathematics*, London, John Murray, 1960, pp. 35–99.

Rosenthal, Evelyn B., *Understanding the New Maths*, London, Souvenir Press, 1965, pp. 113–72.

For some uses of definitions and classification in economics see: Ford, A. G., *Income, Spending and the Price Level,* in this series, pp. 9–31.

Chapter 2

Relations and Functions

2.1 Discovering relations

The purpose of this chapter is to examine some of the ways in which the members of one set may be related to the members of another set. The first chapter dealt with classification and counting, but there is no point in counting things unless the resulting numbers are to be compared with other numbers. Sometimes the comparison of numbers results in the discovery of a neat formula for describing the relation between the members of two sets. More often the relation can be only approximately described by a simple formula. Much of this book concentrates on showing that such simple formulae are useful tools for describing and analysing economic activity. When the simple formulae have been shown to be useful, we can then move on to methods of adapting them to cope with problems which are not always as tidy as we are pretending them to be, but for the moment we concentrate on simplicity.

Suppose there are three wheat farmers. The first has an annual gross revenue from wheat of £3000; the second has a revenue of £6000 and the third a revenue of £4200. Suppose also that we want to explain why their revenues differ even though they farm in the same district and produce the same type of wheat. The most obvious explanation is that they produced and sold different amounts of wheat during the year, so as a first step we can find out the annual quantities sold. The farmer whose revenue was £3000 is discovered to have sold 100 tons, the one with £6000 sold 200 tons, and the one with £4200 sold 140 tons. These pairs of observations (tons, £s) can be written (100, 3000), (200, 6000), and (140, 4200), a pair for each farmer. By convention the number to be explained is written last.

The first number of each pair is a member of the set of quantities sold in tons per annum; call this set X and call each number x, where x is a member of X, $x \in X$. The second number of each pair is a member of the set of revenues in £s per annum; call this set S and each number R, where $R \in S$. (Although capital letters are used or sets, we need not use only small letters for the members of the ets.)

Each pair of numbers giving quantity and revenue, (x, R), is a nember of a new set formed from both X and S. Such a set is nown as a **product set** and is written $X \times S$, spoken 'X times S'. t can be displayed in graphical form by picturing the first set on the orizontal axis and the second set on the vertical axis of a graph, s in Figure 2.1.

Just as a simple set can be pictured in one dimension, a product

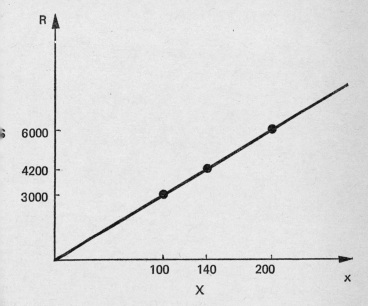

igure 2.1 A relation as a subset of a product set

et can be pictured in two dimensions. A movement of 100 tons east-vards along the quantity axis is matched by a movement north-vards along the revenue axis; a movement of 1 ton eastward is natched by a movement of 30 northward. The relation between and R is given by the formula $R = 30x$. Since revenue equals rice multiplied by the quantity sold, 30 must refer to the price of rheat.

We must also discover in what units price is measured. R is measured in £s per annum and x in tons per annum. The components of the formula $R = 30x$ have units of measurement:

$$R = 30\,x$$

$$\frac{\text{£s}}{\text{years}} = (?)\frac{\text{tons}}{\text{years}}$$

The (?) must be $\dfrac{\text{£s}}{\text{tons}}$ to make the right-hand side of the equation equal the left-hand side, so the price is £30 per ton.

From two sets, X and S, we formed a product set $X \times S$. From studying members of the product set (x, R) we discovered a relation $R = 30x$, and this relation is itself a set; it is a subset of the product set. So now we are dealing with four sets: X, S, $X \times S$, and the relation we discovered, which is a subset of $X \times S$ and is written $\{(x, R) : R = 30x\}$.

There may be relationships between sets of apparently unconnected things: between the use of insecticides and the fertility of eagles, between the national cost of dental care and the production of the iced-lolly industry. Finding the relationships can be very difficult. It involves choosing a suitable way of classifying and until this is found we have to remain sceptical about the hypothesis that there is a relationship; there may not be.

Consider the following problem where the meaning of the sets being compared is understandable, but where the units of measurement are not defined at all. Let X be some measure of the ability to understand mathematical concepts, and let Y be some measure of agility in manipulating mathematical symbols. Each set might have three members: weak, medium, and strong. The product set is pictured in Figure 2.2.

The advocates of the 'new mathematics' hope that by encouraging a high value of X they will also encourage a high value of Y, so that the relationship will follow the crosses on the diagram. Others say that there is time to do only one or the other, and therefore a high value of X will cause a low value for Y, as shown by the circles on the diagram. No one is sure which group is correct. An economist would express the problem in this way: Is X a complement to Y (as shown by the crosses) or is it competing with Y (as shown by the circles)? The immediate problem here is to find some way of measuring X and Y separately. Most methods of testing students' ability at understanding concepts also test their agility at manipulating symbols, so the two component measures are difficult to separate.

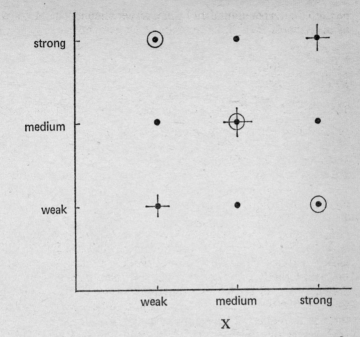

Figure 2.2 Does the relation follow the circles or does it follow the crosses?

2.2 Products of sets

Let x and y be any things, and let (x, y) be a symbol to denote the pair consisting of x and y in that order. Let a and b be another pair of things, and let (a, b) be the pair in that order. Then $(x, y) = (a, b)$ if, and only if, $x = a$ and $y = b$. Compare these ordered pairs with the sets $\{x, y\}$ and $\{a, b\}$. With sets $\{x, y\} = \{a, b\}$ if either $x = a$ and $y = b$, or $x = b$ and $y = a$. With sets the order of writing does not matter, but with ordered pairs it obviously does. Note that sets are displayed in curly brackets.

If X and Y are sets, the product set $X \times Y$ of X and Y is the set of all pairs (x, y) such that $x \in X$ and $y \in Y$. For example, if $X = \{1, 2, 3\}$ and $Y = \{s, t\}$, then

$X \times Y = \{(1, s), (2, s), (3, s), (1, t), (2, t), (3, t)\}$, but
$Y \times X = \{(s, 1), (s, 2), (s, 3), (t, 1), (t, 2), (t, 3)\}$.

If X and Y are finite sets, then $|X \times Y| = |X| \times |Y|$. This follows because if $|X|$ is the number of elements in X there must be $|X|$ ways of choosing the first component of an ordered pair (x, y) and there are $|Y|$ ways of choosing the second component. In the example above, $|X \times Y| = 3 \times 2 = 6$.

Now consider a further example of a product set $X \times Y$, defining X in this case as the set of the first five positive integers $X = \{1, 2, 3, 4, 5\}$, and Y as the set of the first four positive integers $Y = \{1, 2, 3, 4\}$.

$$X \times Y = \{(1, 1), (1, 2), (1, 3), (1, 4),$$
$$(2, 1), (2, 2), (2, 3), (2, 4),$$
$$(3, 1), (3, 2), (3, 3), (3, 4),$$
$$(4, 1), (4, 2), (4, 3), (4, 4),$$
$$(5, 1), (5, 2), (5, 3), (5, 4)\}$$

The product set is pictured in Figure 2.3(a), with the member (x, y) shown as the twenty points.

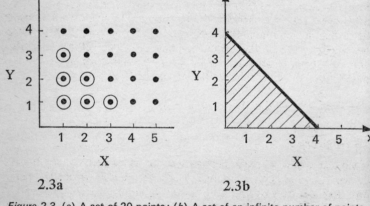

2.3a   2.3b

Figure 2.3 (a) A set of 20 points; (b) A set of an infinite number of points

Let A be the subset of $X \times Y$ containing only those elements where the sum of x and y is less than, or equal to, four. These points are circled in Figure 2.3(a).

$$A = \{(x, y) : x + y \leqslant 4\}$$

Now let us change the definition of X so that it becomes the set of all numbers from 0 to 5, not just the first five integers but all the numbers such as $\frac{2}{3}$, 1, 2, 4·99, 4·9999 and so on. There now are an infinite number of elements in X. Also let Y be the set of all the numbers from 0 to 4, so Y too is an infinite set. The ordered pairs (x, y) which are members of A now fill the whole of the hatched triangle in Figure 2.3(b). A is still a subset of $X \times Y$, but by changing the definition of X and Y we have made X, Y, $X \times Y$ and A into infinite sets.

2.3 The set of production possibilities

The approach of the previous section is particularly useful for finding the various possibilities open to a decision-taker. Once we know what is possible, we can then move on to consider what is best. A simple example of defining the possible is given here and we postpone the decision about what is best until we come to deal with more than two sets at a time.

Suppose that a farmer has 4 acres of land. He can grow either potatoes or barley, or any combination of these. Let x be the number of acres of potatoes that he can grow, and let y be the number of acres of barley. His choice is limited because he has only 4 acres, so he is producing under the constraint that $x + y \leqslant 4$. Also, since he cannot ungrow the crops he must produce either a positive amount or none, so $x \geqslant 0$ and $y \geqslant 0$. If S is his set of production possibilities this can be described formally as:

$$S = \{(x, y) : x + y \leqslant 4, x \geqslant 0, y \geqslant 0\}.$$

2.4 Mappings

If we discover a formula such as $y = 2x$ which relates members of the set X to members of the set Y, the formula is written in such a way that it is easy to find a particular value of y if the value of x is known. By juggling with the formula we can arrange it in such a way that we can find a particular value of x if the value of y is known: we simply write the formula as $x = \frac{1}{2}y$.

An alternative approach is to look at such relations as if they are mapping rules between sets. If X and Y are both sets of all the numbers, and if $x \in X$ and $y \in Y$, then $\{(x, y) : y = 2x\}$ is a subset of $X \times Y$; it is also a relation between x and y, and it is a way of mapping from the set X to the set Y. Figure 2.4 shows two ways of conceptualising a mapping rule.

The word 'mapping' recalls the way in which certain features of our three-dimensional world can be put onto a piece of paper to form a simple two-dimensional map, in the everyday sense of the word. In the case of the rule '$y = 2x$' we can move from X to Y and back

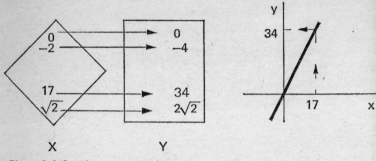

Figure 2.4 One-into-one mapping

again without losing any information: if x is 17, then y is 34; if y is 34, then x is 17. In the case of a simple map we cannot do this. The map-maker may tell us the position of a particular church, but not its height, width, and other details. Only enough information has been selected to answer the question 'How do we get there?' There is not a one-to-one mapping between the real church and

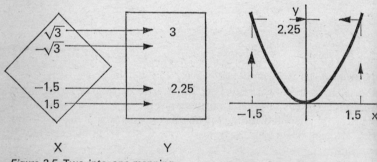

Figure 2.5 Two-into-one mapping

the position on the map. Rather it is a many-into-one mapping, the many details of the church condensed into one point on the map.

An example of a two-into-one mapping is '$y = x^2$' because either $x = +\sqrt{y}$ or $x = -\sqrt{y}$. Two x's correspond to each y; each y

corresponds to two x's. Mapping X into Y maps two into one. This mapping is illustrated in Figure 2.5.

Other mappings may be one-into-many. An example is '$y^2 = x$' which maps each x into two y's, since $y = +\sqrt{x}$ or $y = -\sqrt{x}$. In such a relation knowledge of a particular value of x is not enough to give us an unambiguous value for y. Figure 2.6 illustrates.

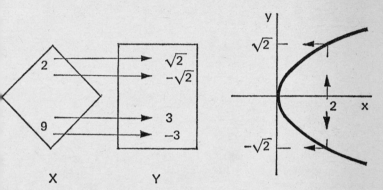

Figure 2.6 One-into-two mapping

2.5 Functions

In economics the most useful relations between two sets of variables are those where a knowledge of the known variable will yield an unambiguous value for the unknown variable. In other words, we want to find one-into-one or many-into-one mappings, and not one-into-many mappings. These useful relations are called functional relations or functions.

If there is a **functional relation** between two sets of variables X and Y, $x \in X$ and $y \in Y$, so that a unique y can be found for any value of x, the relation can be written $y = f(x)$, spoken 'y equals f of x'. A function is a particular type of relation, so a function is a subset of the product set formed from the two sets that the function relates. A function is also a mapping rule, but only one-into-one or many-into-one, not one-into-many. The best known illustration of this is the statement 'y is the wife of x', which is always a relation but is only a function in monogamous tribes.

The formal definition of a function sums this up: a function f from the set X to the set Y is a relation specified by the statement '$y = f(x)$'

such that, if $y \in Y$ exists for a given $x \in X$, then y is unique. A functional relation between the sets X and Y, or between the variables x and y, can be written in symbolic form:

$$f = \{(x, y) : x \in X, y \in Y, y = f(x)\}.$$

Three types of function are illustrated in Figure 2.7. In part (a) the particular function illustrates the amount of interest which must be paid each year on a mortgage loan lasting 10 years. Because interest is paid only on the amount of the loan which is outstanding at any one time, and because a part of the loan is repaid each year,

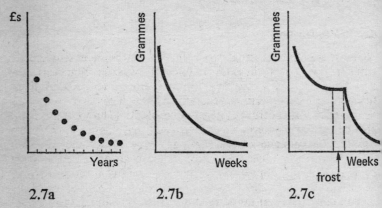

Figure 2.7 (a) Discrete function; (b) Smooth continuous function; (c) Kinked continuous function

the interest payments decrease. However, if interest payments are made only once a year, the function only exists at one point of time each year so it is represented on the diagram as dots. Each ordered pair (years, £s) takes only integral values for years, that is, whole numbers only. Such a function is a **discrete** function.

In part (b) the way in which a dead plant decays is illustrated by showing the ordered pairs (time in weeks, grammes weight). Since we could weigh the plant at any point in time, there are an infinite number of ordered pairs. The function is here represented as a curve. Such a function is a **continuous** function. It is also a **smooth** function because the curve has no kinks in it.

In part (c) another continuous function is illustrated but this one is **kinked**, unlike the smooth function illustrated in (b). As an example we can think of a plant decaying but the process is interrupted by a spell of frost.

The easiest functions to describe and handle are continuous, smooth functions. Of course the world is not always kind enough to behave in a continuous, smooth way, but many relations in the world can be described approximately by using such functions. The properties of the more widely used functions are investigated in the following pages. When investigating their shapes we can think of the functions simply as relations between two sets of numbers. However, when the functions are used to describe real phenomena we have to define the sets involved with care.

2.6 Linear functions

A linear function relating two variables can be represented by a straight line on a diagram. Examples of such functions are: $y = 3x + 2$, $y = 2 - 3x$, $2x + 3y = 4$, $y = x$, $y = 30x$. A **linear function** can be described generally by the formula $y = a + bx$, where a and b are positive or negative constants. (The constants could also be zero. If b is zero, we get the result that y is constant. In this case there is a unique y for any value of x, so y is a function of x.)

The numerical values of a and b will depend on the phenomena being described. Suppose we wish to find the relationship between degrees Fahrenheit and degrees Centigrade. To remind us of the dimensions of the variables we can call them C and F instead of x and y, leaving implicit the definitions of the sets of which C and F are members. To convert Centigrade into Fahrenheit we need the formula $F = a + bC$, and we need two pairs of observations. Since we know that water boils at 212° F or 100° C we can use these figures as one pair, and the other pair is given by the freezing point of water, 32° F or 0° C. We now replace C and F in the formula by their actual values when the temperature is the same, and this gives us two equations:

$$212 = a + b(100)$$
$$32 = a + b(0)$$

The second equation says $32 = a + 0$, so $a = 32$. The first equation says $212 = a + 100b$, but $a = 32$ so $212 = 32 + 100b$. If we subtract 32 from both sides of the equals sign, the two sides will still be equal, so $180 = 100b$ and $b = \dfrac{180}{100} = 1 \cdot 8$. Therefore the formula we are seeking is: $F = 32 + 1\cdot8C$. The numbers 32 and $1\cdot8$ are constants.

In economic theory we are trying to describe wide ranges of phenomena. For example, we may find that most countries have an approximately linear relationship between national income (Y) and total saving (S) of the form $S = a + bY$. Here a and b are constants for each country, but they will be different for different countries. When working out the theoretical implications of changes in the variables, we can leave these symbols in the equation. When we come to apply the theory we shall have to find the numerical values of a and b, and these values will be different for different countries. When constants are used in this way they are called **parameters**. In a sense, a parameter is a constant that varies. In the savings example, a and b will be a constant for different years in the same country, but different for different countries even in the same year.

2.7 Using linear functions and diagrams

Most countries tax their citizens' incomes by a system known as 'progressive taxation'. For over a century there has been a debate about the merits or otherwise of such a system, but only recently has it come to be realised that most people do not know what progressive taxation is. 'Except for a relatively small elite, the very notion of a progressive tax proved to be beyond grasp. By and large people could understand the concept of the wealthy paying more tax than the less wealthy, but they did not comprehend the idea of the wealthy paying more than a proportionately greater tax than the less wealthy. Proportionate and progressive rate schedules were not seen as involving a choice of principles.'[1]

There are many ways of taxing individuals, three of which are: a poll tax (a lump sum of so much per person), a proportionate tax, and a progressive tax. The tax authority will want to know how much tax should be collected from each individual, given the individual's income. The individual will want to know his income after tax, the amount that he can spend, when his income before tax is known.

Let X be the set of incomes before tax, $x \in X$, Y the set of incomes after tax, $y \in Y$, and T the set of amounts taken in tax, $t \in T$, where x, y, and t are measured in £s per annum. We now consider the

1. Blum, Walter J., and Kalven, Harry, Jr.: *The Uneasy Case for Progressive Taxation*, Chicago, 1953, Introduction, p. x. The quotation refers to a small survey made in the United States.

functional relations between X and T and between X and Y in four cases: no tax, a poll tax, a proportionate tax, and a progressive tax. Of course, if we know t as a function of x we automatically know y as a function of x, because $y = x - t$. However, the picture will be clearer if we examine both groups of relations at the same time.

No taxation. Let A be the subset of $X \times T$ which gives the relation between the two sets, X and T, when there is no taxation:

$$A = \{(x, t) : t = 0\}$$

Let B be the subset of $X \times Y$ which gives the relation between the two sets, X and Y, when there is no taxation:

$$B = \{(x, y) : y = x\}$$

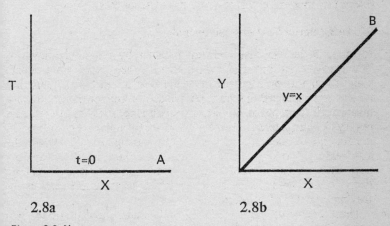

2.8a   2.8b

Figure 2.8 No tax

In Figure 2.8 the two functions are illustrated. The function A is the same as the horizontal axis in part (a). The function B is shown in part (b); provided x and y are measured off in equal measures on the diagram, the line representing B will make an angle of $45°$ with the horizontal axis.

A poll tax of £100 per head. Again taxation does not vary with income. Let C be the subset of $X \times T$ which describes this relation:

$$C = \{(x, t) : t = 100\}$$

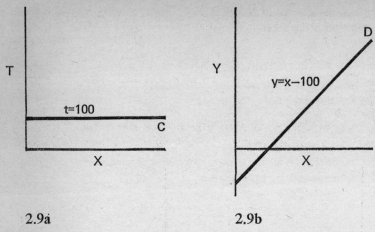

2.9a   2.9b

Figure 2.9 Poll tax

And let D be the corresponding subset of $X \times Y$:

$$D = \{(x, y) : y = x - 100\}$$

How much spending money does a man have when his income is £100 per annum? What happens if his income is less than £100 per annum? Figure 2.9 illustrates.

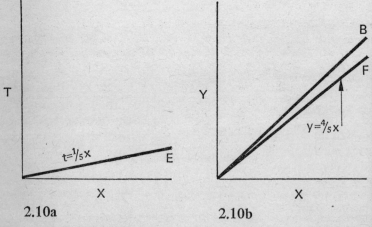

2.10a   2.10b

Figure 2.10 Proportionate tax

A proportionate tax of one-fifth of income. Let E be the subset of $X \times T$ which describes this relation:

$E = \{(x, t) : t = \frac{1}{5}x\}$,

And let F be the corresponding subset of $X \times Y$:

$F = \{(x, y) : y = \frac{4}{5}x\}$

Figure 2.10 illustrates.

A progressive tax. Suppose that the tax law states that of the first £1000 of an individual's income, $\frac{1}{5}$ goes in tax; of the second £1000

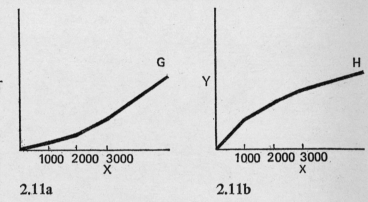

2.11a   2.11b

Figure 2.11 Progressive tax

of income, $\frac{2}{5}$ goes in tax; of the third £1000, $\frac{3}{5}$ goes in tax, and for all income over £3000, $\frac{4}{5}$ goes in tax. This is quite a complicated relation to describe. Let G be the subset of $X \times T$ that gives the relation:

$G = \{(x, t) : t = \frac{1}{5}x$ for $0 < x \leqslant 1000,$
$\qquad t = 200 + \frac{2}{5}(x - 1000)$
$\qquad\qquad$ for $1000 < x \leqslant 2000,$
$\qquad t = 600 + \frac{3}{5}(x - 2000)$
$\qquad\qquad$ for $2000 < x \leqslant 3000,$
$\qquad t = 1200 + \frac{4}{5}(x - 3000)$
$\qquad\qquad$ for $x > 3000\}$

How would H be described, where H is a subset of $X \times Y$ and:

$H = \{(x, y) : y = x - t$ and $t = G(x)\}$?

The symbol $G(x)$ is used in the same way as $f(x)$ was used in section 2.5. The functions G and H are illustrated in Figure 2.11.

Drill

These functions are those defined in the preceding section. Thus
't = A(x)' is the same as 't = 0'; 'y = B(x)' is the same as 'y = x';
't = C(x)' is the same as 't = 100', and so on. Find the value of the
term on the left-hand side of the equals sign when $x = 0$, when
$x = 100$, when $x = 360$, and when $x = 9000$.

1. $t = A(x)$.

2. $y = B(x)$.

3. $t = C(x)$.

4. $y = D(x)$.

5. $t = E(x)$.

6. $y = F(x)$.

7. $t = G(x)$.

8. $y = H(x)$.

Answers

1. 0, 0, 0, 0.
2. 0, 100, 360, 9000.
3. 100, 100, 100, 100.
4. −100, 0, 260, 8900.
5. 0, 20, 72, 1800.
6. 0, 80, 288, 7200.
7. 0, 20, 72, 6000.
8. 0, 80, 288, 3000.

Linear functions and diagrams (continued)

In 1964 about 90 per cent of all income earners in the United Kingdom received incomes of between £400 and £1750 per annum. If we
take into account all the taxes that people pay, not just income tax

but contributions to national insurance, excise duties on drink and tobacco, purchase taxes, etc., the tax system for most people works out to be a proportionate one. For incomes within this range, most people paid about 28 per cent of their income in tax. If we redefine t to cover all taxes and not just income tax, the tax system can be described approximately for 1964 as $t = 0.28x$ for $400 \leqslant x \leqslant 1750$.

We may be more concerned about human welfare than about the amount of tax the government collects from individuals ($t \in T$), or the amount of income left to individuals after tax ($y \in Y$). In order to consider this problem we have to engage in some major reclassification and we have to count complicated groups of numbers. We have to take into account the family responsibilities of the income earner, and also the amount of money and the value of services that the family receives from the state: family allowances, school meals, the value of health and educational services and so on.

Let z be the money value of income minus taxes but plus benefits. There will be a different functional relation between z and x for different classes of income earner because they are now classified according to their family responsibilities. Each function would need several pages to describe it accurately. Let us accept that in 1959, within the income range £400 to £1200, and very approximately, the function for a single man was $z = 200 + 0.6x$, and for a married man with three children it was $z = 250 + 0.9x$. This means that the single man who received a money income before tax of £400 had a 'real' income of $z = 200 + 0.6(400) = £440$. Then for each £1 increase of income before tax his 'real' income increased by £0.6 until $x = 1200$. His break-even income, where taxes paid just equal benefits received, can be found by solving the two equations $z = 200 + 0.6x$ and $z = x$. The solution can be found by putting z for x in the first equation to get $x = 200 + 0.6x$, or $0.4x = 200$, or $x = 500$.

The 'real' income represented by z for the married man with three children can be found in the same way. Note, however, that in this case the break-even income cannot be found, because $z = x$ when $x = 2500$, which is outside the range over which the relation applies, the range where $400 \leqslant x \leqslant 1200$.

2.8 Quadratic functions

A **quadratic function** is one that contains a term in x^2 but no term with a higher power of x. The function may or may not contain a term in x and a constant. Examples are $y = x^2$, $y = 20 + 5x^2$, $y = 2x + x^2$, $y = 20 + 3x + 2x^2$. Quadratic functions are of the form $y = a + bx + cx^2$. If c is positive the function is U-shaped. An average cost function is of this type: X is the set of quantities produced, and $x \in X$, with units of measurement such as tons per annum. Y is the set of average costs of production, with $y \in Y$, and units of measurement such as £s per ton. The average cost declines at first as the overheads (rent, management expenses, etc.) are spread

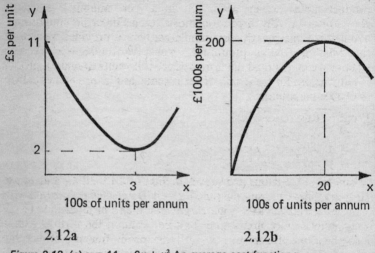

2.12a　　　　　　　　　　2.12b

Figure 2.12 (*a*) $y = 11 - 6x + x^2$ An average cost function; (*b*) $y = 20x - \frac{1}{2}x^2$ A total revenue function

over more and more units and as the division of labour is extended to allow more specialisation, but as production increases further costs tend to rise as more overtime is worked and as the limited equipment and space restrict expansion. Such a function is illustrated in Figure 2.12(*a*).

In this case the precise function is $y = 11 - 6x + x^2$, where x is the number of hundreds of units produced per annum and y is the average cost in £s per unit. If c is negative in the quadratic $y = a + bx + cx^2$, the function is shaped like an inverted U. The relation between the total revenue going to an industry and the total number of units sold will be of this shape. If X is the set of quantities sold, $x \in X$, measured in tons per annum perhaps, and if Y is the set of revenues per annum, $y \in Y$, measured in £s per annum, then y is a function of x. Since there is no revenue when nothing is sold, $y = 0$ when $x = 0$ and the constant a in the general formula is zero. An example of an industry's total revenue function is shown in Figure 2.12(b), where y is revenue in £1000s per annum and x is quantity sold in hundreds of units per annum. This particular function is $y = 20x - \frac{1}{2}x^2$.

We can now consider a simple problem involving quadratics. An industry consists of one firm only, a monopolist. The firm's total revenue (R in £1000s per annum) is a function of the quantity of product sold (x in 100s of units per annum); explicitly $R = 20x - \frac{1}{2}x^2$. The firm's total costs (C in £1000s per annum) are a function of the quantity produced (x, as before, provided we assume that what is sold is produced); explicitly $C = 17 + x^2$. Within what range of x should the firm produce if it wants to make a profit?

Let N stand for the profit, or net revenue as it is sometimes called, in £1000s per annum.

Profit = Revenue $-$ Cost
$$N = R - C$$
$$N = (20x - \tfrac{1}{2}x^2) - (17 + x^2)$$
$$N = -17 + 20x - \tfrac{3}{2}x^2$$

The three functions are shown in Figure 2.13. R, C, and N are each functions of x, so each function can be depicted on a graph with x on the horizontal axis. Since revenue, cost and profit each have the same units of measurement, £1000s per annum, the vertical axis is also the same. Since $N = R - C$, the profit function shows the vertical distance between the revenue and cost functions. If cost is greater than revenue, profit is negative.

There is an important point to make about the way the letters C, R, and N are used here. When stating '$N = R - C$' the three letters are used as variables. Similarly in the statement '$C = 17 + x^2$', C is used as a variable. If Y is the set of numbers which measure £1000s per annum, then $C \in Y$, $R \in Y$, and $N \in Y$ in the same way that $y \in Y$. This is conventional notation in economics. However, we are also referring to C as the total cost function, as that particular mapping from the set X to the set Y that would allow us to find total costs when the quantity is known. We are using C as we would in the expression '$y = C(x)$', which is a particular function relating the variables x and y. In this sense C is a subset of $X \times Y$: $C \subseteq X \times Y$. Similarly, when R and N are used as functions: $R \subseteq X \times Y$ and $N \subseteq X \times Y$.

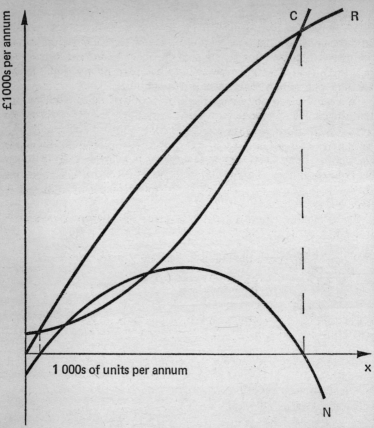

Figure 2.13 Profit is revenue minus cost

The justification for using the same letters for two different things is that it saves notation, and since the context does the defining for us there is little risk of confusion. C, R, and N are abbreviations both for variables (members of sets) and for functions (subsets of product sets).

The problem of finding within what range of x the firm should produce in order to make a profit has now been simplified into finding the two values of x, where $N = 0$. We can find these values either by drawing an accurate graph or by using algebra, as shown in the next section.

2.9 Finding the roots of a quadratic

In the quadratic function $y = a + bx + cx^2$, the roots are the values of x for which $y = 0$. For example, $y = 20x - \frac{1}{2}x^2$ can be written $y = x(20 - \frac{1}{2}x)$ and y is zero either if x is zero or if x is 40; so the roots of this quadratic function are 0 and 40.

(If a quadratic function does not cut the x-axis at all, there are no real values of x for which $y = 0$. For example, $y = 1 + x^2$ becomes $x^2 + 1 = 0$ when y is zero, so $x^2 = -1$ and $x = \pm\sqrt{-1}$. The square root of minus one is an imaginary number. Although it turns out to be very useful in advanced statistics and dynamic economics, it need not concern us here. The average cost function in Figure 2.12(a) cuts the x-axis at imaginary values of x, that is, it does not really cut it.)

The following formula gives the values of x where a quadratic function cuts the x-axis:

If $y = a + bx + cx^2$, then the roots of the equation are

$$x = \frac{1}{2c}\left[-b \pm \sqrt{b^2 - 4ac}\right]$$

For example, if $y = 20x - \frac{1}{2}x^2$, then $a = 0$, $b = 20$, and $c = -\frac{1}{2}$, so:

$$x = \frac{1}{2(-\frac{1}{2})}\left[-20 \pm \sqrt{20^2 - 4(0)(-\frac{1}{2})}\right]$$
$$= -1[-20 \pm \sqrt{20^2}]$$
$$= -1[-20 \pm 20]$$
$$= -1[0, \text{ or } -40]$$
$$= 0, \text{ or } 40$$

The proof is given below for those who do not like to take formulae on trust. This proof is suggested by the pattern which results when an expression such as $(h + x)$ is squared:

$$(h + x)^2 = h^2 + 2hx + x^2$$

Now $(h + x)^2 = 0$ when $x = -h$. If we can arrange $a + bx + cx^2$ into the same pattern as $h^2 + 2hx + x^2$, we may find a formula which will enable us to find the roots of any quadratic. The following manipulation, known as completing the square, shows how the formula is derived:

$$a + bx + cx^2 = 0$$

$$\frac{a}{c} + \frac{b}{c}x + x^2 = 0$$

$$\frac{a}{c} + 2\frac{b}{2c}x + x^2 = 0$$

$$\frac{a}{c} - \left(\frac{b}{2c}\right)^2 + \left(\frac{b}{2c}\right)^2 + 2\left(\frac{b}{2c}\right)x + x^2 = 0$$

$$\frac{a}{c} - \left(\frac{b}{2c}\right)^2 + \left(\frac{b}{2c} + x\right)^2 = 0$$

$$\left(\frac{b}{2c} + x\right)^2 = \left(\frac{b}{2c}\right)^2 - \frac{a}{c}$$

$$\left(\frac{b}{2c} + x\right)^2 = \frac{b^2 - 4ac}{4c^2}$$

$$\frac{b}{2c} + x = \pm\sqrt{\frac{b^2 - 4ac}{4c^2}}$$

$$= \pm\frac{1}{2c}\sqrt{b^2 - 4ac}$$

$$x = -\frac{b}{2c} \pm \frac{1}{2c}\sqrt{b^2 - 4ac}$$

$$= \frac{1}{2c}[-b \pm \sqrt{b^2 - 4ac}]$$

We are now equipped for a return to the problem of the monopolist's profit. Finding those values of x between which profit will be positive is the same problem as finding the values of x which make $N = 0$, where $N = -17 + 20x - \frac{3}{2}x^2$. We substitute in the above formula $a = -17$, $b = 20$, and $c = -\frac{3}{2}$, so:

$$x = \frac{1}{2(-\frac{3}{2})}[-20 \pm \sqrt{(20)^2 - 4(-17)(-\frac{3}{2})}]$$

$$= -\frac{1}{3}[-20 \pm \sqrt{(400 - 102)}]$$

$$= -\frac{1}{3}(-20 \pm 17\cdot31) \quad \text{via logarithms, see Chapter 3}$$

$$= 0\cdot96 \text{ or } 12\cdot44$$

Since x is measured in 100s of units, the firm must produce between 96 and 1244 units if it wants to make a profit. (The most profitable level of production will be calculated in Chapter 5.)

2.10 Cubic functions

A cubic function always contains a term in x^3. It may or may not contain terms in x and x^2 and a constant term. It does not contain terms other than these (no terms in x^4, x^5, $\frac{1}{x}$, for example). The general formula relating x to y as a cubic function is $y = a + bx$

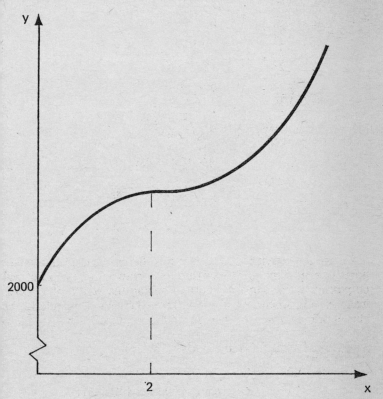

Figure 2.14 A total cost function

$+\, cx^2 + dx^3$. The shape of the cubic function, where a, b, and d are positive but c is negative, is useful for illustrating a common type of total cost function. The graph of the particular function $y = 2000 + 12x - 6x^2 + x^3$ is shown in Figure 2.14.

If we let y be total costs in £s per annum and x be total output in units of product per annum, the function illustrates the way costs often respond to changes in output. When output is zero, $x = 0$ and $y = a$, so £a are the fixed costs. As output expands costs increase, at first less and less quickly as the spare machinery is used instead of lying idle, but later (when $x > 2$) more and more quickly as bottlenecks develop.

Drill

1. Which of the following groups of ordered pairs are definitely not members of functions?

   i. (2, 9), (2, 8), (1, 17), (1, 16).
   ii. (1, 1), (2, 4), (3, 9), (4, 16).
   iii. (17, 1), (19, 2), (21, 3), (25, 4).
   iv. (Henry, Ann Boleyn), (Henry, Anne of Cleves), (Henry, Katherine Parr), (William, Mary).

2. Which of the following relations are functions of the form $y = f(x)$, where $x \in X$ and $y \in Y$?

   i. $x^2 + y^2 = 25$.
   ii. $x^2 + y^2 = 25$ and $x \geqslant 0$.
   iii. $x^2 + y^2 = 25$ and $y \geqslant 0$.

Sketch the relation and illustrate the mapping rule from X to Y in the three cases. State whether the mapping rules are one-into-one, two-into-one, one-into-two, or two-into-two.

3. Graph the following functions.
On the same diagram, from $x = -3$ to $x = 3$.

   i. $y = 2x + 3$.
   ii. $y = 2x - 3$.
   iii. $y = -2x + 3$.
   iv. $y = -2x - 3$.

On a second diagram, from $x = -3$ to $x = 3$.

   v. $y = 2x^2 + 3x$.
   vi. $y = 2x^2 + 3x + 1$.

vii. $y = 2x^2 - 3x$.
viii. $y = 2x^2 - 3x + 1$.

On a third diagram, from $x = -3$ to $x = 3$.

ix. $y = -2x^2 + 3x$.
x. $y = -2x^2 - 3x - 1$.

On a fourth diagram, from $x = 0$ to $x = 6$.

xi. $y = x^3 - 10x^2 + 40x$.
xii. $y = x^3 - 10x^2 + 40x + 20$.

4. In question 3, parts v, vi, vii, viii, ix, and x use the formula for finding the roots of a quadratic to check that the curves cut the x-axis correctly.

5. Is the following statement correct: '{linear functions} $\subseteq$ {smooth functions} $\subseteq$ {continuous functions} $\subseteq$ {functions} $\subseteq$ {relations} $\subseteq$ {product sets}'?

Answers

1. i, iv.
2. Only iii is a function of this form.
 i. $y = \pm\sqrt{25 - x^2}$ is a two-into-two mapping.
 ii. $y = \pm\sqrt{25 - x^2}$, $x \geqslant 0$ is a one-into-two mapping.
 iii. $y = +\sqrt{25 - x^2}$ is a two-into-one mapping, or a function.
4. v. $-1\frac{1}{2}$, 0.
 vi. $-\frac{1}{2}$, -1.
 vii. $1\frac{1}{2}$, 0.
 viii. 1, $\frac{1}{2}$.
 ix. 0, $-1\frac{1}{2}$.
 x. $\frac{1}{2}$, 1.
5. Yes.

Exercise 2

1. The market research department of a firm producing sports cars knows that the firm sells 100 cars a month at a price of £2000. It predicts that a decrease in price of £100 will increase sales to 120, and an increase in price of £100 will decrease sales to 80.

   i. Can the predicted relation between price and sales be stated as a linear function?

   ii. What is quantity sold as a function of price?

   iii. From your knowledge of the market for sports cars would you say that this function accurately predicts the quantity demanded at very low prices?

   iv. Over what range of prices might the function be accurate?

   v. What is price as a function of number of sales per month?

   vi. What is revenue per month as a function of number sold per month?

   vii. What is revenue per annum as a function of number of sales per month?

2. The average tax rate is the proportion of income that a person pays in tax, $\dfrac{t}{x}$. What is the average tax rate for a person earning £4000 per annum if the tax laws can be defined by function A in section 2.7? If by function C? If by function E? If by function G?

3. The marginal tax rate is the proportion of the next £1 of income before tax that will be paid in tax. What are the marginal tax rates for a person earning £2000 per annum before tax, if the tax laws can be defined by function A? If by function C? If by function E? If by function G?

READING

Abbot, P., *Teach Yourself Algebra*, Chapters 13 and 14. (In Abbott the parameters for a quadratic are given as $ax^2 + bx + c$. In this chapter they were given as $a + bx + cx^2$, because this fits better with the conventions of statistics.)

Sawyer, W. W., *Mathematician's Delight*, Chapter 9.

For the use of functions in macroeconomics see: Ford, A. G., *Income, Spending and the Price Level*, Chapter 2.

For illustrations of taxation see: G. H. Peters, *Private and Public Finance*, in this series, pp. 154–6 and 164–84.

Chapter 3

Logarithms

3.1 Introduction

This chapter investigates an important technique of numerical calculation. The technique is also the basis of several types of function. Later in the chapter examples are given of the way in which these functions relate one set of measurements to another set so that predictions can be made about some types of economic behaviour.

3.2 Indices

Indices provide convenient abbreviations, but they become particularly useful as a short-cut in multiplication and division: $a \times a \times a$ can be written more quickly as a^3, spoken 'a cubed', or 'a to the power three', or 'a to the three', and 3 is used here as an index. Some simple examples will illustrate how indices are manipulated. Note in particular the way the indices 0 and 1 are used: any number raised to the power 0 is unity, and any number raised to the power 1 is the number itself.

$$125 = 5 \times 5 \times 5 = 5^1 \times 5^1 \times 5^1 = 5^{1+1+1} = 5^3$$

$$\frac{125}{5} = \frac{5^3}{5^1} = 5^{3-1} = 5^2 = 5 \times 5 = 25$$

$$\frac{5^2}{5^2} = 5^{2-2} = 5^0 = 1$$

$$125 \times 5 = 5^3 \times 5^1 = 5^{3+1} = 5^4$$

$$\frac{125}{1} = \frac{5^3}{5^0} = 5^{3-0} = 5^3$$

In general $a^m \times a^n = a^{m+n}$, and $\dfrac{a^m}{a^n} = a^{m-n}$

The multiplication and division of numbers can be converted to the addition and subtraction of indices. The next group of examples shows a further use of indices where the saving in time spent on calculations is even greater.

$$64 = 8^2 = (2^3)^2 = 2^{3 \times 2} = 2^6$$
$$64 = 4^3 = (2^2)^3 = 2^{2 \times 3} = 2^6$$
$$27^{\frac{1}{3}} = (3^3)^{\frac{1}{3}} = 3^{3 \times \frac{1}{3}} = 3^1 = 3$$
$$625^{\frac{1}{4}} = (5^4)^{\frac{1}{4}} = 5^{4 \times \frac{1}{4}} = 5^1 = 5$$
$$\frac{1}{8^{\frac{1}{3}}} = \frac{1}{(2^3)^{\frac{1}{3}}} = \frac{1}{2^{3 \times \frac{1}{3}}} = \frac{1}{2^1} = 2^{-1}$$

In general $(a^m)^n = a^{m \times n}$, and $(a^m)^{\frac{1}{n}} = a^{\frac{m}{n}}$

The logic of these rules will become clear when we come to deal with logarithmic functions. Note that the square root of a number is that number raised to the power $\frac{1}{2}$. So $\sqrt{a} = a^{\frac{1}{2}}$.

3.3 Logarithms

Another way of saying '$8 = 2^3$' is to say 'the logarithm-to-the-base-2 of 8 is 3'. Similarly, '$100 = 10^2$' is equivalent to 'the logarithm-to-the-base-10 of 100 is 2'. This peculiar way of expressing indices leads to an easier way of multiplying and dividing, particularly if logarithms-to-the-base-10 are used. Because of their popularity, logarithms-to-the-base-10 are known as **common logarithms**.

A common logarithm transforms a number into 10 raised to a particular power. A common logarithm is defined by stating that '$a = 10^m$' is the same as '$\log_{10} a = m$'. If the number is 1000, we know that $1000 = 10^3$ so the common logarithm of 1000 is 3. In general: $a = 10^{\log a}$. The subscript $_{10}$ is the base of the logarithm, but since most of the logarithms used in this book are common logarithms we can omit the subscript without leading to confusion. Tables of common logarithms are readily available and the reader should arm himself with a set before reading further. The following examples are given to show the reader how the eyes can move in a rhythm to spot the meaning of a logarithm.

$10^0 = 1$, so $\log 1 = 0$
$10^{\frac{1}{2}} = \sqrt{10} = 3 \cdot 162$, so $\log 3 \cdot 162 = \frac{1}{2} = 0 \cdot 5$
$10^1 = 10$, so $\log 10 = 1$
$10^{\frac{3}{2}} = 10^{1 + \frac{1}{2}} = 10^1 \times 10^{\frac{1}{2}} = 10 \times 3 \cdot 162 = 31 \cdot 62$, so $\log 31 \cdot 62 = 1 \cdot 5$
$10^2 = 100$, so $\log 100 = 2$

By working out many such examples a graph of the function $y = \log x$ can be obtained. This is illustrated in Figure 3.1. Note how large increases in x are matched by smaller and smaller increases in y, when x is greater than 1.

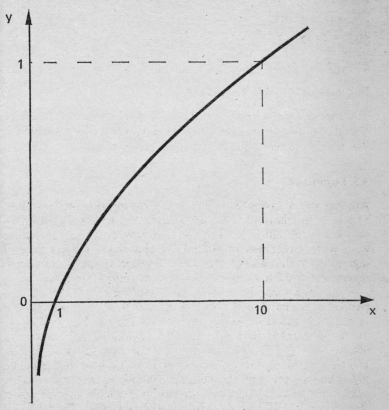

Figure 3.1 y as a logarithmic function of x

Tables of logarithms are confusing to use at first. They appear to show the logarithms of those numbers from 10·00 to 99·99. However, the logarithms in the tables range from 0 to 1, and we know that 0 is log 1 (since $10^0 = 1$) and that 1 is log 10 (since $10^1 = 10$). Therefore we have to remember that although the tables say the numbers range from 10·00 to 99·99, they mean from 1·000 to 9·999. (Some modern log tables actually say what they mean.)

Once this difficulty has been overcome a second one presents itself. What happens if the number whose logarithm we want to know does not lie between 1 and 10? The following examples illustrate how a number is converted so that its logarithm can be found from the log tables.

$$\begin{aligned} \log 326\cdot3 &= \log (100 \times 3\cdot263) \\ &= \log 100 + \log 3\cdot263 \\ &= 2 + \log 3\cdot263 \\ &= 2 + 0\cdot5136 \text{ since } \log 3\cdot263 = 0\cdot5136 \\ &= 2\cdot5136 \end{aligned}$$

$$\begin{aligned} \log 0\cdot08 &= \log (0\cdot01 \times 8) \\ &= \log 0\cdot01 + \log 8 \\ &= -2 + \log 8 \\ &= -2 + 0\cdot9031 \text{ since } \log 8 = 0\cdot9031 \end{aligned}$$

This is sometimes written for convenience as $\bar{2}\cdot9031$. The minus sign over the 2 means that only the 2 is negative, the remainder of the expression being positive.

What is 8 per cent of £362·3? To answer this we have to find $0\cdot08 \times 326\cdot3$. To solve the multiplication problem we convert the numbers to logarithms via the log tables, add the logarithms, and then convert back to numbers via the anti-log tables. (An anti-logarithm converts the power of 10 into an ordinary number.)

$$\begin{aligned} 326\cdot3 \times 0\cdot08 &= \text{antilog} (\log 326\cdot3 + \log 0\cdot08) \\ &= \text{antilog} (2\cdot5136 - 2 + 0\cdot9031) \\ &= \text{antilog} (1\cdot4167) \\ &= 26\cdot10 \qquad \text{since antilog } 0\cdot4167 = 2\cdot610 \end{aligned}$$

so 8 per cent of £326·3 is £26·1.

The next example illustrates the reason for using logarithms, which is that adding is easier than multiplying. The problem is to find $360^{0\cdot95}$. First a few words about what the expression means. $360^{0\cdot01}$ means that expression which, if we took 100 of such expressions and multiplied them together, would give us 360: if $x = 360^{0\cdot01}$, then $x^{100} = 360$. The expression $360^{0\cdot95}$ results from multiplying 95 of such x's together, each x being $360^{0\cdot01}$. Problems involving numbers like this often occur in economics.

The approach is to keep taking logarithms until the stage is reached where we can add instead of having to multiply.

$\log 360^{0.95} = 0.95 \times \log 360$

$$\begin{aligned}
\log (\log 360^{0.95}) &= \log 0.95 + \log (\log 360) \\
&= \bar{1}.9777 + \log (2.5563) \\
&\qquad \text{since } \log 0.95 = \bar{1}.9777 \\
&\qquad \text{and } \log 360 = 2.5563 \\
&= \bar{1}.9777 + 0.4075 \\
&\qquad \text{since } \log 2.5563 = 0.4075 \\
&= -1 + 0.9777 + 0.4075 \\
&= -1 + 1.3852 \\
&= 0.3852
\end{aligned}$$

$$\begin{aligned}
\log 360^{0.95} &= 2.428 && \text{since antilog } 0.3852 = 2.428 \\
360^{0.95} &= 267.9 && \text{since antilog } 2.428 = 267.9
\end{aligned}$$

Once the principles are understood, some time can be saved by doing the calculations in clearly labelled columns:

Number	log	log log
$360^{0.95}$	2.5563*	0.4075*
	0.95	$+\bar{1}.9777*$
267.9†	2.428†	0.3852

* via log tables   † via anti-log tables

3.4 Log linear functions

Linear relations are very easy to use, but many relations in the world are not linear. There is a group of non-linear functions which can be manipulated into a form that allows them to be handled with the same ease as linear functions. These are functions of the form $s = ap^b$, where s and p are variables; a and b are parameters. If we take the logarithm of both sides of the equal sign the two sides will still be equal, so

$$\begin{aligned}
\log s &= \log ap^b \\
&= \log a + \log p^b \\
&= \log a + b \log p
\end{aligned}$$

Put $y = \log s$ and $x = \log p$; also note that if a is constant so is $\log a$. This gives the expression $y = (\text{constant}) + bx$ which is of the same form as a linear function. $s = ap^b$ is not a linear relation between the variables, but it is a linear relation between the logarithms of the variables. Such a function is called **linear in logarithms** or in short **log linear**.

There are many examples of such relationships. Two of them are sufficiently important in economics to warrant sections to themselves later in the chapter. First we give an interesting everyday example.

A vehicle is liable to aquaplane and go out of control if it is

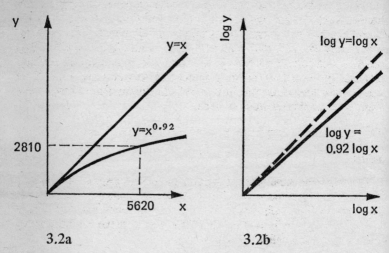

3.2a   3.2b

Figure 3.2 (a) y as a power function of x; (b) Log y as a linear function of log x

driven fast on a surface covered with water, as on a road in heavy rain. The highest safe speed depends on the tyre pressure. If s is the highest safe speed in miles per hour, and p is the tyre pressure in pounds per square inch, the relationship is $s = 9p^{\frac{1}{2}}$. Of course if one is lucky enough to have a car whose tyre pressure is 25 lb. per sq. in. the formula is easy to work out: maximum safe speed is $9(25)^{\frac{1}{2}} = 9 \times 5 = 45$ m.p.h. For less obvious pressures the formula can be converted to logarithmic form and the solution found from log tables, a difficult task at 70 m.p.h. in a thunderstorm, but not at a desk.

$$s = 9p^{\frac{1}{2}}$$
$$\log s = \log 9 + \tfrac{1}{2} \log p$$

Log linear relations also allow us to invent a simpler progressive tax system than the one given in section 2.7. Let the relation between income before tax (x) and income after tax (y) be of the form $y = x^b$. We have to decide what value we should make the parameter b in order to have a reasonable tax system. If $b = 0$, $y = x^0 = 1$, so everyone is left with £1 per annum of pocket money. If $b = 1$, $y = x$ so there is no tax. A progressive tax should allow y to increase as x increases in order to reward people for working harder, but y should increase less and less rapidly with increases in x. This will happen provided b is greater than 0 but less than 1, $0 < b < 1$. An example which would give a tax system which was fiercely progressive compared with the present system would be $y = x^{0.92}$. This function is pictured in two ways in Figure 3.2. In part (a) the relation between the variables shows y increasing less and less quickly as x increases, but, as shown in part (b), the relationship between the logarithms of the variables is linear.

Drill

1. Draw on the same sheet of graph paper the graphs of $y = \frac{1}{2}x^2$, $y = \frac{1}{2}x^1$, $y = \frac{1}{2}x^{\frac{1}{2}}$, and $y = \frac{1}{2}x^0$ over the range from $x = 1$ to $x = 4$. The approach in each case is to find the ordered pairs (x, y) for $x = 1$, $x = 2$, $x = 3$, and $x = 4$. Then sketch in the smooth curve joining the points defined by these pairs.

2. Draw on a second sheet of graph paper the graphs of $y = \frac{1}{2}x^2$, $y = \frac{1}{2}x^1$, and $y = \frac{1}{2}x^{\frac{1}{2}}$ from $x = 0$ to $x = 1$. Compare the behaviour of the curves when x is greater than one with x less than one.

3. Draw on a third sheet of graph paper the curves for $y = x^{-\frac{1}{2}}$, $y = x^{-1}$, and $y = x^{-2}$ from $x = 0$ to $x = 3$. Note that as x approaches zero, $\dfrac{1}{x}$ moves towards infinity.

4. Sketch the shapes of $y = \frac{1}{2}x^2$, $y = \frac{1}{2}x$, $y = \frac{1}{2}x^{\frac{1}{2}}$, $y = x^{-\frac{1}{2}}$, $y = x^{-1}$, and $y = x^{-2}$ when $\log x$ is plotted on the horizontal axis and $\log y$ on the vertical axis.

5. Draw the graph of $y = 3^x$ from $x = -1$ to $x = 1 \cdot 5$.

3.5 Learning by doing

In many industries the cost of producing a unit of product falls rapidly as the experience of the labour force increases. This reduction in costs has been particularly true for the Swedish iron-ore industry and the American air-frame industry, but it is being noticed in other industries as more records become available and as investigators know what to look for.

If U is the cost of producing the Nth unit, the relation between U and N is log linear: $U = aN^{-b}$, where a and b are positive parameters particular to the industry concerned. Note that there is no mention of time in the units of measurement. We are not dealing with the annual output of an industry but with the total output produced to date. The learning occurs because of the number of units which have been produced by that industry over the whole of history. The production process builds up a stock of knowledge.

The cost of the first unit produced is the cost when N is 1: $U = a(1)^{-b} = a$. Since the index of N is negative, the cost declines as N increases. Figure 3.3 illustrates. Figure 3.3 also illustrates the way in which a continuous function can be used to give the relationship between discrete variables. N takes only integral values. We do not want to know, nor could we find, the cost of the 9·87th airframe produced, but the relation does allow us to find the cost of the whole units.

3.6 Zipf's Law

A fascinating relation is that discussed by Zipf in his book *Human Behaviour and the Principle of Least Effort*.[1] A reasonable supposition is that housewives will visit a shopping centre less frequently the further they have to travel to get there. If x is the travelling time in minutes and y is the number of visits made each month, one can often predict y if x is known. It has also been found that the more letters there are in a word, the less frequently is the word used. If x is the number of letters in the word and y is the number of times the word appears in print, there is often a rough relationship between y and x. Both of these are examples of relationships between the amount of effort expended in order to perform some task (x) and

1. Zipf, G. K., *Human Behaviour and the Principle of Least Effort*, New York, Hafner, 1965.

the number of times this task is performed (y). There are many others, but the surprising aspect of these relationships is that they often fit the form $y = ax^{-b}$. Only the parameters vary with the phenomena being studied.

There is no doubt that this relation occurs frequently in the world. However, as a general 'law' the relationship has been refuted often, so if a log linear relation is suspected between two variables this suspicion must be tested by taking observations. The procedure is simple. First find a set of some measurement of effort such as the

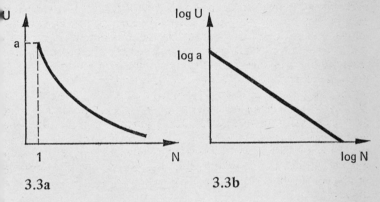

3.3a   3.3b

Figure 3.3 The learning curve

distances travelled by housewives from their homes to a shopping centre, and let x be a member of this set. Next find a set which gives the frequency with which people enjoy the fruits of this effort, such as the number of visits made to the shopping centre each month. Then take ordered pairs of observations (x, y), one pair for Mrs Smith, another for Mrs Jones, a third for Mrs Brown and so on. Finally, plot the pairs (log x, log y) on a sheet of graph paper. If the points are on or near a straight line, this is an example of Zipf's Law since the law says that $y = ax^{-b}$, and this becomes $\log y = \log a - b \log x$, which is a log linear function. Once the parameters are known the relation becomes particularly useful for planning car-parks, shopping centres, bus routes and so on. Functions of this type are used in geography, librarianship and linguistics as well as in economics.

3.7 Summary of widely used continuous functions

Linear: $\qquad y = a + bx$

Quadratic: $\quad y = a + bx + cx^2$

Cubic: $\qquad y = a + bx + cx^2 + dx^3$

Log linear: $\quad y = ax^b$, or $\log y = \log a + b \log x$

Logarithmic: $y = \log x$. If the logarithms are to the base 10, this logarithmic function is the same shape as $x = 10^y$, although the one expresses y as a function of x and the other expresses x as a function of y.

Power: $\qquad y = 10^x$. This power function is the same shape as $x = \log y$. Note that y as a logarithmic function of x is the same shape as x as a power function of y.

Exercise 3

1. A firm is considering moving to a different site where all equipment and buildings will be new. The engineers and accountants make estimates of the costs of producing various amounts of output. When logarithms of these costs and outputs are plotted on a graph the resulting points fall on a straight line, so that the relation between total costs (C in £s) and output (x in units of product) is approximately: $\log C = 1 \cdot 0792 + 3 \log x$. Show that total cost as an algebraic function of output is $C = 12x^3$.

2. An aero-frame manufacturer finds that the cost, U, of the Nth aero-frame made is given by the function $U = aN^{-\frac{1}{3}}$, where a is the cost in £(million) of the first aero-frame. For a particular supersonic model the cost of the first frame is £100(million) and the market price is £10(million). How many must be produced before the cost per frame becomes less than the selling price?

3. A local authority considers that a learning process occurs as more and more slag-heaps are made safe and beautiful. The cost of tackling the first slag-heap is estimated to be £10 000, and the cost of tackling the tenth slag-heap is estimated to be £4000. Calculate the formula for finding the cost of making safe and beautifying the Nth slag-heap, on the assumption that the formula for learning-by-doing applies. What is the estimate of the cost of tackling the 100th slag-heap?

4. Describe in symbols and illustrate with diagrams the relation

between time in hours (t) and distance in feet (s) in the following cases. (Assume that s is a function of t, and put t on the horizontal axis.)

    i. A tortoise proceeding steadily at 1 m.p.h. from now.

    ii. A tortoise who thinks about it for an hour and then proceeds steadily at 1 m.p.h.

    iii. A tortoise who is already one mile on his way and then proceeds steadily at 1 m.p.h.

    iv. A tortoise who proceeds at $\frac{4}{5}$ m.p.h. for the first hour and $\frac{6}{5}$ m.p.h. thereafter.

    v. A tired tortoise who is moving, but more and more slowly.

READING

Abbot, P., *Teach Yourself Algebra*, Chapters 15, 16, and 17.

Land, Frank, *The Language of Mathematics*, Chapter 8 and pp. 117–39 of Chapter 9.

Sawyer, W. W., *Mathematician's Delight*, Chapter 6.

Chapter 4

Equilibrium

4.1 The set of market possibilities

If a survey was conducted of all the firms in a particular industry, a result might emerge which showed that the firms in total were prepared to produce and sell 1000 units per annum, but only if the price was at least £10·5 per unit. A further result might show that the firms were prepared to sell a total of 6000 units per annum if the price was greater than or equal to £13 per unit. Analysis of these and other results might show that the range of prices (p) necessary to call forth a particular quantity per annum of the good (x) can be described by the supply relation:

$$p \geqslant 10 + \frac{1}{500}x$$

This relation is pictured in Figure 4.1(a) as the hatched area together with the line S.

Now suppose that a second survey is carried out, this time on the prospective buyers of the product. This survey might show that buyers would buy 1000 units per annum if the price was not more than £19·67 per unit; they would buy 6000 units provided the price was less than or equal to £18. Further analysis of the survey might show that the range of prices (p) necessary to persuade buyers to buy a particular quantity of the good each year (x) is given by the demand relation:

$$p \leqslant 20 - \frac{1}{3000}x$$

This is pictured as the hatched area together with the line D in Figure 5.1(b).

Usually producers cannot unmake goods and consumers cannot demand negative quantities, so x will not be negative. However, producers may decide to offer none of the good for sale (if the price falls below £10) and consumers may decide to buy none of the good (if the price climbs above £20). Therefore common-sense tells us that $x \geqslant 0$.

We have now defined a set of combinations of prices and quantities which could be found in the market for this good. This set of market possibilities, call it M, is illustrated in Figure 4.1(c) as the cross-hatched area. M is a set of possible values of ordered pairs (x, p). It shows those combinations of quantity and price which will both persuade the suppliers to produce and the consumers to purchase.

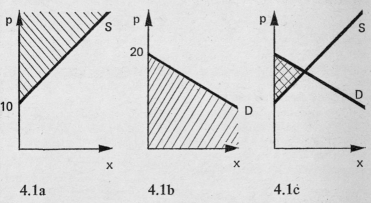

4.1a   4.1b   4.1c

Figure 4.1 (a) Possible price–quantity combinations for sellers; (b) Possible price–quantity combinations for buyers; (c) The set of market possibilities

If P is the set of all prices, $p \in P$, and X is the set of all quantities per annum, $x \in X$, then M is a subset of $X \times P$.

$$M = \{(x, p) : p \geqslant 10 + \frac{1}{500}x,$$
$$p \leqslant 20 - \frac{1}{3000}x,$$
$$x \geqslant 0\}$$

4.2 Supply and demand functions

Although the set of market possibilities defines a range of quantity-price combinations, it cannot explain a particular price and quantity, nor can it predict how prices and quantities will change in response to changes in supply and demand conditions. In order to do this we need the more precise tools provided by functions.

When using functions to describe real phenomena we are usually describing cause and effect. In a causal relation, 'the thing that does the explaining' is called the independent variable and 'the thing to be explained' is called the dependent variable. The following four statements can often be used with the same meaning:

Quantity supplied is caused by the price.
Quantity supplied depends on the price.
Quantity supplied is a function of price.
$x = f(p)$.

If we know the precise function we can write it out explicitly, for example, $x = 500p - 5000$, where x is units offered for sale per annum and p is the price in £s per unit.

It is conventional to write the independent variable (in this case p) on the right-hand side of the equals sign and the dependent variable on the left-hand side. Of course, when we are doing calculations we move the variables about as we like. Conventions about where to write what are guides to understanding. Like all conventions they can be broken if they become inconvenient, but breaking them may cause confusion if the context does not make the position clear.

For example, $x = 500p - 5000$

becomes $\dfrac{1}{500} x = p - 10$

Therefore $\quad p = 10 + \dfrac{1}{500}x$

This is the straight line S, illustrated in Figure 4.1(a). However, the function $x = 500p - 5000$ is not the same as the relation $p \geqslant 10 + \dfrac{1}{500}x$.

A demand function can be described in a similar way to the supply function. The quantity demanded depends on the price, or quantity demanded is a function of price. We have already used the notation '$x = f(p)$' to describe the supply function, so we have to use a different way of describing the demand function. We could use '$x = g(p)$' to show that g and f are different functions, and write that 'x is the quantity demanded' to remind us that we are dealing with a different set of quantities. However, it is less confusing at first to use subscripts on x, writing x_s for quantity supplied and x_d for quantity demanded.

We can describe the supply and demand functions in a way that is more easily remembered by using S and D instead of f and g.

$$x_s = S(p)$$
$$x_d = D(p)$$

An example of a precise demand function is $x_d = 60\,000 - 3000p$ where x_d is the quantity demanded in units per annum and p is the price in £s per unit. (Check that this demand function can be represented by the same line that was used to represent the boundary of the relation $p \leqslant 20 - \dfrac{1}{3000}x$, the line D in Figure 4.1(b).)

Economic theory tells us that a market is in equilibrium when the quantity demanded equals the quantity supplied, so provided the supply and demand functions are known we can find the equilibrium price. In our example:

$$x_s = 500p - 5000$$
$$x_d = 60\,000 - 3000p$$
$$x_s = x_d$$

These are three equations in three unknowns, x_s, x_d, and p. Two of the equations are functions and one is an equilibrium condition.

Since $x_s = x_d$
$$500p - 5000 = 60\,000 - 3000p$$
$$3500p = 65\,000$$
Therefore $p = £18 \cdot 57$ per unit

Also by substituting this value of p into either the supply or the demand functions: $x_s = x_d = 4286$ units per annum. The price of £18·57 per unit brings equilibrium to the market so that 4286 units will be traded each year, unless the supply and demand functions change.

Such equations do not always have a solution. One can imagine an industry which becomes more and more efficient as it becomes larger. Specialised suppliers of parts develop and trade associations grow to keep everyone well informed. However, if the industry shrank these specialised firms would go out of business; there would be less division of labour. The supply function would slope downward from left to right. It is just possible, though very improbable, that such an industry would have a supply function, over the range in which we were interested, such as:

$$x_s = 40\,000 - 3000p$$
$$x_d = 60\,000 - 3000p$$

If this supply function is compared with the demand function, it is seen that the two would be parallel lines on a diagram. They do not intersect and in practice there would be no equilibrium in such a market.

It is also possible to have a supply function which, if plotted on a diagram, would be above the demand function for all positive values of x. Not only is this possible; it is also very common. It accounts for the vast list of products which nobody bothers to produce.

Finally, we could have a supply function which intercepts the demand function at a negative price, although the quantity is positive. Suppliers are prepared to pay to get rid of the good, and demanders will only accept the good if they are given money to do so. Such a good is rubbish.

4.3 Supply and demand diagrams

In mathematics there is a convention that the independent variable is pictured on the horizontal axis of a diagram, and the dependent variable on the vertical axis. If we were to picture a supply function we would be conventional mathematicians if we put price on the horizontal axis and quantity on the vertical axis. In economics the convention is to put price on the vertical axis. This may be to emphasise that the equilibrium price is the dependent variable, the thing to be explained, and it is explained by both the supply function and the demand function. However, we must remember that the approach taken here does not include dates. We tend to ignore the problem of what happened first and we concentrate on the final result, the equilibrium position. Analysis which does not mention the order in time when something happened is known as **Static Analysis**. This type of analysis involves simpler concepts than the more realistic dynamic analysis, but it can lead to some confusion about which variables are independent and which are dependent. Often the easiest way is simply to think of the dependent variable as the one we do not know yet.

The following two functions and one equilibrium condition form a simple **model** of a market:

$$x_s = S(p) = 2p - 200 \quad \checkmark$$
$$x_d = D(p) = -\tfrac{1}{2}p + 600$$
$$x_s = x_d$$

Check that the equilibrium price is 320 monetary units and the equilibrium quantity is 440 units of the good per period of time. The economist's way of picturing this is given in Figure 4.2(*a*) and the mathematician's in Figure 4.2(*b*).

Negative quantities do not interest us in this problem so we can ignore the area to the left of the *p*-axis in Figure 4.2(*a*), or the area below the *p*-axis in Figure 4.2(*b*). We shall always assume that $x_s \geqslant 0$ and $x_d \geqslant 0$.

When the supply and demand functions are clearly labelled there is

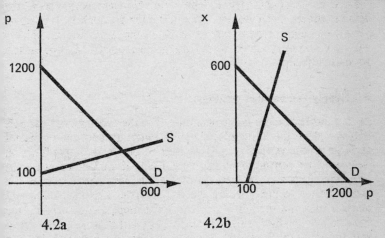

4.2a   4.2b

Figure 4.2 Supply and demand; (*a*) The economist's picture;
(*b*) The mathematician's picture

often no need to use the subscripts on x_s and x_d because the context does the defining for us. Both x_s and x_d are members of the set of quantities of the good per period of time (such as vehicles per month, or tons of wheat per annum). If we call this set *X*, then $x \in X$ and this is often sufficient. Of course $x_s \in X$ and $x_d \in X$.

4.4 Shifts of the demand function

Suppose that the number of consumers doubles but that the tastes and income of the typical consumer stay the same. At each price, twice the amount would be bought as was the case before. Quantity demanded will increase from $(-\tfrac{1}{2}p + 600)$ to $(-p + 1200)$. Since tastes and average income have stayed the same, a price of 1200 monetary units will result in zero quantity demanded both before and after the increase in the number of potential customers. To find the new equilibrium price and quantity we use the new demand function, the unchanged supply function and the usual equilibrium

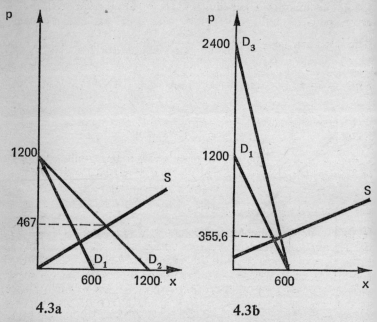

4.3a   4.3b

Figure 4.3 Shift of the demand function; (*a*) More consumers; (*b*) Higher income

condition. The subscripts on *D* are used to distinguish between the different demand functions.

Before the change $x_d = D_1(p) = -\frac{1}{2}p + 600$
After the change $x_d = D_2(p) = -p + 1200$
$$x_s = S(p) = 2p - 200$$

$x_s = x_d$ when $2p - 200 = -p + 1200$, so the new equilibrium is when $p = 466{\cdot}67$ and this leads to a quantity traded of $x_s = x_d = 733{\cdot}33$ units per time period. This case is illustrated in Figure 4.3(*a*).

Now consider the case where tastes change but the number of

customers in the market does not. If consumers decide that the good is more attractive to them than it was before, they will be prepared to pay higher prices for each particular quantity. A simple example of this would be the case where consumers are prepared to pay twice the price for each quantity that they demand. The demand function changes from D_1 to D_3 as illustrated in Figure 4.3(b) and in the algebra below:

Before the change $x_d = D_1(p) = -\frac{1}{2}p + 600$ ✓

so $\qquad\qquad\qquad\qquad 2x_d = -p + 1200$

and $\qquad\qquad\qquad\qquad\quad p = 1200 - 2x_d$

After the change $\qquad\qquad\quad p = 2400 - 4x_d$

$\qquad\qquad\qquad\qquad\qquad \frac{1}{4}p = 600 - x_d$

So the new function is $x_d = D_3(p) = 600 - \frac{1}{4}p$

As before $\qquad\qquad x_s = S(p) = 2p - 200$

$x_s = x_d$ when $2p - 200 = 600 - \frac{1}{4}p$, giving a new equilibrium price of 355·6 which leads to a quantity traded of $x_s = x_d = 511\cdot2$.

4.5 A tax of £t per unit of quantity

In this section we show that the results of imposing a tax are different from those which are popularly supposed. Continuing with the simple market which we invented in the previous sections, we now consider the case where the government imposes a tax of £t per unit on the suppliers of the product. The quantity offered for sale at each price will change because of the tax. When the supply function is $x_s = S(p) = 2p - 200$, a price of £400, for example, will cause 600 units to be offered for sale. After the tax is imposed, the sellers will need a price of more than £400 to persuade them to offer 600 units because the tax authority is taking £t per unit. The new price will have to be £t greater than the old price in order to persuade suppliers to offer the same amount. The price which causes a particular quantity to be offered can be found from the supply function.

If $x_s = 2p - 200$, then $p = 100 + \frac{1}{2}x_s$, provided there is no tax. But in order to persuade suppliers to offer x_s for sale in spite of the tax, the price must be raised to $p = 100 + \frac{1}{2}x_s + t$. After the tax the supply function changes. Call the new supply function $S_t(p)$ and it is found from manipulating the above expression for the new price.

$2p = 200 + x_s + 2t$

$x_s = S_t(p) = 2p - 200 - 2t$

The new equilibrium is found by combining this new supply function with the original demand function:

$$x_d = D(p) = -\tfrac{1}{2}p + 600$$

and $x_s = x_d$ when $2p - 200 - 2t = -\tfrac{1}{2}p + 600$, so the equilibrium price is when $p = 320 + 0.8t$ and the quantity traded is $440 - 0.4t$. Compare this with the old equilibrium: $p = 320$ and $x_s = x_d = 440$. The price rises by £$0.8t$ and the quantity traded declines by the number of units given by $0.4t$. The extent of the change depends on t. Figure 4.4(a) illustrates.

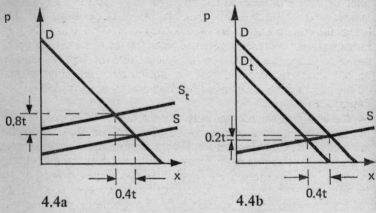

Figure 4.4 (a) A tax on the sellers; (b) A tax on the buyers

Suppose that the tax had been levied from the buyers instead of from the sellers. What happens to price and quantity in this case? Before the tax a price of £500, for example, would have persuaded the buyers to buy $x_d = -\tfrac{1}{2}(500) + 600 = 350$ units. After the tax the buyers will require a price of less than £500 to persuade them to buy 350 units because they are going to have to pay £t per unit to the tax authority in addition to the price they pay to the sellers. In order to persuade them to buy 350 units the price will have to be £$(500 - t)$. The old demand relation was $x_d = D(p) = -\tfrac{1}{2}p + 600$, so the old price could be expressed as $p = -2x_d + 1200$. The new price must be $p = -2x_d + 1200 - t$, giving a new demand function:

$$x_d = D_t(p) = -\tfrac{1}{2}p + 600 - \tfrac{1}{2}t.$$

The new equilibrium is found by combining this new demand function with the original supply function:

$$x_s = S(p) = 2p - 200$$

and $x_s = x_d$ when $2p - 200 = -\frac{1}{2}p + 600 - \frac{1}{2}t$, so the equilibrium price is $320 - 0\cdot2t$ and the quantity traded is $440 - 0\cdot4t$. Figure 4.4(b) illustrates.

A tax imposed on the buyer leads to a decline in quantity of $0\cdot4t$, just the same as when the tax was imposed upon the sellers. The changes in price in the two cases are different: taxing the sellers leads to a rise in price of $0\cdot8t$; taxing the buyers leads to a decline in price of $0\cdot2t$. However, when the buyer pays the tax he pays the market price of £($320 - 0\cdot2t$) plus the tax of £t per unit, and this brings the cost to him of his purchase up to £($320 + 0\cdot8t$) which is the same as the cost of his purchase when the tax was imposed upon the seller. Imposing the tax on the sellers shifts the supply function up but leaves the demand function unchanged. Imposing the tax on the buyers shifts the demand function down but leaves the supply function unchanged.

Who is paying the tax, the sellers or the buyers? The people who pay in the end are not necessarily the same as those upon whom the tax was imposed. The incidence of the tax depends upon a comparison of the slope of the demand function with the slope of the supply function. In this example, the supply function slopes upward by $\frac{1}{2}p$ for each unit change in x_s; the demand function slopes down by $2p$ for each unit change in x_d. For each unit change in price, x_s will change by two units, but x_d will change by only half a unit. The demanders are less willing to adjust to the new situation than are the suppliers. The change in x_d is only a quarter of the change in x_s. The suppliers are four times as successful as the demanders in adjusting their trading so that they can avoid the tax. The demanders pay four times as much tax as the suppliers. The buyers pay £$0\cdot8t$ per unit and the sellers £$0\cdot2t$.

Figure 4.5(a) is an enlarged version of Figure 4.4(a) and illustrates the case where the tax is on the sellers. Point a is the equilibrium price and quantity before the tax is imposed. Point b is the equilibrium price and quantity after the tax. Point c is at the same quantity as point b, but in the vertical direction point c shows the revenue per unit that will be received by the suppliers, the price minus the tax. The distance between c and d is the reduction in the suppliers' revenue per unit due to the tax (in this example £$0\cdot2t$). The distance between d and b is the increase in market price due to the tax (in this sample £0·8t, so consumers 'pay' 80 per cent of this tax and producers 20 per cent).

Figure 4.5(b) illustrates the case when the tax is on the buyers. Point a is as before. Point e is the market equilibrium price and quantity after the tax. The cost per unit to the buyer is the price plus the tax, and this is the point f because the old demand function is exactly the distance t above the new demand function. The distance between g and e is the reduction in market price due to the tax (in this example

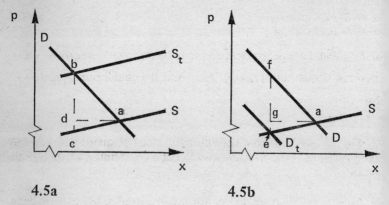

4.5a   4.5b

Figure 4.5 The incidence of the tax is the same

£0·2t) and this part of the tax must be borne by the sellers. The distance from g to f is the amount that must be borne by the buyers. The incidence of the tax is the same regardless of whether it is formally imposed on the buyers or the sellers.

4.6 The identification problem introduced

We have been able to predict the equilibrium price and quantity in a market by using three equations: the demand function, the supply function, and the equilibrium condition. Can we reverse the process? Can we use the observed values of equilibrium price and quantity to find the supply and demand functions? We cannot, and the following drill illustrates why not.

Drill

1. Show that each of these pairs of supply and demand functions will yield an equilibrium price of 12 and an equilibrium quantity of 76.

  i. $x_d = D(p) = 100 - 2p, x_s = S(p) = -20 + 8p$.
  ii. $x_d = D(p) = 90 - \frac{7}{6}p, x_s = S(p) = -8 + 7p$.
  iii. $x_d = D(p) = 76(12)^{\frac{1}{2}}p^{-\frac{1}{2}}, x_s = S(p) = p^3 - 1652$.

2. In the linear demand and supply functions

$$x = D(p) = a + bp$$
$$x = S(p) = c + dp$$

$a, b, c,$ and d are parameters and may be positive or negative. Show that the equilibrium price is $\dfrac{a - c}{d - b}$ and the equilibrium quantity is $\dfrac{ad - bc}{d - b}$.

3. Put the numbers from the linear functions of question 1 into the parameters of question 2 and check that $p = 12$ and $x = 76$ in both cases.

4. Now assume that we do not know $a, b, c,$ and d, but that we have observed $p = 12$ and $x = 76$ in equilibrium, also that we are satisfied that linear functions will give good approximations. Use the equations: $12 = \dfrac{a - c}{d - b}$ and $76 = \dfrac{ad - bc}{d - b}$ to satisfy yourself that each unknown must be expressed in terms of another, so the solution to the pair of equations is indefinite.

There are an infinite number of possible supply and demand relations which would fit the observations. The problem is to identify the right ones. Compare this problem of finding four parameters, $a, b, c, d,$ from two equations with the problem of finding equilibrium values for three variables, $x_s, x_d,$ and p, from three equations.

4.7 Solutions to the identification problem

If the market for a product is competitive, equilibrium price and quantity are decided by the supply and demand functions. Therefore it would be circular reasoning to try to identify these functions by the equilibrium price and quantity alone. When both the supply and demand functions are shifting, the solution to the identification problem is extremely complex. However, there are two simple situations which illustrate the method of solution.

Assume that careful observation of the market convinces us that tastes and incomes have remained constant so that there is no reason to suspect that demand has shifted. However, the industry is known to have gone though a period of technical progress which has reduced costs of production and shifted the supply curve to the right. We have three observations of equilibrium price and quantity at

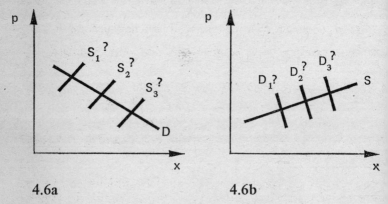

4.6a   4.6b

Figure 4.6 (*a*) Identifying the demand function; (*b*) Identifying the supply function

three different moments in time. We know that the supply function has shifted, although we do not know what the function is at any point of time. However, we now have enough information to identify the demand function. Figure 4.6(*a*) illustrates the case. The supply curves are labelled with question marks after them because the only part of each supply curve that we know is the point which is fixed by the observation of equilibrium price and quantity. Only the demand curve can be identified.

Another simple case is illustrated in Figure 4.6(*b*). Assume that we can observe no reason to suspect that the supply function has shifted, but we know that the industry has engaged in a massive advertising campaign which has shifted the demand function. We cannot identify any of the demand functions, but we can identify the supply function under these circumstances.

Equilibrium prices and quantities are insufficient to identify supply and demand functions. We have to know something extra about supply in order to identify a demand function, and we have to know something extra about demand in order to identify a supply function.

Exercise 4

1. The demand function for a good is $x = D(p) = a + bp$ and the supply function is $x = S(p) = c + dp$, where a, b, c, and d are parameters.

   i. If the good is of the usual type, what are the signs of a, b, c, d?

   ii. Show that if $\dfrac{c - a}{b - d}$ is less than zero, the 'good' is rubbish.

2. Sketch the set M, where $M = \{x, p) : p \geqslant 20 + x,$
$$p \leqslant 10 - x,$$
$$x \geqslant 0\}$$

What type of a set is M? Do many goods have a set of market possibilities of this type?

3. In an imaginary economy, the demand for unskilled workers is given by the function $x = D(w) = 40 - 2w$, where w is the wage in £s per week and x is the quantity demanded in millions of men per week. The supply of such workers is given by the function $x = S(w) = \frac{1}{3}w - 2$, where w is as before and x is the number of millions of men offering themselves for work at this wage.

   i. What is the equilibrium wage and how many men are employed?

   ii. The government imposes on employers a weekly contribution to National Insurance of £2 per employee. What is the new equilibrium wage and how many men are employed?

   iii. If unemployment benefit of £7 per man per week is paid by government, how much extra revenue has the government collected?

4. We have used the equals sign in three different ways: first, 'is by definition' (or 'is identical to'); second, 'is caused by'; third, 'equals in equilibrium'. In which of these ways is it used in the following contexts?

i. Gross National Product = Those goods and services produced
for consumption and gross investment, plus those goods and services produced by government, plus goods and services exported
minus those imported.

ii. Output of a factory = f(labour, machines, raw material,
management skills, technical knowledge, etc.).

iii. What is bought = what is sold.

iv. Either the quantity demanded = the quantity supplied, or the
price will change.

v. $A \cup B = \{x : x \in A$ or $x \in B\}$.

vi. Quantity demanded = a function of price.

5. Explain the meaning of the brackets (   ) in the following contexts.

i. $y = f(x) = 16x^2$.

ii. $y = (a + b)x = ax + bx$.

iii. $y = (a + x)^2$.

iv. $A = \{(x, y) : x + y = 1\}$.

v. The Minister of Housing said that it was all a question of supply
and demand (loud laughter).

vi. $x = x(p) = 25 - \frac{1}{2}p$.

vii. $R = px = p(25 - \frac{1}{2}p)$.

6. Explain the meaning of the juxtaposition of the terms on the left-
hand side of the following equalities.

i. $1\frac{1}{3} = \frac{4}{3}$.

ii. $a\dfrac{b + c}{3} = \dfrac{ab + ac}{3}$.

iii. English men = $E \cap M$.

iv. $37 = 30 + 7$.

v. $ab = a^3 + 7a$, when b is $a^2 + 7$.

READING

Henry, S. G. B., *Elementary Mathematical Economics*, London,
Routledge and Kegan Paul, 1969, Chapter 1.

For illustrations of equilibria in microeconomics see: Harbury,
C. D., *An Introduction to Economic Behaviour*, in this series, Chapter
3, 4 and 5. For illustrations in macroeconomics see Ford, *Income
Spending and the Price Level*, Chapter 3.

For the incidence of taxation see Peters, *Private and Public Finance*,
pp. 158–64.

Chapter 5

The Margin

5.1 Introduction

The word 'marginal' often occurs in economics: marginal cost, marginal revenue, marginal propensity to save, marginal tax rates and so on. The concept of the margin contributes to the explanation of equilibria, to the prediction of changes which will take place in economic variables and to the prescription of courses of action which enable a businessman or government to attain some objective. However, the concept also has applications outside economics. It facilitates the study of all smooth changes. In this chapter we shall see that apparently widely differing concepts such as margin, velocity, gradient, growth, and decay have an underlying unity which enables them to be handled by the same analytical technique.

As an example consider the case of a small businessman whose total costs (C) are related to the number of units produced per week (x) by the function $C = 30 + 16x^2$. At present he is producing 10 units per week. The price per unit is £650, and the market is competitive, so he need not reduce his price in order to persuade customers to buy a greater quantity. Should he increase production?

If he produces one more unit the addition to his costs is the cost of producing 11 units, which we can write as $C(11)$, minus the cost of producing 10 units, $C(10)$.

$$C(11) = 30 + 16(11)^2 = 30 + 1936$$
$$C(10) = 30 + 16(10)^2 = 30 + 1600$$
$$C(11) - C(10) = 336$$

For an additional (or marginal) cost of £336 he receives an additional revenue of £650, obviously a worthwhile move. If the calculation is repeated we find that although the additional cost of the twentieth unit, $C(20) - C(19)$, is £624, which is still profitable, the additional cost of the twenty-first unit is $C(21) - C(20) = £656$, so this unit costs more to produce than is received from its sale. The producer should therefore expand production until he is producing 20 units per week.

This type of calculation is tedious, but the figures which result are used to guide decisions. Provided the market is competitive so that increased sales do not lower price appreciably and changes in price can be ignored, the rule is: if marginal cost is less than price expand production, if greater than price reduce production, and produce up to that level of output where marginal cost equals price. Since this is such a crucial variable a functional relationship between marginal cost and the quantity produced would clearly be convenient. Such a relation can be found by manipulating the total cost function. The next few pages show how this is done, but first we assume that we have found it so that we can illustrate the way in which a marginal cost function cuts out much tedious calculation. If total cost $= 30 + 16x^2$, then marginal cost $= 32x$, as shown later. The most profitable output is where marginal cost $=$ price, or where $32x = 650$, so produce $x = \dfrac{650}{32} = 20 \cdot 3$ units per week, or 20 units to the nearest integer.

5.2 Limits

Analysis of the relation between totals and marginals involves studying the way very small changes in the totals behave. For example, by studying the change in the slope of the cubic function illustrated in Chapter 2, it can be seen that the slope of the function becomes less and less steep at first but then becomes more and more steep as x increases. The concept of the limit is an aid to the understanding of small changes. We start by studying the limiting values of algebraic expressions as the variables become very large, and then study the limiting values of expressions as the variables become very small.

If the same positive number is added to both the numerator and the denominator of a fraction, the value of the fraction is nearer to unity than it was before. For example:

$$\frac{1}{2} = 0 \cdot 5, \text{ but } \frac{1+1}{2+1} = \frac{2}{3} \approx 0 \cdot 67$$

$$\frac{3}{2} = 1 \cdot 5, \text{ but } \frac{3+1}{2+1} = \frac{4}{3} \approx 1 \cdot 33$$

In general, if a and b are constants and x is a positive variable, $\dfrac{a+x}{b+x}$ will tend to unity as x tends to infinity. Note that we can say 'as x tends to infinity, $\dfrac{1+x}{2+x}$ tends to 1', but we should not say '$\dfrac{1 + \text{infinity}}{2 + \text{infinity}} = 1$', because infinity is thought of as a direction rather than a number.

The reader is also reminded that a fraction which has zero for the denominator is meaningless. In order to illustrate this, the graph of $y = \dfrac{1+x}{2+x}$ is shown in Figure 5.1. Note how the value of y approaches

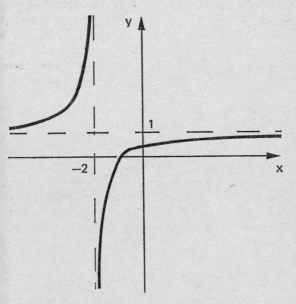

Figure 5.1 The function $y = \dfrac{1 + x}{2 + x}$ does not exist when $x = -2$

both plus infinity and minus infinity as x tends to -2. The expression does not exist when its denominator is zero.

If x tends to infinity, $\dfrac{1}{x}$ tends to zero. In symbols:

$$\frac{1}{x} \longrightarrow 0 \text{ as } x \longrightarrow \infty.$$

Consider the expression $\dfrac{3x+1}{x}$, which can be written $3 + \dfrac{1}{x}$. As x

tends to infinity, $\frac{3x+1}{x}$ tends to 3. The **limiting value** of $\frac{3x+1}{x}$, as x tends to infinity, is 3.

In symbols:

$$\lim_{x \to \infty} \frac{3x+1}{x} = 3$$

We can check that this seems reasonable by substituting increasing values of x in the function:

$$f(x) = \frac{3x+1}{x}$$

$f(0)$ does not exist

$$f(1) = \frac{3(1)+1}{1} = 4$$

$$f(2) = \frac{3(2)+1}{2} = 3 \cdot 5$$

$$f(10) = \frac{3(10)+1}{10} = 3 \cdot 1$$

$$f(100) = \frac{3(100)+1}{100} = 3 \cdot 01$$

We now turn to the problems arising when one of the variables in an expression tends to zero. The limit of $(x+h)$, as h tends to zero, is x. In symbols:

$$\lim_{h \to 0} (x+h) = x$$

There is no limit to $\frac{x}{h}$ as h tends to zero, because the value of the expression becomes larger and larger as the value of h becomes smaller and smaller. Similarly, there is no limit to $\frac{(x+h)^2}{h}$ as h tends to zero:

$$\frac{(x+h)^2}{h} = \frac{x^2 + 2xh + h^2}{h} = \frac{x^2}{h} + 2x + h$$

The expression on the right-hand side contains three terms. As h tends to zero, $\frac{x^2}{h}$ is limitless; $2x$ is $2x$ regardless of what happens to h; and h tends to zero as h tends to zero. If the sum of several terms contains a term with no limit, the sum has no limit.

However, the expression $\dfrac{(x+h)^2 - x^2}{h}$ does have a limit as h tends to zero because h can be eliminated from the denominator.

$$\frac{(x+h)^2 - x^2}{h} = \frac{x^2 + 2xh + h^2 - x^2}{h} = \frac{2xh + h^2}{h} = 2x + h \quad \text{and}$$

$\lim_{h \to 0} (2x + h) = 2x$. It is expressions similar in pattern to this which have great practical significance.

Drill

1. Find the values of $\dfrac{x}{x+1}$, when x is 0, 1, 2, 9, 99, and 999.

2. Find the values of $\dfrac{x}{x+1}$, when x is $-0{\cdot}9$, $-0{\cdot}99$, and $-0{\cdot}999$. Where does $\dfrac{x}{x+1}$, seem to be going as x tends to minus one?

3. Find the values of $\dfrac{x}{x+1}$, when x is $-1{\cdot}1$, $-1{\cdot}01$, and $-1{\cdot}001$. Now where does $\dfrac{x}{x+1}$ seem to be going as x tends to minus one?

4. Draw the graph of $y = \dfrac{x}{x+1}$.

5. Express as decimals $\dfrac{1}{2^{-1}}, \dfrac{1}{10^{-1}}, \dfrac{1}{10^{-6}}$.

6. Express as decimals $2^{-1}, 10^{-1}, 10^{-6}$.

7. If $f(x) = 16x^2$, what are $f(0), f(1), f(2), f(5)$?

8. If $f(x) = x^3 + x^2 + 8x + 4$, what are $f(0), f(1), f(2)$?

9. If $f(x) = ax^4 + bx + c$, where a, b, and c are constants, what are $f(0), f(1), f(2), f(3)$?

10. If $f(x) = 12x^2 - 2x$, what are $f(1), f(a), f(3), f(b), f(a+h)$?

11. If $f(x) = 16x^2$, what is $f(a+h) - f(a)$?

12. If $f(x) = x^3$, what is $f(a+h) - f(a)$?

13. If $f(x) = 2x^2$, what is $\dfrac{f(a + h) - f(a)}{h}$?

14. What is the limiting value as h tends to zero of each of the following expressions?

   i. $7a + h$.

   ii. $ax^2 + bx + c + h$.

   iii. $ahx^2 + bx + c$.

   iv. $ax^2 + bhx + ch$.

   v. $\dfrac{32hx + 3h^2}{h}$.

   vi. $\dfrac{x^2 + 32hx + 3h^2}{h}$.

   vii. $\dfrac{x^2 + 32hx + 3h^2 - x^2}{h}$.

15. If $y = f(x)$, the 'derivative of y with respect to x' is defined as:

$$\operatorname*{Lim}_{h \to 0} \frac{f(x + h) - f(x)}{h}$$

What is the derivative of y with respect to x when $y = x^2$, when $y = 2x^2$, when $y = 16x^2$ and when $y = 30 + 16x^2$?

Answers

1. $0, \frac{1}{2}, \frac{2}{3}, 0\cdot9, 0\cdot99, 0\cdot999$.

2. $-9, -99, -999$, minus infinity.

3. $+11, +101, +1001$, plus infinity.

5. $2, 10, 10\,000\,000$.

6. $0\cdot5, 0\cdot1, 0\cdot000\,000\,1$.

7. $0, 16, 64, 400$.

8. $4, 14, 32$.

9. $c, a + b + c, 16a + 2b + c, 81a + 3b + c$.

10. $0, 12a^2 - 2a, 102, 12b^2 - 2b,$
    $12a^2 + 24ah + 12h^2 - 2a - 2h$.

11. $32ah + 16h^2$.

12. $3a^2h + 3ah^2 + h^3$.

13. $4a + 2h$.

14. i. $7a$; ii. $ax^2 + bx + c$; iii. $bx + c$; iv. ax^2; v. $32x$; vi. no limit; vii. $32x$

15. $2x, 4x, 32x, 32x$.

5.3 Average velocity and point velocity

In this section the familiar ideas involved in time, distance, and speed are used to illustrate some analytical techniques. The techniques can then be used to gain a better understanding of economic relationships.

Suppose that we are asked to find the relation between the velocity of a falling object and the time the object has taken in falling. Such a problem would arise if we were concerned at the amount of

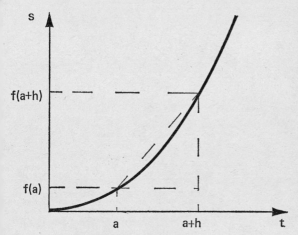

Figure 5.2 Average velocity during h seconds

damage the object would do if it hit something. The damage depends on the weight of the object and its velocity *at the moment of impact*. If the weight of the object is known, we need only find the velocity at the moment of impact.

The relation between the distance in feet, s, which an object falls after t seconds is given by the function $s = f(t) = 16t^2$. Let a be some particular value of t, so $f(a)$ is the distance corresponding to a. In this example $f(a) = 16a^2$, but if we stay with the more general notation we may come up with a more general solution.

Velocity is distance travelled per unit of time, so we want some interval of time during which to measure the velocity. Let us measure it between a and $a + h$ seconds. The distance travelled in $a + h$ seconds will be $f(a + h)$. Figure 5.2 illustrates.

Distance travelled during the interval of time: $f(a + h) - f(a)$
Interval of time: $(a + h) - a = h$

$$\text{Velocity} = \frac{\text{distance}}{\text{time}} = \frac{f(a + h) - f(a)}{h}$$

If h is 10 seconds, the average velocity during this 10 seconds is:

$$\frac{f(a + 10) - f(a)}{10} = \frac{16(a + 10)^2 - 16a^2}{10}$$

$$= \frac{16a^2 + 320a + 1600 - 16a^2}{10}$$

$$= \frac{320a + 1600}{10}$$

$$= 32a + 160$$

Now this tells us the average velocity during the 10 seconds after the object has already been falling for a seconds. The average velocity between 0 and 10 seconds is $32(0) + 160 = 160$ feet per second. Between 1 and 11 seconds, average velocity is $32(1) + 160 = 192$ feet per second; between 2 and 12 seconds it is $32(2) + 160 = 224$ feet per second.

However, we want to know the velocity at the moment of impact. We have to make a distinction between 'average velocity' and 'point velocity'. (The same distinction is made in practice by the driver who suspects he is exceeding the speed limit: he looks at his speed-ometer, not at mileposts at the side of the road and his watch. 'Point velocity' is a difficult concept to work out without any mathematical technique, but the driver who has a gadget to work it out for him finds the gadget useful.)

We can get nearer to point velocity by finding the average speed during the next second, putting $h = 1$:

$$\frac{f(a + 1) - f(a)}{1} = 16(a + 1)^2 - 16a^2 = 32a + 16$$

And we would be even more accurate if we put $h = 0.1$:

$$\frac{f(a + 0.1) - f(a)}{0.1} = \frac{16(a + 0.1)^2 - 16a^2}{0.1}$$

$$= \frac{16(a^2 + 0.2a + 0.01) - 16a^2}{0.1}$$

$$= 32a + 1.6$$

The velocity actually at time a is the velocity when h tends to zero:

$$\text{Lim}_{h \to 0} \frac{f(a + h) - f(a)}{h} = \text{Lim}_{h \to 0} \frac{16(a + h)^2 - 16a^2}{h}$$
$$= \text{Lim}_{h \to 0} (32a + 16h)$$
$$= 32a$$

The symbol 'a' was used to show that some particular time was being discussed. In fact 'a' could be any particular time so 'a' can be replaced by 't'. If distance is a function of time, $s = f(t)$, then:

$$\text{velocity} = \text{Lim}_{h \to 0} \frac{f(t + h) - f(t)}{h}$$

The notation which is used to show the way s reacts to changes in t is $\frac{d}{dt}(s)$, spoken '$d\,d\,t$ of s'. If a real phenomenon is being investigated, $\frac{d}{dt}(s)$ can be looked upon as the velocity, the way distance responds to changes in time. An alternative approach is to look upon $\frac{d}{dt}(\ )$ as an instruction: 'Perform the operation of finding the derivative with respect to t of the term inside the bracket.' Thus $\frac{d}{dt}(16t^2) = 32t$. For this reason $\frac{d}{dt}$ is sometimes called an **operator**.

Similarly, if $y = f(x)$, then $\frac{d}{dx}(y)$ means 'perform the operation of finding the derivative of y with respect to x'. If $y = 16x^2$, then the derivative of y with respect to x is $\frac{d}{dx}(16x^2)$ which is $32x$.

The notation $\frac{d}{dt}(s)$ is often abbreviated to $\frac{ds}{dt}$, spoken '$d\,s$ by $d\,t$', $\frac{d}{dx}(y)$ is abbreviated to $\frac{dy}{dx}$, '$d\,y$ by $d\,x$'. It is as well to remember that these are abbreviations even though they are widely used. Historically the letter 'd' was used to suggest the Greek capital delta, Δ, which is commonly used to mean 'a little bit of'. An expression such as $\frac{\Delta y}{\Delta x}$ means $\frac{\text{a small change in } y}{\text{a small change in } x}$, and $\frac{dy}{dx}$ is the limiting value of $\frac{\Delta y}{\Delta x}$ as Δx tends to zero.

5.4 The derivative of x^n

There is a particular short-cut to this process which is the key to the rapid calculation of derivatives. The proof is tedious, but since the result is easy to remember it is given here without proof:

$$\frac{d}{dx}(x^n) = nx^{n-1}$$

e.g. $\frac{d}{dx}(x^2) = 2x$, $\frac{d}{dx}(x^3) = 3x^2$, $\frac{d}{dx}(x^{10}) = 10x^9$

To illustrate how this general rule arises, note that:

$$\frac{d}{dx}(x^n) = \lim_{h \to 0} \frac{(x+h)^n - x^n}{h}$$

and perform the calculation for $n = 1, 2, 3$, and 4.

n	$(x+h)^n$	$\dfrac{(x+h)^n - x^n}{h}$
1	$x + h$	1
2	$x^2 + 2xh + h^2$	$2x + h$
3	$x^3 + 3x^2h + 3hx^2 + h^3$	$3x^2 + 3xh + h^2$
4	$x^4 + 4x^3h + 6x^2h^2$ $+ 4xh^3 + h^4$	$4x^3 + 6x^2h + 4xh^2 + h^4$

As h tends to zero all the terms in the right-hand column disappear except the first term in each expression. We accept therefore that:

$$\frac{d}{dx}(x^n) = nx^{n-1}$$

The following two statements can also be proved:

$$\frac{d}{dx}(ax^n) = anx^{n-1}$$

$$\frac{d}{dx}(ax^n + bx^m) = anx^{n-1} + bmx^{m-1}$$

A word of caution is necessary when considering $\frac{dy}{dx}$ in the case where $y = x$. If $y = x$, then $\frac{dy}{dx} = \frac{d}{dx}(x) = 1 \cdot x^{1-1} = x^0 = 1$. The way x responds to changes in x is one-to-one. Do not look upon the expression $\frac{d}{dx}(x)$ as a fraction $\frac{dx}{dx}$, where the numerator and the denominator cancel out. By remembering that $\frac{d}{dx}$ is an operator, the generality of the concept is not lost.

A constant term does not change as a variable changes, so the derivative of a constant term is zero. Consider first the mechanical approach. If $y = b$, this can also be written $y = bx^0$, and $\frac{d}{dx}(bx^0) = b \cdot 0 x^{0-1} = 0$, since anything multiplied by 0 is 0.

Next consider the approach using limits. Suppose that an object is standing still b feet from the point of origin for measurement. What is its velocity in feet per second? From first principles:

$$s = f(t) = b$$

$$\text{velocity} = \frac{ds}{dt} = \lim_{h \to 0} \frac{f(a + h) - f(a)}{h}$$

$$= \lim_{h \to 0} \frac{b - b}{h}$$

$$= \lim_{h \to 0} \frac{0}{h}$$

$$= \lim_{h \to 0} 0$$

$$= 0$$

This trivial example is illustrated in Figure 5.3, which is similar to Figure 5.2 except for the function being considered. In the manipulation of the symbols, note that h does not tend to zero until the limit sign is removed, but the limit sign is removed after h has disappeared from the expression, because $\frac{1}{h}$ times 0 is 0. The problem of $\frac{0}{0}$ never arises.

Derivation provides a method of calculating the slope of the tangent to a curve. Consider the function $y = 16x^2$. Its slope depends on the value of x and is given by $\frac{dy}{dx} = \frac{d}{dx}(16x^2) = 32x$. Now consider the point on the curve where $x = 3$. This will be the point (3, 144) since $y = 16(3)^2 = 144$. The slope of the curve at this point will be $\frac{dy}{dx} = 32(3) = 96$ units of y for each unit of x.

If we know the equation of a curve, we can find the equation of the tangent to that curve at any point on the curve. Since the tangent is a straight line, its equation is of the form $y = a + bx$. But the slope of the tangent is the same as the slope of the curve. Again consider the tangent to the curve $y = 16x^2$ at the point (3, 144), as shown in Figure 5.4. The slope of the curve and the tangent is $\frac{d}{dx}(16x^2) = 32x = 32(3) = 96$, so the equation of the tangent is $y = a + 96x$. We can find a because we know that the tangent passes through the point (3, 144), so $144 = a + 96(3)$, hence $a = 144 - 288 = -144$. Therefore the equation of the tangent to $y = 16x^2$

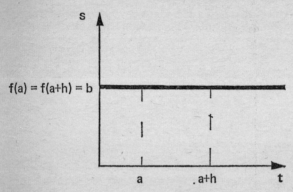

Figure 5.3 Zero velocity

at the point (3, 144) is $y = -144 + 96x$. Note that the slope of the tangent is measured in units of y per unit of x.

The following examples of derivation show that the formulae apply to all indexes, positive or negative, integers or fractions:

If $y = 3x^2$, $\frac{dy}{dx} = 3(2)x^{2-1} = 6x$

If $y = -2x^{10}$, $\frac{dy}{dx} = -2(10)x^{10-1} = -20x^9$

If $y = x^{-10}$, $\frac{dy}{dx} = (-10)x^{-10-1} = -10x^{-11}$

If $y = -2x^{-10}$, $\frac{dy}{dx} = -2(-10)x^{-10-1} = 20x^{-11}$

If $y = \sqrt{x} = x^{\frac{1}{2}}$, $\frac{dy}{dx} = (\frac{1}{2})x^{\frac{1}{2}-1} = \frac{1}{2}x^{-\frac{1}{2}} = \frac{1}{2x^{\frac{1}{2}}} = \frac{1}{2\sqrt{x}}$

If $y = x^{1\cdot1}$, $\frac{dy}{dx} = (1\cdot1)x^{1\cdot1-1} = 1\cdot1x^{0\cdot1}$

If $y = x^{0 \cdot 9}$, $\dfrac{dy}{dx} = (0 \cdot 9)x^{0 \cdot 9 - 1} = 0 \cdot 9x^{-0 \cdot 1}$

If $y = 30x^{\frac{3}{4}}$, $\dfrac{dy}{dx} = 30(\tfrac{3}{4})x^{\frac{3}{4} - 1} = \dfrac{90}{4}x^{-\frac{1}{4}}$

If $y = 30x + x^2$, $\dfrac{dy}{dx} = 30(1)x^{1-1} + (2)x^{2-1} = 30 + 2x$

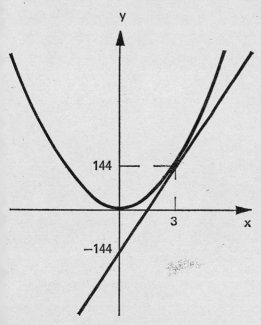

Figure 5.4 A tangent to a curve

Drill

1. Find the derivative with respect to x of:

    i. $x^4 + x^3 + x^2 + x.$
    ii. $\frac{1}{5}x^5 + \frac{1}{4}x^4 + \frac{1}{3}x^3 + \frac{1}{2}x^2 + x.$
    iii. $a + bx + cx^2 + kx + m.$
    iv. $x^2 + x + a + b + c.$
    v. $ax + bx + cx.$

vi. $x^{21} + x^{\frac{1}{2}}$.

vii. $x^{-2} + x^{-3}$.

viii. $\dfrac{9}{x^2} + \dfrac{7}{x^3}$.

ix. $-\dfrac{9}{x} - \dfrac{7}{2x^2}$.

2. The relation between a firm's total revenue (R) and the quantity sold (x) is found to be $R = 20x - \frac{1}{2}x^2$. What is the relation between average revenue, $\dfrac{R}{x}$, and x? What is the relation between marginal revenue, $\dfrac{dR}{dx}$, and x?

3. A firm's total costs as a function of quantity are:

$C = ax^3 - bx^2 + cx + k$.

What is average cost as a function of quantity? What is marginal cost as a function of quantity?

4. A total cost function is $C = 1000 + x^2$. What are the average and marginal cost functions?

5. The relation between the flow of aggregate saving in a year (S) and the flow of aggregate income in a year (Y) is given by $S = 20 + \frac{1}{5}Y$. What is the average propensity to save, $\dfrac{S}{Y}$, expressed as a function of income? What is the marginal propensity to save, $\dfrac{dS}{dY}$?

6. The relation between a country's imports (M) and income (Y) is given by $M = 10 + \frac{1}{6}Y^2$. What is the marginal propensity to import, $\dfrac{dM}{dY}$?

7. The relation between tax paid (t) and annual personal income (x) is given by $t = x - x^{0.95}$. What is marginal taxation, $\dfrac{dt}{dx}$, expressed as a function of income?

8. If the demand function is $x = D(p) = 20 - 3p$, how does quantity demanded respond to changes in price, i.e. what is $\frac{dx}{dp}$?

9. If the supply function is $x = S(p) = \frac{1}{2}p = 2000$, how does quantity supplied react to changes in price?

10. It sometimes saves notation if we write 'y is a function of x' as $y = y(x)$ instead of $y = f(x)$. This may lead to confusion with 'y times x' but in practice the context usually makes the meaning clear.

    i. If $y = y(x) = 2x$, what are $y(0)$, $y(1)$, $y(10)$?
    ii. If $y = y(x) = x^2$, what are $y(1)$, $y(3)$?
    iii. If $u = u(x) = 7x$, what are $u(0)$, $u(2)$?
    iv. If $v = v(x) = 12x^2 + 3$, what are $v(1)$, $v(3)$?
    v. If $y = 3x + 2$, what is xy expressed in terms of x?

Answers

1. i. $4x^3 + 3x^2 + 2x + 1$.
  ii. $x^4 + x^3 + x^2 + x + 1$.
  iii. $b + 2cx + k$.
  iv. $2x + 1$.
  v. $a + b + c$.
  vi. $21x^{20} + \frac{1}{2}x^{-\frac{1}{2}}$.
  vii. $-2x^{-3} - 3x^{-4}$.
  viii. $-18x^{-3} + 21x^{-4}$.
  ix. $9x^{-2} + 7x^{-3}$.

2. $\frac{R}{x} = 20 - \frac{1}{2}x, \frac{dR}{dx} = 20 - x$.

3. $\frac{C}{x} = ax^2 - bx + c + \frac{k}{x}, \frac{dC}{dx} = 3ax^2 - 2bx + c$.

4. $\frac{C}{x} = \frac{1000}{x} + x, \frac{dC}{dx} = 2x$.

5. $\frac{S}{Y} = \frac{20}{Y} + \frac{1}{5}, \frac{dS}{dY} = \frac{1}{5}$.

6. $\frac{dM}{dY} = \frac{1}{3}Y$.

7. $\frac{dt}{dx} = 1 - 0 \cdot 95x^{-0 \cdot 05}$.

8. —3.

9. $\frac{1}{2}$.

10. i. 0, 2, 20.

  ii. 1, 9.

  iii. 0, 14.

  iv. 15, 111.

  v. $xy = 3x^2 + 2x$.

5.5 The derivative of the product of two functions

Sometimes the easiest way to find the derivative of the product of two functions is to multiply them out and then take the derivative of the expression for the product. For example:

If $u = u(x) = x^3 + 2$

  $v = v(x) = x^2 + 1$

  $y = u . v = (x^3 + 2)(x^2 + 1)$

then $\dfrac{dy}{dx} = \dfrac{d}{dx}(u . v) = \dfrac{d}{dx}(x^5 + x^3 + 2x^2 + 2)$

$$= 5x^4 + 3x^2 + 4x$$

For many functions, multiplying out is tedious or even impossible. A more general rule for finding the derivative of the product of two functions will prove particularly helpful in understanding monopoly when we come to consider this in the next chapter. This more general rule is:

If $y = u . v$, where $u = u(x)$ and $v = v(x)$

then $\dfrac{dy}{dx} = u . \dfrac{dx}{dv} + v . \dfrac{du}{dx}$

In the above example:

$u = x^3 + 2$, so $\dfrac{du}{dx} = 3x^2$

$v = x^2 + 1$, so $\dfrac{dv}{dx} = 2x$

$y = u . v$, so $\dfrac{dy}{dx} = u . \dfrac{dv}{dx} + v . \dfrac{du}{dx}$

$$= (x^3 + 2) . 2x + (x^2 + 1) . 3x^2$$

$$= 5x^4 + 3x^2 + 4x$$

For those readers who do not like to take formulae on trust, the proof of the product rule is given in the last section of this chapter.

Drill

Use the product rule to find the derivative with respect to x of:

1. $(x^{\frac{3}{2}} + 1)(x^2 - 2)$.

2. $(x + a)(x^3 - bx^2 + c)$.

Answers

1. $\frac{5}{2}x^{\frac{3}{2}} - x^{-\frac{1}{2}} + 2x$.
2. $4x^3 + (3a - 3b)x^2 - 2abx + c$.

5.6 The inverse function rule

Consider the demand function $x = 20 - 3p$, where x is tons demanded and p is price per ton. Quantity reacts to changes in price at the rate of $\dfrac{dx}{dp} = -3$ tons per £.

If the market for this good were controlled by a monopolist the causal relation of price determining quantity demanded need no longer apply. The monopolist is not a price-taker but a price-maker. He can decide either at what price he will sell or what quantity he will sell, though not both because we assume at this stage that he has to accept the demand function as it is. If he decides to control quantity, the demand relation can be used to tell him what price he should charge:

The demand relation $x = 200 - 3p$

becomes $$p = \frac{200}{3} - \tfrac{1}{3}x$$

How does price react to changes in the quantity sold? $\dfrac{dp}{dx} = -\tfrac{1}{3}$£ per ton. Compare these units of measurement with those for $\dfrac{dx}{dp}$. Provided the change in the units of measurement is borne in mind, then, in numerical terms:

$$\frac{dp}{dx} = \frac{1}{\dfrac{dx}{dp}}$$

The inverse function rule states in general:

If $y = f(x)$, then $\dfrac{dx}{dy} = \dfrac{1}{\dfrac{dy}{dx}}$

Note again that $\dfrac{dy}{dx}$ is not a fraction: it is an operator giving the instruction 'find the derivative of y with respect to x'. Similarly, $\dfrac{dx}{dy}$ gives the instruction 'find the derivative of x with respect to y'.

5.7 Price for the monopolist and for the competitive firm

The monopolist faces a downward sloping demand function. If he increases his price, the quantity he sells will decrease; if he increases the quantity he sells, the price he charges will have to decrease. His total revenue (R) is price (p) times quantity (x). Total revenue can be expressed as a function of quantity by treating price as a function of quantity. For the monopolist:

$R = p \cdot x$, where $p = p(x)$

Marginal revenue $= \dfrac{dR}{dx} = p \cdot \dfrac{dx}{dx} + x \cdot \dfrac{dp}{dx}$, by the product rule

$$= p + x \cdot \frac{dp}{dx}$$

Since $\dfrac{dp}{dx}$ is negative, $x \cdot \dfrac{dp}{dx}$ is also negative, so price is always greater than marginal revenue for the monopolist.

The producer in a perfectly competitive market is in a different position. He has to take the price as given. Price to him is a parameter, a constant so far as his decisions are concerned. For the competitive producer:

$R = p \cdot x$, where p is constant

Marginal revenue $= \dfrac{dR}{dx} = p$

For both types of producer, average revenue is the same as price, because revenue is defined as price times quantity. Average revenue $= \frac{R}{x} = \frac{p \cdot x}{x} = p$, but p is a function of x for the monopolist and a parameter for the competitive producer.

5.8 Second derivatives

The derivative of total revenue with respect to output is marginal revenue and this shows how total revenue reacts to changes in the quantity sold. In order to find out how marginal revenue reacts to changes in quantity we have to find the derivative of marginal revenue. However, marginal revenue is itself a derivative, so we are finding the derivative of a derivative. The derivative of marginal revenue is called the second derivative of total revenue. For example:

If $R = 200x - x^2$

then $\frac{dx}{d}(R) = \frac{dR}{dx} = 200 - 2x$

and $\frac{d}{dx}\left(\frac{dR}{dx}\right) = \frac{d}{dx}(200 - 2x) = -2$

The expression $\frac{d}{dx}\left(\frac{dR}{dx}\right)$ is usually abbreviated to $\frac{d^2R}{dx^2}$, spoken '$d\,2\,R$ by $d\,x$ squared'. It is the second derivative of R with respect to x.

One can take as many derivatives as one likes. In the above example, $\frac{d^3R}{dx^3} = \frac{d}{dx}(-2) = 0$. Similarly, if $y = x^4$, $\frac{dy}{dx} = 4x^3$, $\frac{d^2y}{dx^2} = 12x^2$, $\frac{d^3y}{dx^3} = 24x$, $\frac{d^4y}{dx^4} = 24$, $\frac{d^5y}{dx^5} = 0$, $\frac{d^6y}{dx^6} = 0$, and so on.

Drill

1. Total costs (C) are a function of quantity produced (x): $C = 2000 + 3x$. What are marginal costs? What is the rate of change of marginal costs?

2. If $C = 20 + \frac{1}{200}x^2$, what are $\frac{dC}{dx}$ and $\frac{d^2C}{dx^2}$?

3. If output in units of product (Q) is related to labour input in man-

hours (L) by the expression $Q = 100L^{\frac{3}{4}}$, what is the marginal product of labour, $\frac{dQ}{dL}$? Show that the marginal product of labour diminishes as more output is produced.

4. Aggregate saving (S) is a function of aggregate income $(Y): S = -a + bY^n$, where a and b are positive constants and n is greater than one. Show that saving increases as income increases, i.e. find the marginal propensity to save and show that it is positive. By finding $\frac{d^2S}{dY^2}$ and studying the parameters, show that there is an increasing marginal propensity to save as income increases.

Answers

1. $\frac{dC}{dx} = 3, \frac{d^2C}{dx^2} = 0.$

2. $\frac{1}{100}x, \frac{1}{100}.$

3. $75L^{-\frac{1}{4}}, -\frac{75}{4}L^{-\frac{5}{4}}$, which is negative.

4. $\frac{dS}{dY} = bnY^{n-1}$, which is positive.

$\frac{d^2S}{dY^2} = bn(n-1)Y^{n-2}$. Since b and n are positive, and $(n-1)$ is positive, the whole expression is positive.

5.9 Cost functions.

In most cases cost functions are assumed to be of such a shape that there will eventually be increasing marginal costs after some stage of increasing output. The J-shaped marginal cost curve found in most text-books is derived from a total cost function which is a cubic: $C = a + bx - cx^2 + kx^3$, where a, b, c, k are positive constants. Such a curve is illustrated in Figure 5.5(a). Fixed costs are those costs incurred even when output is zero, which is a in this case. The marginal cost function derived from this is a quadratic: $\frac{dC}{dx} = b - 2cx + 3kx^2$. Marginal costs will be increasing if the slope of the marginal cost curve is positive, that is if marginal costs react positively to increases in x, which is when $\frac{d}{dx}\left(\frac{dC}{dx}\right)$ is greater than zero.

$\frac{d}{dx}\left(\frac{dC}{dx}\right) = \frac{d}{dx}(b - 2cx + 3kx^2) = -2c + 6kx$, and this expression is positive when $6kx > 2c$, or when $x > \frac{c}{3k}$. If x is less than

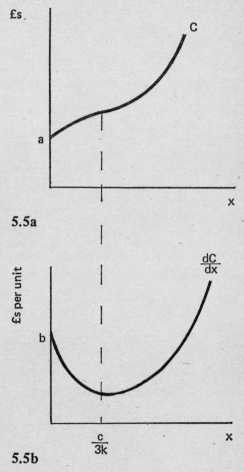

5.5a

5.5b

Figure 5.5 Total cost and marginal cost

$\frac{c}{3k}$, marginal costs are diminishing as x increases; if x is greater than $\frac{c}{3k}$, marginal costs are increasing as x increases, and marginal costs are at a minimum when $x = \frac{c}{3k}$. The marginal cost curve corresponding to the total curve is shown in the lower part of Figure 5.5(b).

Note how the two diagrams in Figure 5.5 are formed. If X is the set of quantities per time period, $x \in X$, and T is the set of totals in £s, $C \in T$, then the total cost function is a subset of $X \times T$. In order to save notation we are using C to represent both total costs and the function relating total costs to quantities. Used as a variable, $C \in T$; used as a function, $C \subseteq X \times T$. We could have put $C = f(x) = a + bx - cx^2 + kx^3$, in which case we would label the curve in Figure 5.5(a) f, and label the vertical axis C. However, the context makes the meaning clear so there is no need to complicate the notation by using two different symbols.

Figure 5.5(b) is formed from a different product set. If M is the set of marginal costs measured in £s per unit, then the marginal cost function is a subset of $X \times M$. We cannot illustrate this function on the same vertical axis as the total cost function because the units of measurement are different. However, a set A consisting of all possible average costs would allow the product set $X \times A$ to be formed, and an average cost function would be a subset of $X \times A$. This could be illustrated on the same diagram as marginal costs because average costs use the same units of measurement, £s per unit of quantity.

Drill

1. The relation between time in seconds (t) and distance in feet (s) of a falling object is $s = 16t^2$.

i. What is the object's velocity after t seconds, and what are the units of measurement of this velocity?

ii. What is its acceleration after t seconds (either put $v =$ velocity and find $\frac{dv}{dt}$, or find $\frac{d^2s}{dt^2}$), and what are the units of measurement of this acceleration?

2. If a body is propelled upwards by a given force, the relation between distance and time is found to be $s = 120t - 16t^2$.

i. What is its velocity after t seconds?

ii. After how many seconds does it reach its greatest height? (Find when it stops going up but has not quite started to come down, when its velocity upwards is neither positive nor negative).

iii. What is the greatest height reached?

iv. What is its acceleration upwards? and downwards?

3. A monopolist faces a demand relation for his product of $x = \frac{15}{2} - \frac{1}{16}p$.

i. Find price as a function of quantity demanded.

ii. What is the relation between total revenue and quantity sold?

iii. What is marginal revenue?

iv. At what quantity is total revenue a maximum?

v. What is maximum total revenue?

vi. Show that marginal revenue diminishes.

Answers

1. i. $32t$ feet per second.
   ii. 32 feet per second per second.
2. i. $120 - 32t$.
   ii. 3·75 seconds.
   iii. 225 feet.
   iv. -32, $+32$.
3. i. $p = 120 - 16x$.
   ii. $R = 120x - 16x^2$.
   iii. $120 - 32x$.
   iv. 3·75.
   v. 225.
   vi. $\dfrac{d^2R}{dx^2}$ is negative.

5.10 Profit maximisation

Profit in the sense used here is total revenue minus total cost. Total revenue is a function of quantity sold, but total cost is a function of quantity produced, so for ease of analysis we assume that what is produced is sold, and this amount is x. Both total cost, C, and total revenue, R, are functions of x. Let N stand for net revenue or profit. Since $N = R - C$ by definition, but $R = R(x)$ and $C = C(x)$ we have $N = N(x)$.

When profit is at a maximum it is just at that point where it has stopped going up but is not yet going down, so its rate of change is zero: $\frac{dN}{dx} = 0$.

$$N = R - C$$
$$\frac{dN}{dx} = \frac{dR}{dx} - \frac{dC}{dx}$$

So when $\frac{dN}{dx} = 0$, $\frac{dR}{dx} = \frac{dC}{dx}$, that is marginal revenue equals marginal cost.

Two different total revenue functions are illustrated in the top parts of Figure 5.6(a) and (b), in each case with a quadratic total cost function. In Figure 5.6(a), the revenue function for a firm in a competitive market is shown and this is a straight line since $R = px$, where p is constant. In Figure 5.6(b), the revenue function for a monopolist is shown and this is a curve since $R = px$, where $p = p(x)$ and $\frac{dp}{dx} < 0$.

In the middle diagrams the profit functions are shown. These could have been shown in the top diagrams but are shown separately to avoid cluttering. The bottom diagrams illustrate the marginal functions.

This is a convenient place at which to make the distinction between **necessary** and **sufficient** conditions. It is necessary to breathe in order to be healthy, but a patient can be breathing and still be very ill, so breathing is a necessary but not a sufficient condition for health. On the other hand, an athlete may pass an extremely strict medical test and he would only have passed it if he were healthy. The fact that he has just passed the test is sufficient for us to believe that he is healthy, but passing the test is not a necessary condition for health; he could have been healthy whether he took the test or not.

The equality of marginal cost with marginal revenue is a condition for profit maximisation. It is a necessary condition, so if profit is to be maximised then marginal cost must equal marginal revenue. It is not a sufficient condition, so if the equality holds we do not always find that output where profit is maximised. The diagrams in Figure 5.7 illustrate two cases where this is not so. In Figure 5.7(a), total

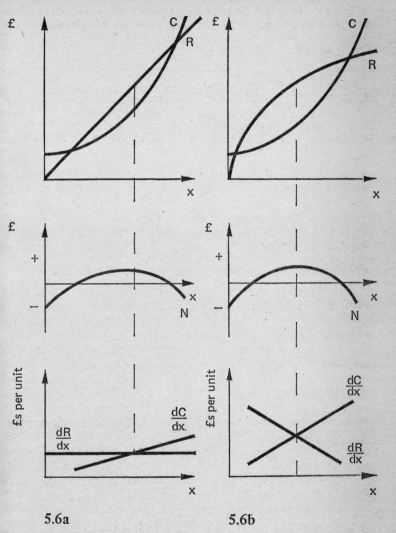

Figure 5.6 The profit-maximising quantity; (*a*) With constant price and a linear marginal cost function; (*b*) With monopolistic price and a linear marginal cost function

costs are always greater than total revenue, so the condition results in finding that quantity where losses are minimised.

Figure 5.7(*b*) shows the most important case. Here marginal revenue equals marginal cost at two different levels of output, because of the J-shape of the marginal cost curve. At one output profit is maximised but at the other output loss is maximised, so a blind application of the condition could lead to precisely the result that is least desirable. It is not enough that the rate of change of profit (or loss) is zero. We have to ensure that when profit is not changing it has just stopped going up and is just about to go down. A study of the top diagrams shows that this will occur when total revenue is increasing more slowly than total cost. Or, as shown in the middle diagrams, when the rate of change of profit is decreasing, when $\frac{d}{dx}\left(\frac{dN}{dx}\right) < 0$.

The results which we found by using common-sense and diagrams can be found more briefly by manipulating the symbols. Since $N = R - C$, $\frac{dN}{dx} = \frac{dR}{dx} - \frac{dC}{dx}$, and N will be at a maximum or at a minimum when $\frac{dN}{dx} = 0$, which is when $\frac{dR}{dx} = \frac{dC}{dx}$. This is known as the **first order condition** for profit maximisation. In order to ensure that profit is at a maximum, $\frac{d^2N}{dx^2}$ must be less than zero, but:

$$\frac{d^2N}{dx^2} = \frac{d}{dx}\left(\frac{dR}{dx} - \frac{dC}{dx}\right)$$
$$= \frac{d^2R}{dx^2} - \frac{d^2C}{dx^2}$$

and when $\frac{d^2N}{dx^2} < 0$, $\frac{d^2R}{dx^2} < \frac{d^2C}{dx^2}$. This is the **second order condition** for profit maximisation.

In a competitive market a firm's marginal revenue is constant, so $\frac{d^2R}{dx^2}$ is zero. Provided marginal costs are increasing the second order condition will be met.

A monopolist has a marginal revenue function which decreases, so the second order condition will be met either if marginal costs are increasing or if marginal costs are constant.

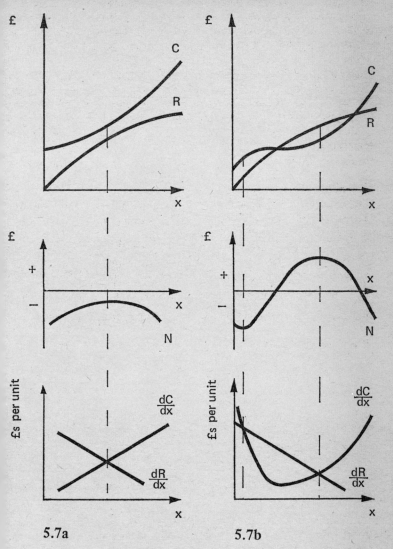

Figure 5.7 (*a*) The loss-minimising quantity; (*b*) The ambiguous result of first-order conditions when the marginal cost function is J-shaped

5.11 The proof of the product rule

This is an interesting example of the way mathematicians use patterns to suggest solutions to problems. The statement with which we are now familiar is:

If $y = y(x)$, then $\dfrac{dy}{dx} = \underset{h \to 0}{\text{Lim}} \dfrac{y(x + h) - y(x)}{h}$ (1)

The statement defining the derivative of the product of two functions can be written in the same way:

If $y = u(x) \cdot v(x)$, then $\dfrac{dy}{dx} = \underset{h \to 0}{\text{Lim}} \dfrac{u(x + h) \cdot v(x + h) - u(x) \cdot v(x)}{h}$

(2)

Now although we know how to manipulate (1) we do not know much about (2). It looks strange. The objective therefore is to rearrange (2) until it looks more like (1). The first problem is how to eliminate the product terms. This could be done by factoring, but there is no common factor. However, if we both add and subtract an extra term, $u(x + h) \cdot v(x)$, the value of the expression will not be changed, but in its new form it will lend itself to manipulation. So (2) becomes:

$$\underset{h \to 0}{\text{Lim}} \frac{\begin{aligned}u(x + h) \cdot v(x + h) \\ - u(x + h) \cdot v(x) + u(x + h) \cdot v(x) - u(x) \cdot v(x)\end{aligned}}{h}$$

$$= \underset{h \to 0}{\text{Lim}} \frac{u(x + h)[v(x + h) - v(x)] + v(x)[u(x + h) - u(x)]}{h}$$

$$= \underset{h \to 0}{\text{Lim}} \left[u(x + h) \frac{v(x + h) - v(x)}{h} + v(x) \frac{u(x + h) - u(x)}{h} \right]$$

and since the limit of the sum of two terms equals the sum of the limit of each term:

$$= \underset{h \to 0}{\text{Lim}} \left[u(x + h) \frac{v(x + h) - v(x)}{h} \right] + \underset{h \to 0}{\text{Lim}} \left[v(x) \frac{u(x + h) - u(x)}{h} \right]$$

The expression inside each of the big brackets is almost the same as the expression in (1). If we remove $u(x + h)$ from within the limit sign, we must let h tend to zero as we remove it: $u(x + h)$ tends to $u(x)$ as h tends to zero, so the expression becomes:

$$u(x) \underset{h \to 0}{\text{Lim}} \frac{v(x + h) - v(x)}{h} + v(x) \underset{h \to 0}{\text{Lim}} \frac{u(x + h) - u(x)}{h}$$

$= u(x) \cdot \dfrac{dv}{dx} + v(x) \cdot \dfrac{du}{dx}$, since the expressions within the limit signs have been manipulated until they are of exactly the same pattern as (1).

Now prove by using limits that if $R = p \cdot x$, where $p = p(x)$, then $\dfrac{dR}{dx} = p + x \cdot \dfrac{dp}{dx}$.

Exercise 5

1. A monopolist faces the demand function $x = D(p) = 500 - 5p$.
   i. What is the relation between total revenue and quantity sold?
   ii. Writing revenue as a function of x, $R = R(x)$, find $R(11) - R(10)$ and $R(10) - R(9)$.
   iii. What is the relation between marginal revenue and quantity sold?
   iv. What is marginal revenue at the point where $x = 10$?

2. The relation between a firm's total cost, C, and the quantity produced per annum, x, is $C = x^3 - 4x^2 + 8x$. Draw the average and marginal cost curves over the range from $x = 0$ to $x = 4$.

3. The long run is that period of time over which all resources can be varied. A firm's total costs, C, are related to total output, x, over a five-year period by the function $C = ax^3 - bx^2 + cx$, where a, b, and c are positive constants.

   i. Is five years 'the long run' for this firm?
   ii. What is the average cost function?
   iii. At what output are average costs a minimum?
   iv. What is the marginal cost function?
   v. At what output does average cost equal marginal cost? Substitute the numbers in question 2 for the constants in question 3 and check that your graphs in question 2 are correct.

4. i. If the supply function for a good is $x = S(p) = p - 10$, and the demand function is $x = D(p) = 20 - \frac{1}{2}p$, what are the equilibrium price and quantity?
   ii. If a monopolist takes over this market, what are his total and average revenues expressed as functions of quantity sold?
   iii. The monopolist takes over all the plant in the industry so that

his marginal cost function is the same as the old supply relation when this relation is expressed as a function of x. How much will he produce for maximum profit and what price will he charge?

iv. The monopolist introduces more efficient plant so that his marginal cost function changes to $\frac{dC}{dx} = 11 + \frac{1}{4}x$. How much will he now produce and what price will he charge?

5. The price of wheat is £31 per ton.

i. A wheat farmer's total costs are £$(2000 + x + 0\cdot03x^2)$, where x is the quantity produced in tons per annum. How much should he produce and sell to maximise profit? How much profit will he make?

ii. Another wheat farmer estimates that his total costs are £$(5000 + 25x)$. If his estimate is correct, how much should he produce to break even? How much should he produce to maximise profit, if the price of wheat stays constant? Do you think his estimate is correct?

READING

Henry, S. G. B., *Elementary Mathematical Economics*, Chapter 2.

Sawyer, W. W., *Mathematician's Delight*, Chapters 8, 10, 11, and 12.

Chapter 6

Elasticity

6.1 Problems of comparison

When analysing the way in which quantity demanded reacts to changes in price we can use the demand function $x = D(p)$ to derive $\frac{dx}{dp}$. This derivative will have a dimension such as 'tons per change of £1'. However, when we try to compare the responsiveness to price changes of different products, these products will usually have different units of measurement. A figure for coal in tons might be compared with a figure for electricity in kilowatt-hours, and the comparison means nothing without far more information. When comparing the same product in different countries, the prices will be in different currencies. Conversion from one currency to another for the purpose of comparing the prices of the same good in two countries are very difficult because the two price systems are formed from different tastes and different productive resources. These problems of dimension can be overcome by using the concept of elasticity.

The unit of measurement is not the only difficulty which arises when contrasting the responsiveness of different products to price changes. A second problem arises because of the proportions with which we are dealing. A price change of £1 is significant to the price of a pair of shoes but insignificant to the price of a house. A change in quantity of 1 ton is significant in the world market for diamonds but not in the wheat market. It is the proportionate change in price or quantity compared with the price or quantity before the change that is significant when we are measuring responsiveness.

The **average price elasticity of demand** is the proportionate response of quantity demanded to changes in price. Writing Δ for 'a small amount of', a price change from p to $p + \Delta p$ is a proportionate change of $\frac{\Delta p}{p}$. If a price change from p to $p + \Delta p$ causes a change in quantity demanded from x to $x - \Delta x$, then the average price elasticity of demand is:

$$\frac{\text{proportionate change in quantity demanded}}{\text{proportionate change in price}} = \frac{\frac{\Delta x}{x}}{\frac{\Delta p}{p}} = \frac{p}{x} \cdot \frac{\Delta x}{\Delta p}$$

The problem of proportion is solved by measuring proportionate changes. The problem of dimension is also solved because $\frac{x}{p}$ has the dimension $\frac{\text{price units}}{\text{quantity units}}$ and $\frac{\Delta x}{\Delta p}$ has the dimension $\frac{\text{quantity units}}{\text{price units}}$.

When the two are multiplied together the result is dimensionless: it is just a number. Dimensionless expressions are always easy to apply because they avoid the problems of proportion and of different units of measurement. For example, the statement 'the quantity of wheat demanded declined by 3 million tons in response to a £1 increase in price' is uninformative unless there are additional data on previous price and quantity, but the statement 'the price elasticity of demand for wheat is $-0\cdot2$' tells us that a 1 per cent increase in price will lead to only one-fifth of a per cent decrease in the quantity demanded, so there is little responsiveness to price changes.

Drill

1. When the price of wheat is £30 per ton, 2 million tons per month are demanded. When the price of wheat is £31 per ton, 1·98 million tons are demanded. What is the average price elasticity of wheat between the prices of £30 and £31 per ton?

2. When the price of wheat is £32, 1·96 million tons are demanded. What is the average price elasticity of demand between £31 and £32 per ton?

3. When the price of wheat is £33, 1·94 million tons are demanded. Show that the average price elasticity of demand is greater between £32 and £33 than between £31 and £32.

4. Show that the demand function $x = D(p) = 2\cdot6 - 0\cdot2p$, where x is quantity demanded in millions of tons per annum and p is price in £s per ton, is consistent with the observations.

Answers

1. $-0\cdot300$.
2. $-0\cdot313$.
3. $-0\cdot326$.

6.2 Point elasticity

Point elasticity is the limiting value of average elasticity. The limiting value of $\frac{p}{x} \cdot \frac{\Delta x}{\Delta p}$ as Δp tends to zero is $\frac{p}{x} \cdot \frac{dx}{dp}$. Point elasticity has many advantages over average elasticity and for the rest of this book we shall mean point elasticity whenever the word elasticity is used by itself.

The first advantage is that elasticity can be expressed in terms of either the price variable or the quantity variable. If the demand function is $x = 2\cdot6 - 0\cdot2p$, the point elasticity of demand, e_d, is $\frac{p}{x} \cdot \frac{dx}{dp}$. Now $\frac{dx}{dp}$ is $-0\cdot2$, so $e_d = -0\cdot2\left(\frac{p}{2\cdot6 - 0\cdot2p}\right)$. Usually it is more helpful to express elasticity as a function of quantity. To do this we express the demand relation in terms of price as a function of quantity. In this example, $p = 13 - 5x$. To find $\frac{dx}{dp}$ we use the inverse function rule:

$$\frac{dx}{dp} = \frac{1}{\frac{dp}{dx}} = \frac{1}{-5} = -0\cdot2$$

so $e_d = \frac{p}{x} \cdot \frac{dx}{dp} = \left(\frac{13 - 5x}{x}\right)(-0\cdot2) = \frac{5x - 13}{5x}$

Another advantage of point elasticity is that it avoids any ambiguity in the measure of proportionate change. If quantity changes from 100 to 105, the proportionate change is $\frac{105 - 100}{100} = 0\cdot0500$; but if quantity changes from 105 to 100 the proportionate change is $\frac{100 - 105}{105} = -0\cdot0476$. Other advantages appear when the elasticities of non-linear functions are to be measured.

There are three types of elasticity which are particularly interesting in economics:

The price elasticity of demand, which is the elasticity of quantity demanded in response to changes in price:

$e_d = \dfrac{p}{x} \cdot \dfrac{dx}{dp}$, where x is quantity demanded and p is price. Since

demand curves always slope downward, and $\dfrac{dx}{dp}$ is the inverse of the

slope of the demand curve, $\dfrac{dx}{dp}$ will be negative. The crucial value for

for e_d is -1. When e_d is less than -1 (for example, -2), demand is elastic. When e_d is greater than -1 (for example, -0.5), demand is inelastic.

In text-books where derivatives are not used, the price elasticity

of demand is given by $\dfrac{p}{x} \cdot \dfrac{\Delta x}{\Delta p}$, and since the direction of change is not

taken into account this expression will not be negative. In order to avoid confusion we can think of the **absolute value** of e_d. Absolute values are always positive or zero. The notation for the absolute value of the elasticity is $|e_d|$. Examples: $|-1| = 1$, $|-2.0| = 2.0$, $|1| = 1$, $|-0.5| = 0.5$, $|0| = 0$, $|-3| = 3$. (The notation for absolute values is the same as that for the number of elements in a set, which is also always positive or zero. See sections 1.9 and 1.10.)

The income elasticity of demand, which is the elasticity of quantity demanded in response to changes in income:

$e_y = \dfrac{y}{x} \cdot \dfrac{dx}{dy}$,

where x is quantity demanded and y is income per head in the relevant group of people.

If $e_y > 1$, then an increase in income leads to a more than proportionate increase in the quantity demanded of the good. For example, if income increases by 1 per cent and other things remain constant, 10 per cent more bottles of champagne may be bought. If $0 < e_y < 1$, then an increase in income leads to a less than proportionate increase in the quantity of the good which is purchased. For example, if income goes up by 1 per cent, the number of loaves of bread which are purchased may increase by only $\frac{1}{2}$ of 1 per cent. There is also the unusual case of a good with a negative income elasticity. This states that an increase in income will lead to a decrease in the quantity purchased, and a decrease in income will lead to an increase in the quantity purchased. For example, if potatoes are the cheapest food, and if income decreases, then less will be spent on meat and milk, but stomachs must be filled somehow so more potatoes are bought.

The income elasticity of demand is sometimes used to define three types of goods:

A **luxury** is a good where $e_y > 1$.
A **necessity** is a good where $0 < e_y < 1$.
An **inferior good** is one where $e_y < 0$.

The elasticity of supply, which is the elasticity of quantity supplied in response to changes in price:

$e_s = \dfrac{p}{x} \cdot \dfrac{dx}{dp}$, where x is quantity supplied and p is price.

If $y = f(x)$, where x and y are any variables, the elasticity of y in response to changes in x is defined as $\dfrac{x}{y} \dfrac{dy}{dx}$. (Do not confuse this definition, involving any two variables, with the definition of the income elasticity of demand, involving income and quantity demanded.) So the elasticity of any function is the slope of that function divided by the average, because:

$$\frac{x}{y} \frac{dy}{dx} = \frac{\dfrac{dy}{dx}}{\dfrac{y}{x}} = \frac{\text{marginal function}}{\text{average function}} = \frac{\text{'slope'}}{\text{'average'}}$$

If y is a linear function of x, the slope will be constant but the elasticity will not, because the average changes as x changes. The one exception to this, when y is a linear function of x, is a function such as $y = bx$, that is, a straight line which passes through the origin. This can be proved by considering any linear function $y = a + bx$, where $\dfrac{dy}{dx} = b$ and $\dfrac{y}{x} = \dfrac{a}{x} + b$. The average, $\dfrac{y}{x}$, is constant only if $a = 0$.

We now illustrate the concept of elasticity by studying the price elasticity of demand for three types of demand function: linear, log linear, and a demand function where the revenue of the sellers is constant regardless of the changes in price and quantity.

Consider the demand function $x = a - bp$.

$$e_d = \frac{p}{x} \cdot \frac{dx}{dp} \qquad\qquad \text{but } \frac{dx}{dp} = -b$$

$$\text{and } p = \frac{a - x}{b}$$

$$\text{so } e_d = \left(\frac{a - x}{bx}\right)(-b)$$

$$= -\frac{a - x}{x}$$

$$= \frac{x - a}{x}$$

$$= 1 - \frac{a}{x}$$

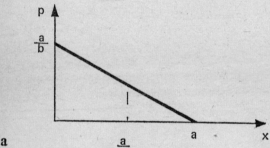

6.1a

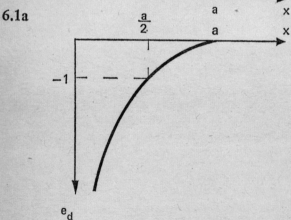

6.1b

Figure 6.1 A demand function and the corresponding elasticity function

This demand function is illustrated in Figure 6.1(a). When $p = \frac{a}{b}$ nothing is demanded, and when $p = 0$, a is demanded. In Figure 6.1(b), the elasticity is illustrated as a function of x. As x tends to zero, e_d tends to minus infinity. This is what we expect. Above a certain price, $\frac{a}{b}$, nothing is purchased. As price falls, something is purchased. In proportion to what was bought before, the responsiveness is infinite.

When $x = a$, e_d is zero. Provided the good has a positive price, the responsiveness of quantity to changes in price is negative. This also is what we expect: if p and x are positive the sign of e_d depends upon the sign of $\frac{dx}{dp}$, but this is always negative because demand curves always slope downward.

Now consider the elasticity of the log linear demand function $x = kp^{-c}$, where k and c are positive parameters. This elasticity is easier to calculate as if it were a function of price:

$$e_d = \frac{p}{c} \cdot \frac{dx}{dp} \qquad \text{but} \frac{dx}{dp} = -ckp^{-c-1}$$

$$\text{so } e_d = \frac{p}{kp^{-c}}(-ckp^{-c-1})$$

$$= \frac{-ckp^{-c}}{kp^{-c}}$$

$$= -c$$

With a log linear demand function the elasticity is simply the index of p.

Before calculating the price elasticity of demand for a good where the revenue of producers remains constant regardless of price, we must first find the demand function. Since revenue is price times quantity, and in this case revenue is constant, the demand function can be found from the definition of revenue:

$$R = p \cdot x, \text{ where } R \text{ is constant}$$

$$\text{so } x = \frac{R}{p} = Rp^{-1}$$

This is a special case of the log linear demand function given above. Here $c = 1$, so the elasticity of demand is -1. The demand function

$x = Rp^{-1}$ is of unit elasticity. No product has such a demand function, except for small ranges of price, but it provides a useful guide when classifying types of demand, rather as north on the compass is useful even though we may not want to go north.

Drill

1. Give the relationship between the price elasticity of demand, e_d, and the quantity demanded, x, for each of the following demand functions:

 i. $x = 20 - 2p$.
 ii. $x = 10 - p$.
 iii. $x = 5 - \frac{1}{2}p$.
 iv. $x = \dfrac{10}{p}$.
 v. $x = \dfrac{5}{p}$.

2. For each relation in question 1, find the quantity bought when the price elasticity of demand is -1.

3. What would be the marginal revenue functions if a monopolist faced each of the demand functions of question 1?

4. In each case, at what quantity is marginal revenue zero?

5. Compare the answers to questions 2 and 4 and explain.

6. What are the absolute values of -273, $\frac{19}{2}$, 0, 23, and -19?

7. Give the relation between the income elasticity of demand, e_y, and the quantity demanded, x, when the relation between consumers' income, y, and x is as follows:

 i. $y = 100x$.
 ii. $y = x^2$.
 iii. $y = -10 + 30x$.

8. Give the relation between the elasticity of supply, e_s, and the quantity supplied, x, for each of the following supply functions:

 i. $x = p$.
 ii. $x = 0\cdot5p$.

iii. $x = 0.01p$.

iv. $x = bp$, where b is some constant.

v. $x = (p - 7)^{\frac{1}{2}}$.

vi. $x = -40 + 0.01p$.

Answers

1. i. $\dfrac{x - 20}{x}$; ii. $\dfrac{x - 10}{x}$; iii. $\dfrac{x - 5}{x}$; iv. -1.

2. i. 10; ii. 5; iii. $\frac{5}{2}$; iv. indeterminate (any x).

3. i. $10 - x$; ii. $10 - 2x$; iii. $10 - 4x$; iv. 0.

4. i. 10; ii. 5; iii. $\frac{5}{2}$; iv. all x.

5. Marginal revenue $= 0$ when $e_d = -1$.

6. 273, $\frac{19}{2}$, 0, 23, 19.

7. i. 1, ii. $\frac{1}{2}$; iii. $\dfrac{3x - 1}{3x}$.

8. i. 1; ii. 1; iii. 1; iv. 1; v. $\dfrac{x^2 + 7}{2x^2}$; vi. $\dfrac{x + 40}{x}$.

6.3 Monopoly and competition

The price elasticity of demand is a measure which can be used to find whether a market is competitive in the way prices are formed. In order to show the influence of monopoly on elasticity we first show the relation between elasticity, price, and the monopolist's marginal revenue: $R = p \cdot x$, where $p = p(x)$. Marginal revenue is related to price and quantity.

$$\frac{dR}{dx} = p + x \cdot \frac{dp}{dx} \quad \text{(from section 5.7)}$$

In order to relate marginal revenue to elasticity, we remember that $e_d = \dfrac{p}{x} \cdot \dfrac{dx}{dp}$ and see if the above expression can be manipulated until it includes a term of the same pattern:

$$\frac{dR}{dx} = p + \frac{p}{p} \cdot x \cdot \frac{dp}{dx}$$

$$= p\left(1 + \frac{x}{p} \cdot \frac{dp}{dx}\right)$$

$$= p\left(1 + \frac{1}{e_d}\right)$$

For a monopolist, e_d is always negative, so the term inside the bracket will always be less than one, and marginal revenue will always be less than price.

In the model of a market known as **perfect competition**, the market demand function for a good is of the usual type, with $\dfrac{dx}{dp}$ negative. To the individual firm, however, as it looks at the market from its position as one supplier among many, the demand relation appears to be of the form: $p = $ constant. If we arrange markets in order of their nearness to the theoretical extreme of perfect competition, the demand relation tends to look more and more like '$p = $ constant' so far as the individual producers in such a market are concerned. If $\dfrac{dp}{dx}$ moves from a negative value towards $\dfrac{d}{dx}$(constant), its value is moving from a negative direction towards zero. Therefore its inverse, $\dfrac{dx}{dp}$, is tending towards minus infinity and so is $\dfrac{p}{x} \cdot \dfrac{dx}{dp}$. The expression $\left(1 + \dfrac{1}{e_d}\right)$ tends to unity, and marginal revenue tends to equal price.

Some numerical values for the elasticity of demand will clarify this chain of reasoning. If $e_d = -1\cdot5$, demand is elastic and:

$$\frac{dR}{dx} = p\left(1 + \frac{1}{e_d}\right) = p\left(1 - \frac{1}{1\cdot5}\right) = \tfrac{1}{3}p$$

Marginal revenue in this case is positive. A monopolist might decide to sell in such a market, although whether he does sell will depend on his marginal costs.

If demand is of unit elasticity, $e_d = -1$, and:

$$\frac{dR}{dx} = p\left(1 - \frac{1}{1}\right) = 0$$

If marginal revenue is zero, there is no reason to expand sales because no extra revenue results. The monopolist can increase profit by cutting back sales, thus moving back up the demand function until marginal revenue becomes positive. Even if he could produce at zero cost there is no profit in expanding production when marginal revenue is zero.

If $e_d = -0\cdot5$, demand is inelastic and:

$$\frac{dR}{dx} = p\left(1 - \frac{1}{0\cdot5}\right) = -p$$

Now marginal revenue is negative. In order to persuade customers to buy a larger quantity, price must be reduced by a greater proportion than the increase in sales. Such a level of sales is even more unprofitable than the level where $e_d = -1$.

As e_d tends to minus infinity, as it will do for the firm in a competitive market, marginal revenue will tend to price:

$$\frac{dR}{dx} = p\left(1 + \frac{1}{e_d}\right) \text{ tends to } p(1 + 0) = p$$

Figure 6.2 illustrates the relation between total revenue, marginal revenue and the elasticity of demand (measured in absolute values). When total revenue is at its peak, marginal revenue is zero and $|e_d|$ is unity. As total revenue increases from 0 to its peak, marginal revenue is positive and $|e_d|$ is greater than one, or elastic. As total revenue decreases, marginal revenue is negative and $|e_d|$ is less than one, or inelastic.

If a demand function is log linear, the elasticity of demand is easy to measure:

$$x = kp^{-c}$$
$$\log x = \log k - c \log p$$

When observations of price and quantity are made and then the logarithms of these observations are plotted on a graph, the slope of the line is the elasticity of demand. Such techniques can be used to assess whether a market is dominated by a monopolist, provided the Identification Problem has been solved.

For many years there has been controversy over the way the American medical profession restricts entry into the medical schools. Critics said this was done to enable the profession to restrict the quantity of medical care available, increase its price, and thus increase the incomes of doctors. It has been found that $|e_d|$ for physicians' services in the US in the 1950s was 0·2.[1] If American doctors were both ruthless profit-maximisers and able to control the quantity of medical care sold, they would have decreased the quantity of medical care sold until $|e_d|$ climbed above one, thereby getting more money for less work.

1. Feldstein, Paul J., and Severson, Ruth M., 'The Demand for Medical Care', *Report of the Commission on the Cost of Medical Care*, vol. 1, Chicago, American Medical Association, 1964, pp. 57–76.

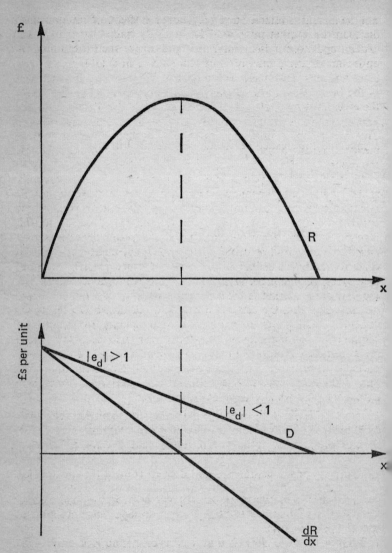

Figure 6.2 Elasticity is unity when total revenue is a maximum and marginal revenue is zero

6.4 The mark-up

The economist is interested in analysing the effects of businessmen's decisions on market price and the quantity traded, so that he can explain and predict the overall effect of many such decisions. The approach of the economist, standing apart and looking at many firms and their customers, is often very different from the approach of the businessman who actually runs a particular firm. As a result, the economist may talk one language and the businessman another. The economist uses concepts like elasticity and marginal revenue. The businessman uses expressions like sellers' market, buyers' market, and the mark-up. How do we translate one language into the other?

Many writers have pointed out that firms usually do not know the shape of the demand function for their product. Businessmen do not decide price by equating marginal revenue with marginal cost, because they cannot derive marginal revenue if they cannot find the demand function. What they say they do is to calculate 'unit costs' and then add a fixed percentage for profit. They use a mark-up over costs to decide the selling price. However, when pressed, businessmen agree that the mark-up is not a fixed percentage but varies with the state of the market. If the firm uses a mark-up over marginal cost, we can show that the size of the mark-up demonstrates the firm's implicit opinion about the price elasticity of demand for its product. Methods of making explicit what previously had been left unsaid are extremely useful tools for the economist. They allow more comparisons to be made than would be possible otherwise, and often they point out inconsistencies in economic behaviour which were unintended and which can be easily corrected.

When a businessman talks of a mark-up of 10 per cent over marginal cost, he means that he is pricing his product at 110 per cent of marginal cost, so $p = (1 + 0.10) \frac{dC}{dx}$. For a mark-up of $100m$ per cent, $p = (1 + m) \frac{dC}{dx}$; so for $m = 0.01$ the mark-up is 1 per cent, for $m = 0.05$ the mark-up is 5 per cent. If the businessman knows his marginal costs and if he has decided what mark-up to use, the price follows.

What we want to show is that a decision about m is really a decision about the price elasticity of demand, assuming as usual that the businessman is a profit-maximiser. If the businessman is successful in selling that output which maximises his profit, he will have equated marginal revenue with marginal cost, even though this may have been accomplished by trial and error rather than by direct calculation.

From $p = (1 + m)\dfrac{dC}{dx}$

we have $\dfrac{dC}{dx} = \dfrac{p}{1 + m}$

But $\qquad \dfrac{dR}{dx} = \dfrac{dC}{dx}$ when profit is maximised,

so $\qquad \dfrac{dR}{dx} = \dfrac{p}{1 + m}$ when profit is maximised.

In the previous section we found an expression relating marginal revenue, price and the elasticity of demand:

$$\frac{dR}{dx} = p\left(1 + \frac{1}{e_d}\right)$$

We now have one expression relating the mark-up to marginal revenue (providing the firm is maximising profit), and we have a second expression relating elasticity to marginal revenue. By equating the two we can find the relation between elasticity and the mark-up:

$$\frac{p}{1 + m} = p\left(1 + \frac{1}{e_d}\right)$$
$$\frac{1}{1 + m} = 1 + \frac{1}{e_d} = \frac{e_d + 1}{e_d}$$
$$e_d = (1 + m)(1 + e_d) = 1 + m + e_d + m . e_d$$
$$m . e_d = -(1 + m)$$
$$e_d = -\left(\frac{1 + m}{m}\right)$$
$$|e_d| = \frac{1 + m}{m}$$

If the mark-up is known, the firm's assessment of the elasticity of demand for its product can be found. As the mark-up tends to zero, $|e_d|$ tends to infinity and the market approaches perfect competition. This situation is illustrated in Figure 6.3(a), showing the horizontal demand curve as it looks to the producer in perfect competition. Production occurs at that quantity where price equals marginal cost, and there is no mark-up. The demand curve appears to be infinitely elastic.

If the firm is using a mark-up, there must be some element of monopoly in the market for the firm's product. Figure 6.3(*b*) illustrates this position. The firm has not used the rule of equating marginal revenue with marginal cost in order to decide what quantity to sell and what price to charge, because it cannot calculate marginal revenue when the demand function is not known. Instead it has

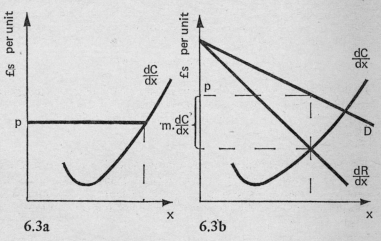

6.3a   6.3b

Figure 6.3 (*a*) No mark-up in a competitive market; (*b*) A mark-up over marginal cost in a monopolistic market

found the most profitable quantity and mark-up by trial and error, and by judgement. The analysis which we have done shows that this process is really the same as finding the elasticity of the demand function over the relevant range.

Exercise 6

1. A producer finds that the price elasticity of demand for his product is -0.9. Prove that he cannot be both a profit maximiser and a monopolist.

2. The relation between price (p) and quantity demanded (x) for a monopolist's product is $p = \dfrac{70}{x + 7}.$

i. What prices should he charge if he wants to sell 0, 3, 693, and 6993 units per time period? Sketch the curve.

ii. The rule for finding the derivative of a quotient is as follows:

If $R = \dfrac{u}{v}$, where $u = u(x)$, and $v = v(x)$,

then $\dfrac{dR}{dx} = \dfrac{1}{v^2}\left(v \cdot \dfrac{du}{dx} - u \cdot \dfrac{dv}{dx}\right)$

What is the monopolist's marginal revenue as a function of x?

iii. What is the relation between x and the price elasticity of demand for this demand function?

3. In an imaginary economy, the demand function for National Health Service prescriptions is $x = \dfrac{70}{p} - 7$, where p is the price per prescription in £s and x is the quantity demanded in millions of prescriptions per annum.

i. How much would be demanded when the price is £0·125 and how much when prescriptions are free?

ii. Prescriptions are rationed partly by doctors for medical reasons, partly by consumers for ethical and social reasons and partly by consumers because they do not like queuing. Assume that the cost of queuing is the only relevant factor, and that only 28 (million) prescriptions are provided when there is no charge. What is the value to the average consumer of the time spent in queuing for each prescription?

4. i. If a firm sells in a competitive market, what mark-up over marginal cost will it use to decide its selling price?

ii. If a firm uses a mark-up over marginal cost of 10 per cent to decide its selling price, what implicit assumption is the firm making about the price elasticity of demand for its product?

iii. If a firm sells at a price equal to marginal cost, what assumption is it making about the price elasticity of demand for its product?

Chapter 7

Discrete Functions

7.1 Introduction

This chapter presents some simple techniques for handling those functions which are not continuous. It should be emphasised that 'continuous' and 'discrete' refer to the analytical approach to problems and not to the phenomena being investigated. For example, in Chapter 3 we used a continuous function to relate cost per aero-frame to the number of aero-frames built, although we were interested only in whole units. Conversely, we could describe the flow of a river as x million gallons per annum, although the flow is continuous and not one large deluge of water once a year.

Discrete functions are often used as brief ways of describing rates of change. The analytical problem which usually arises is: when the way something changes is known, how do we find the total quantities involved? Compare this with the problems presented in the previous two chapters: when the totals are known, how do we find the rates of change?

7.2 Simple growth

Consider an economy where imports are £100 in week 0, £105 in week 1, £110 in week 2 and so on. Imports in week t are $100 + 5t$. If M_t is imports in week t, the relation between M_t and t can be described by the expression $M_t = 100 + 5t$. This is a discrete function and it is handled in a rather different way from a continuous function. Note that t is always an integer in this function, not a continuous variable; t is used to label particular weeks.

If $M = 100 + 5t$ were a continuous function, with M standing for imports per week, we could find how imports react to changes in time by finding $\dfrac{dM}{dt} = 5$ (this is analogous to acceleration; the units of measurement are '£s per week per week', which are similar to the units of measurement used for the acceleration of a body 'feet per second per second'). By using a discrete function we are describing imports as though they were arriving in lumps each week. It is like studying icebergs breaking off a glacier each week rather than studying the continuous melting of a block of ice.

If a graph is used to picture a discrete function, care must be taken with the way it is drawn. For example, graphs of imports are often drawn as in Figure 7.1(a). Strictly there are two mistakes in this manner of presentation, both of which are corrected in Figure 7.1(b).

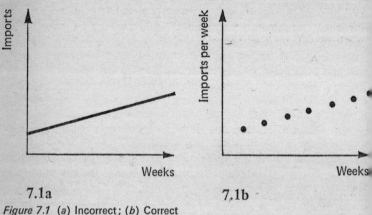

7.1a   7.1b

Figure 7.1 (a) Incorrect; (b) Correct

Firstly, the labelling of the vertical axis should make clear that imports are a flow so a time dimension should be stated. Secondly, a discrete function exists only at points on the graph. However, sometimes a continuous line is a helpful and quick device for visualising a trend provided the context makes the meaning clear.

If imports are 100 in week 0 and increase by 5 each week, in week 51 they will be $100 + 5(51)$. But what is the total flow of imports during the year, the 52 weeks from week 0 to week 51? (We shall see that the calculations are simplified by labelling the first week as week 0.)

The terms 100, $100 + 5$, $100 + 10$, $100 + 15$, ... are in arithmetical progression. The total of imports during the year is $100 + 100 + 5(1) + 100 + 5(2) + \cdots + 100 + 5(51)$. This expression is the sum of the terms of an arithmetical progression. A short-cut to find this sum is given in section 7.4, but first we introduce a formula that is helpful and an abbreviation which is used when handling the sums of discrete functions.

7.3 The sum of the first n integers

Consider the sum $1 + 2 + 3 + 4$. We can express this sum in symbols by letting i stand for integer, capital sigma $\sum$ for 'the sum of', $\sum i$ for 'the sum of the integers i', and $\sum_{i=1}^{4} i$ for 'the sum of the integers i, from $i = 1$ to $i = 4$ inclusive'. That is $\sum_{i=1}^{4} i = 1 + 2 + 3 + 4$. Now consider two different ways of arranging the sum of the first four integers: $1 + 2 + 3 + 4$ and $4 + 3 + 2 + 1$. Now note the pattern when we add these two sums together:

$$\sum_{i=1}^{4} i = 1 + 2 + 3 + 4$$

$$\sum_{i=1}^{4} i = 4 + 3 + 2 + 1$$

$$2\sum_{i=1}^{4} i = 5 + 5 + 5 + 5$$

Therefore $\sum_{i=1}^{4} i = \tfrac{1}{2}(5 + 5 + 5 + 5) = 10$

We can now generalise this approach to n integers, where n is any whole number. The regularity which appeared with four integers also appears for n integers, and this allows us to find a general formula:

$$\sum_{i=1}^{n} i = 1 + \quad 2 \quad + \quad 3 \quad + \cdots + n$$

$$\sum_{i=1}^{n} i = n + (n - 1) + (n - 2) + \cdots + 1$$

$$2\sum_{i=1}^{n} i = (n + 1) + (n + 1) + (n + 1) + \cdots + (n + 1)$$

$$= n(n + 1) \quad \text{since there are } n \text{ terms.}$$

Therefore, in general $\sum_{i=1}^{n} i = \dfrac{n}{2}(n + 1)$.

7.4 The sum of the terms of an arithmetical progression

Let a = the amount at the start, b = the amount added each time, n = the number of times the addition occurs (which is one less than the number of terms in the expression), and AP_{n+1} = the sum of an arithmetical progression with $n + 1$ terms.

So
$$\begin{aligned}
AP_{n+1} &= a + (a + b) + (a + 2b) + \cdots + (a + nb) \\
&= (n + 1)a + (b + 2b + 3b + \cdots + nb) \\
&= (n + 1)a + (1 + 2 + 3 + \cdots + n)b \\
&= (n + 1)a + \frac{n}{2}(n + 1)b \quad \text{from section 7.3} \\
&= (n + 1)(a + \frac{n}{2}b) = \frac{(n + 1)(2a + nb)}{2}
\end{aligned}$$

Returning to the example given in section 7.2, the total flow of imports over the 52 weeks is found by putting $n = 51$, $a = 100$, and $b = 5$, so:

$$\sum_{t=0}^{51} M_t = \frac{(52)(200 + 255)}{2} = 11\ 830 \text{ £s per year.}$$

7.5 Compound growth

We now consider another extraordinary economy, one where imports are £100 during week 0, and grow at 5 per cent per week compound. During week 1 imports are 5 per cent up on week 0 so they are £100(1·05). During week 2 imports are 5 per cent up on week 1 so they are £100(1·05)(1·05) = £100(1·05)^2, and during week 51 imports are £100(1·05)^{51}. What is the flow of imports during the year, the 52 weeks from week 0 to week 51 inclusive?

The terms 100, 100(1·05), 100(1·05)^2, ..., are in geometrical progression. Their sum is given by: 100 + 100(1·05) + 100(1·05)^2 + $\cdots$ + $\cdots$ + 100(1·05)^{51}. The short-cut to finding this sum will prove useful in a wide range of problems: growth, decay, the multiplier, bank loans, hire purchase, investment appraisal, and many of the problems in economics where time is important.

7.6 The sum of the terms of a geometrical progression

Let a = the amount at the start, k = the amount by which a is multiplied each time, n = the number of times a is multiplied (so there are $n+1$ terms in the whole expression) and $GP_{n+1} =$ the sum of a geometrical progression of $n+1$ terms.

So $GP_{n+1} = a + ak + ak^2 + \cdots + ak^n$.

This expression needs simplifying before it can be handled with ease. The most untidy part is the group of terms in the middle. Each term is k times the term before, so if we multiply each side of the equals sign by k we shall get a second expression with many of the same terms as the first. Subtracting one from the other will leave a third expression much tidier than the first:

$$GP_{n+1} = a + ak + ak^2 + \cdots + ak^n$$
$$kGP_{n+1} = \quad\; ak + ak^2 + ak^3 + \cdots + ak^n + ak^{n+1}$$
$$(k-1)GP_{n+1} = -a + ak^{n+1}$$
$$= a(k^{n+1}-1)$$

Therefore $GP_{n+1} = \dfrac{a(k^{n+1}-1)}{k-1}$ provided k does not equal 1.

Returning to the problem of section 7.5, the flow of imports over the 52 weeks is found by putting $n = 51$, $a = 100$, and $k = 1.05$ to obtain:

$$\sum_{t=0}^{51} M_t = \frac{100(1.05^{52}-1)}{0.05} = 2000(1.05^{52}-1)$$
$$= 2000(13.77 - 1)$$
$$= 25\,540\,\text{£s per annum}$$

Compare the magnitude of the difference between arithmetical and geometrical growth over the year in the two examples.

A reminder: $1.05^{52} = 10^{\log 1.05^{52}} = 10^{52 \log 1.05}$
$$= 10^{52 \times 0.0212*} = 10^{10\log 52 + \log 0.0212}$$
$$= 10^{100.0423*} = 10^{1.102\dagger} = 12.65\dagger$$
$$* \text{ via log tables}$$
$$\dagger \text{ via antilog tables}$$

7.7 Decay

Decay is the reverse of growth, but it can be handled analytically in a similar way. Examples of arithmetical and geometrical decay illustrate the similarity.

Suppose imports are £100 in week 0 and decrease by £5 each week.

The formula for imports during week t would be $M_t = 100 - 5t$. After 20 weeks there would be no imports. The total of imports for the year from week 0 to week 51 can be found by applying the formula for the sum of the terms of an arithmetical progression:

$$AP_{n+1} = \frac{(n+1)(2a + nb)}{2} \text{ where } n = 51, \ a = 100, \text{ and } b = -5,$$

so:

$$\sum_{t=0}^{51} M_t = \frac{(51+1)(200 - 5 \cdot 51)}{2} = -1430$$

(For a descriptive technique such as this, we can interpret negative imports as exports.)

If imports are declining by 5 per cent each week from a level of £100 in week 0, their value is £100(0·95) in week 1, £100(0·95)^2 in week 2 and so on. Total imports during the year is found from the formula for the sum of the terms of a geometrical progression:

$$GP_{n+1} = \frac{a(k^{n+1} - 1)}{k - 1}, \text{ where } n = 51, \ a = 100, \text{ and } k = 0·95, \text{ so:}$$

$$\sum_{t=0}^{51} M_t = \frac{100(0·95^{52} - 1)}{0·95 - 1}$$

This expression is neater if both the numerator and denominator are multiplied by minus one:

$$\sum_{t=0}^{51} M_t = \frac{100(1 - 0·95^{52})}{1 - 0·95} = 2000(1 - 0·07) = 1860$$

A reminder on calculating that $0·95^{52} = 0·07$:

Number	log		log log
$0·95^{52}$	$\bar{1}·9777* \times 52$		$\bar{1}·9902*$
	$= -52 + 52 \times 0·9777$	$0·9777$	$1·7160*$
	$= -52 + 50·84$	$52·$	
$0·06918†$	$= \bar{2}·84$	$50·84†$	$1·7062$
$\approx 0·07$			

* via log tables
† via anti-log tables

7.8 The multiplier

The multiplier is an example of geometrical decay. If £100 of additional investment is injected into an under-employed economy in which the marginal propensity to consume is $\frac{2}{3}$, how much extra income is generated? Note that neither income nor investment has a time dimension in this problem. Each is measured in £s, not in £s per time period. We are considering a once-and-for-all lump sum of additional investment of £100, not an increase of £100 per annum. We want to find the effect on income of this lump sum increase in investment. The total effect on income will also be a lump amount of additional income, not a permanent increase in the annual flow of income.

A £100 injection adds £100 to the flow of income. Those who obtain this additional income will themselves spend $\frac{2}{3}$ of it, so the second round of spending will be £100$(\frac{2}{3})$. The third round of spending will generate £100$(\frac{2}{3})^2$ extra income, and so on. Each round of spending is only two-thirds of the previous round. The rounds get smaller in a process of geometrical decay.

The total of additional income generated apparently goes on increasing indefinitely, although by the twelfth round it is £100$(\frac{2}{3})^{11}$ which is only about £1. The total will not exceed a limit which can be found by studying the formula $GP_{n+1} = \dfrac{a(1 - k^{n+1})}{1 - k}$, where $a = 100$, $k = \frac{2}{3}$, but n tends to infinity because we want to find the maximum amount of income generated.

Consider k^{n+1} as n tends to infinity. If k were greater than one, k^{n+1} would tend to infinity as n tends to infinity. If $k = 1$, so does k^{n+1} no matter what happens to n. But if k is less than one, k^{n+1} will get smaller as n increases. For example, if $k = \frac{2}{3}$ then $k^2 = 0.444$; $k^3 = 0.296$; $k^4 = 0.198$; $k^{11} = 0.012$ and so on. If $k < 1$, then k^{n+1} tends to zero as n tends to infinity, so:

$$\underset{\to \infty}{\text{Lim}} \frac{a(1 - k^{n+1})}{1 - k} = \frac{a}{1 - k} \quad \text{for } k < 1$$

In our example $\dfrac{a}{1 - k} = \dfrac{100}{1 - \frac{2}{3}} = 300$, so the maximum amount of income generated is £300. Since the marginal propensity to consume is $\frac{2}{3}$, the marginal propensity to do things that withdraw spending power from the circular flow of income (saving, imports) must be $\frac{1}{3}$.[1] So the multiplier is the reciprocal of the marginal propensity *not* to consume.

Conceptually, the multiplier is an aid to understanding how to avoid major unemployment. Multipliers are also used in practical problems such as finding the effects of extra investment on the income of a region within a national economy. The size of the figure for a regional multiplier for the first year after an injection might be somewhere between 1·2 and 1·8, depending on the type of investment and the region. Note that in a practical problem a time dimension is included. For example, we might find that a £100 injection of additional investment would lead to an increase in the region's income of £120 during the year after the investment was made, but its effect in succeeding years would be ignored.

7.9 The generation of credit

If all money passes through banks, and all banks keep at least 8 per cent cash in hand for all the money they borrow, what is the maximum amount of credit that will be generated by a £100 loan to a bank from the monetary authority?

The bank owes £100 as soon as it receives the loan. It then lends up to £92 to people who themselves will deposit the money in banks or spend it with people who will. The series is again a geometrical progression with k less than one. The limiting value is:

$$100 + 100(0·92) + 100(0·92)^2 + \cdots = \frac{100}{1 - 0·92} = £1250.$$

Drill

1. What is the sum of the first eleven integers? Of the first hundred integers?

2. A firm writes off its capital equipment in its accounts by deducting 10 per cent of the purchase price from its book value each year. How long will it take to write off half the value of a new piece of equipment?

3. A firm writes off 15 per cent of the previous year's book value of

1. Taxation has a similar effect, but see Ford, in this series, Chapter 10.

a piece of equipment to allow for depreciation. How long will it take to write off half the value of a new piece of equipment?

4. What is the multiplier when the marginal propensity to consume is 0·8?

5. If the capital stock of an economy is £100 million in year 0, and if it increases at 3 per cent per annum, what is the capital stock in year 10? In year 20?

Answers

1. $\sum_{i=1}^{11} i = \frac{11}{2}(11 + 1) = 66$, $\sum_{=1}^{100} i = \frac{100}{2}(100 + 1) = 5050$.

2. 5 years.

3. $V(0·85)^t = 0·5V$

$$t = \frac{\log 0·5}{\log 0·85} = \frac{\bar{1}·6990}{\bar{1}·9294} = \frac{-0·3010}{-0·0706} = 4·26 \text{ years.}$$

4. 5.

5. $100(1·03)^{10} = £134·3$ million.
   $100(1·03)^{20} = £180·3$ million.

7.10 Present values and investment appraisal

An **interest rate** is a price for loanable funds. In equilibrium it strikes a balance between those people who are prepared to forgo using their funds immediately, provided there is some reward, and those people who want funds now and are prepared to pay for their immediate availability. If the rate of interest is 5 per cent, then £100 lent now will become £100(1·05) = £105 in one year's time, £100(1·05)² in two year's time, and £100(1·05)ᵗ in t years.

A **rate of time preference** is a numerical way of describing the preference for funds now rather than funds next year. Different economic units will have different rates of time preference and there will be considerable variety between individuals, between firms and even between government departments. For example, a student may prefer £100 now to the certainty of £140 in one year's time, in which case his rate of time preference is over 40 per cent.

A **discount rate** is a rate which is used in the calculation of present values. If a businessman discounts the future at 5 per cent, then the promise of £105 in one year's time is worth only $£\dfrac{105}{1\cdot05} = £100$ to him now; the promise of £100 in one year's time is worth only $£\dfrac{100}{1\cdot05} = £95\cdot23$ now. In the examples which follow we shall assume that the appropriate discount rate to use is the rate of interest (the price of loanable funds). However, this is not always the case. Sometimes a calculation is more helpful if the decision-maker's rate of time preference is used instead.

Let R_t = the receipts expected in t years' time,
$100i$ per cent = the rate of interest (so $i = 0\cdot08$ means a rate of interest of 8 per cent),
PVR = the present value of R_t,
then PVR $= \dfrac{R_t}{(1 + i)^t}$

When trying to appraise the worth of an investment project, there will be both costs and revenues to take into account and these will vary over the years. Future costs are less expensive than costs now, just as future revenues are worth less than revenues now. The net revenue in year t will be the revenue in that year, R_t, minus the costs in that year, C_t. In some years $R_t - C_t$ will be negative, particularly at the start of a project. The problem is to find some numerical criterion for judging the pay-offs from investment projects so that different projects can be compared and those with the highest pay-offs carried out. The present value of the net revenues provides such a measure.

Let R_t = the revenue in year t, C_t = the costs in year t, i = the rate of interest, T = the length of life of the project in years, and PVNR = the present value of the net revenues, so:

$$\text{PVNR} = R_0 - C_0 + \frac{R_1 - C_1}{1 + i} + \frac{R_2 - C_2}{(1 + i)^2} + \cdots + \frac{R_T - C_T}{(1 + i)^T}$$

Since $(1 + i)^0 = 1$ and $(1 + i)^1 = 1 + i$, the following abbreviation can be used:

$$\text{PVNR} = \sum_{t=0}^{T} \frac{R_t - C_t}{(1 + i)^t}$$

For major investment projects R_0 will be zero and C_0 will be the capital costs and therefore very large. To emphasise this we can put $R_0 = 0$ and $C_0 = K$. The series can then be summed ignoring year 0;

$$PVNR = \sum_{t=1}^{T} \frac{R_t - C_t}{(1 + i)^t} - K$$

Drill

One of a group of proposed investment projects is estimated to cost £100 initially. At the end of the first year costs will be £80 and returns £120. At the end of the second year costs will be £60 and returns £180. The project closes at the end of the second year. The rate of discount is 8 per cent.

1. Prepare a table giving the year t in the first column, the returns R_t in the second column, and the costs C_t in the third.

2. Find the present value of the net revenues.

3. Find separately the present value of the revenues and the present value of the costs. Check that the difference between them agrees with question 2.

4. A second project has a present value of revenues PVR of £1 000 265 and a present value of costs PVC of £1 000 225. What is the present value of the net revenues? Which project seems the better proposition?

5. Compare the two projects by using as criterion the ratio $\frac{PVR}{PVC}$. Which is the best proposition on this criterion?

Answers

1.

t	R_t	C_t
0	0	100
1	120	80
2	180	60

2. $-100 + \dfrac{120 - 80}{1 + 0\cdot08} + \dfrac{180 - 60}{(1 + 0\cdot08)^2} = 40.$

3. $265 - 225 = 40$.

4. 40. A blind application of the PVNR criterion shows both projects to be equally ranked, but the second has £1 million tied up in costs.

5. $\frac{265}{225} = 1 \cdot 8$ which is greater than $\frac{1\,000\,265}{1\,000\,225} = 1 \cdot 00 \ldots$

7.11 The internal rate of return

The calculation of present values requires that the discount rate be known. The discount rate will be either the rate of interest or the rate of time preference. The rate of time preference depends on opinions and usually there is difficulty in persuading decision-takers to express in numerical terms their preference for present rather than future funds. The interest rate is a price, but different types of loan have different prices and the markets for all types of funds are imperfect. In an attempt to overcome these difficulties another method of summarising the worth of an investment project has become increasingly popular.

The present value methods involve finding the costs each year, the revenues each year and the discount rate. These data allow the calculation either of the present value of the net revenues, PVNR = PVR — PVC, or of the ratio of present values $\frac{\text{PVR}}{\text{PVC}}$. The third method is to use as a criterion that discount rate which would make PVNR equal zero. If R_t and C_t are known for each year from $t = 0$ to $t = T$, then:

$$0 = \sum_{t=0}^{T} \frac{R_t - C_t}{(1 + r)^t},$$

where r is the internal rate of return, sometimes known as the discounted cash flow rate of return.

In the example given in the drill, page 149, the internal rate of return would be calculated by solving the following equation for r:

$$0 = \frac{0 - 100}{(1 + r)^0} + \frac{120 - 80}{(1 + r)^1} + \frac{180 - 60}{(1 + r)^2} = -100 + \frac{40}{1 + r} + \frac{120}{(1 + r}$$

$$0 = -100(1 + r)^2 + 40(1 + r) + 120$$

$$0 = -60 + 160r + 100r^2$$

and from section 2.9:

$$r = \frac{1}{2 \times 100}[-160 \pm \sqrt{160^2 - 4(100)(-60)}]$$

$$= \frac{1}{200}(-160 \pm \sqrt{49600})$$

$$= \frac{1}{200}(62\cdot7 \text{ or } -382\cdot7)$$

$$= 0\cdot31 \text{ or } -1\cdot91$$

The second solution can be ignored since in this example it is obviously unrealistic. The rate of return is $r = 0\cdot31$ which is 31 per cent.

This example is given simply to demonstrate what is the rate of return. In most practical examples the solution is complicated and can be most easily found by graphical techniques. Sometimes solving a problem by algebraic methods can give two equally realistic figures (see question 3 of Exercise 7).

7.12 Interest compounded more than once a year

If a sum of £a is left to accumulate interest at $100i$ per cent per annum, the amount at the end of t years is $a(1 + i)^t$. If A_{t1} is the accumulated total after t years when interest is compounded annually, then $A_{t1} = a(1 + i)^t$. The first subscript on A refers to the number of years that the sum accumulates, and the second refers to the number of times per annum that interest is compounded. For A_{t1}, t takes integer values only.

For calculating the total when interest is added twice yearly, a simple rule of thumb is to add half the interest twice as often. Defining A_{t2} as the accumulated total after t years when interest is added twice yearly, $A_{t2} = a\left(1 + \frac{i}{2}\right)^{2t}$, where t takes integer and half values. However, A_{t2} is greater than A_{t1}, as can be seen by comparing the totals after one year:

$$A_{1,1} = a(1 + i)^1 = a(1 + i)$$

$$A_{1,2} = a\left(1 + \frac{i}{2}\right)^2 = a\left(1 + i + \frac{i^2}{4}\right), \text{ which is greater than } A_{1,1} \text{ by}$$

$a\left(\frac{i^2}{4}\right)$. The difference is not great, although it is an amount worth having. For example, if $a = £10\,000$ and $i = 0{\cdot}08$ the amount is £16.

The difference between four-monthly (thrice yearly) and six monthly compounding is far less. In one year:

$$A_{1,2} = a\left(1 + \frac{i}{2}\right)^2 = a\left(1 + i + \frac{i^2}{4}\right),$$

but $A_{1,3} = a\left(1 + \frac{i}{3}\right)^3 = a\left(1 + i + \frac{i^2}{3} + \frac{i^3}{27}\right),$

and the difference is $a\left(\dfrac{i^2}{12} + \dfrac{i^3}{27}\right)$, which for £10 000 at 8 per cent is only £5·52.

The amount which can be obtained by compounding more and more frequently tends to a limit. This limit turns out to be an extremely important aid to analysis. The next chapter shows that it provides a bridge between the discrete functions mentioned here and the continuous functions of earlier chapters.

Exercise 7

1. Imports and exports are exactly in balance at the start of month 0. Exports increase by £10 million per month and imports by £15 million per month. By how much have exports increased in the 12 months from the start of month 0 to the end of month 11? What is the 'trade gap' at the end of the year?

2. By what percentage per annum must national income grow if it is to double every 15 years?

During the 1950s, West Germany's national income increased by 7·6 per cent per annum. Did it double over the decade?

3. A firm received a government grant of £1000 in January 1966 in order to persuade it to engage in a particular project. In January 1967 it paid out in costs £2110, and in January 1968 it received in revenue £1111. The project then ended. Show that if the firm had predicted costs and revenues accurately at the start of the project, the calculation of the internal rate of return would have yielded a figure of either 1 per cent or of 10 per cent.

4. A student's grant is £100 a term. He spends one-third of it on the morning of the first day of term, one-third of what is left on the

morning of the second day and so on, spending one-third of what is left on the morning of each day. If his fare home is £1 and if he always goes home when broke, how long can he stay at university?

READING

Abbott, P., *Teach Yourself Algebra*, Chapter 21, 'Series'.

Sawyer, W. W., *Mathematician's Delight*, Chapter 14, pp. 200–204.

Carr, J. Laurie, *Investment Economics*, London, Routledge and Kegan Paul, 1969, especially pp. 19–32.

For uses of discrete functions in macroeconomics see: Ford, A. G., *Income, Spending and the Price Level*, Chapters 4 and 5.

Chapter 8

Growth and Natural Logarithms

8.1 Euler's number

In Chapter 7 we found the formula for the amount of money which accumulates after t years, where a is the amount at the start and i is the rate of interest, to be $A_{t1} = a(1 + i)^t$ if interest is compounded annually and $A_{t2} = a\left(1 + \dfrac{i}{2}\right)^{2t}$ if interest is compounded twice yearly. If interest is compounded n times per annum $A_{n,t} = a\left(1 + \dfrac{i}{n}\right)^{nt}$. How much is £1 worth at the end of one year with interest at 100 per cent per annum compounded n times per annum? Here $a = 1$, $t = 1$, and $i = 1$, so the total depends on n: $A_{1n} = \left(1 + \dfrac{1}{n}\right)^n$. Now as n increases this total moves toward a finite limit. Calculations with log tables would yield the following approximate values:

n	1	10	100	1000	10 000
$\left(1 + \dfrac{1}{n}\right)^n$	2	2·594	2·704	2·717	2·718 ...

This limit turns out to be a number which is approximately 2·718 ... It is given the symbol 'e' whose definition is:

$$e = \lim_{n \to \infty} \left(1 + \frac{1}{n}\right)^n.$$

By letting n tend to infinity we are assuming that interest is accumulating continuously over time instead of in jumps each year, quarter, month, or day.

The number e is called **Euler's number** after the mathematician who first appreciated its importance. It cannot be expressed exactly as a decimal, but it can be calculated as accurately as is necessary for the problem in hand. It is similar in some ways to π. The number π is the area of a circle of unit radius. However, π cannot be expressed exactly as a ratio so it is called an **irrational number**. Approximately, π is 3·1416, but this is only approximate. Euler's number is also irrational. Approximately it is 2·7183, but more usually it is written as e. This chapter explains why e is useful.

8.2 Exponential growth

The expression for the accumulated total when n tends to infinity can be converted into a simpler expression involving e. First the expression is rearranged so that it forms a similar pattern to the definition of e:

$$a\left(1 + \frac{i}{n}\right)^{nt} = a\left(1 + \frac{i}{n}\right)^{\frac{n}{i}it}$$

$$= a\left(1 + \frac{1}{m}\right)^{mit}, \text{ where } m = \frac{n}{i}$$

$$= a\left[\left(1 + \frac{1}{m}\right)^{m}\right]^{it}$$

But since $m = \frac{n}{i}$, where i is a positive constant, m will tend to infinity when n tends to infinity, so:

$$\text{Lim}_{n \to \infty} a\left(1 + \frac{i}{n}\right)^{nt} = \text{Lim}_{m \to \infty} a\left[\left(1 + \frac{1}{m}\right)^{m}\right]^{it}$$
$$= a[e]^{it} = ae^{it}$$

In other mathematical work the symbol i is used for the square root of minus one, so we will avoid the possibility of confusion if we change our notation and remember the expression: $y = ae^{rt}$. This continuous function relates y, the accumulated total, to t, time. The parameters a and r will vary with the phenomena being studied and with the units of measurement. It is the formula for exponential growth. a is the value of y when t is zero, the moment when the process starts. We shall see below that r is the rate of growth. If r is negative the relation gives the formula for exponential decay. Figure 8.1 illustrates.

The power to which e is raised, in this case rt, is called the exponent. Sometimes the function is written: $y = a \cdot \exp(rt)$.

The symbol e can be looked upon as an abbreviation either for 'Euler's number' or for 'exponent'.

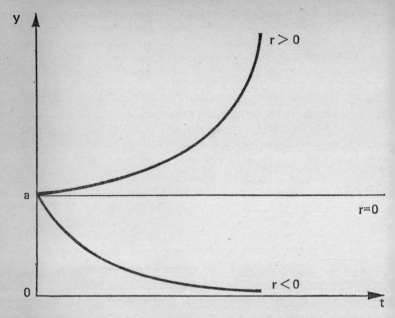

Figure 8.1 $y = a$ exp (rt) depicts growth, constancy, or decay, depending on the value of r

8.3 Natural logarithms

Until now we have used the abbreviation 'log' to mean common logarithm or logarithm-to-the-base-10. If $y = 10^x$ then $x = \log_{10} y$ with the base stated explicitly, and $y = 10^{\log y}$ with the base assumed.

For many purposes logarithms-to-the-base-e are more convenient. If $y = e^x$ then $x = \log_e y$. These logarithms are called natural logarithms. A frequently used abbreviation for a natural logarithm is '1n', and we shall use this so that we do not have to write in the base each time.

Of course, a logarithm can be to any positive base. For example, the base 2 is used in the theory of information. The two abbreviations used in this book are as follows:

Common logarithm: If $y = 10^x$, then $x = \log_{10} y = \log y$.
Natural logarithm: If $y = e^x$, then $x = \log_e y = 1n\ y$.

The two types of logarithm are related:

If $y = e^x$, then $x = \ln y$, so $y = e^{\ln y}$.
If $y = 10^z$, then $z = \log y$, so $y = 10^{\log y}$.
When y is the same, $e^{\ln y} = 10^{\log y}$.
However, $e = 10^{\log e}$, so $e^{\ln y} = (10^{\log e})^{\ln y}$.
Therefore $10^{\log e \cdot \ln y} = 10^{\log y}$
and $\qquad \log e \cdot \ln y = \log y$

$$\ln y = \frac{1}{\log e}\log y$$

or approximately $\ln y = (2 \cdot 3026) \log y$.

8.4 The derivative of $\ln x$

In Figure 8.2 the function $y = \ln x$ is illustrated (remember that
this is the same shape as $x = e^y$). As with all logarithms when $x = 1$,

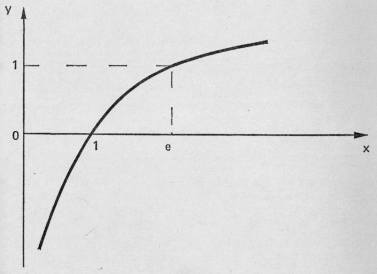

Figure 8.2 The natural logarithmic function

$y = 0$ since any number raised to the power zero is 1. Also when
$x = e$, $y = 1$ since $e^1 = e$. The function becomes less and less steep

as x increases, although the slope is always positive. The slope of $y = \ln x$ is actually $\dfrac{1}{x}$. To express this in symbols

$$\frac{d}{dx}(\ln x) = \frac{1}{x}$$

The proof is complicated. First the standard definition of a derivative is used to express the derivative of $\ln x$.

If $y = f(x)$, then $\dfrac{dy}{dx} = \underset{h \to 0}{\mathrm{Lim}} \dfrac{f(x+h) - f(x)}{h}$

so $\dfrac{d}{dx}(\ln x) = \underset{h \to 0}{\mathrm{Lim}} \dfrac{\ln(x+h) - \ln x}{h}$

Then the rules of logarithms are used to arrange this expression into a pattern which is similar to the pattern for the definition of e:

$$\frac{\ln(x+h) - \ln x}{h} = \frac{1}{h} \ln \frac{x+h}{x}$$

$$= \ln \left(\frac{x+h}{x} \right)^{\frac{1}{h}}$$

$$= \ln \left(1 + \frac{h}{x} \right)^{\frac{1}{h}}$$

$$= \frac{x}{x} \ln \left(1 + \frac{h}{x} \right)^{\frac{1}{h}}$$

$$= \frac{1}{x} \ln \left(1 + \frac{h}{x} \right)^{\frac{x}{h}}$$

so $\dfrac{d}{dx}(\ln x) = \underset{h \to 0}{\mathrm{Lim}} \dfrac{1}{x} \ln \left(1 + \dfrac{h}{x} \right)^{\frac{x}{h}}$

The logarithm of a number always increases as the number itself increases, so the limit of the logarithm of an expression will be the same as the logarithm of the limit of that expression. This allows us to write:

$$\frac{d}{dx}(\ln x) = \frac{1}{x} \ln \left[\underset{h \to 0}{\mathrm{Lim}} \left(1 + \frac{h}{x} \right)^{\frac{x}{h}} \right]$$

$$= \frac{1}{x} \ln \left[\underset{\frac{1}{h} \to \infty}{\mathrm{Lim}} \left(1 + \frac{h}{x} \right)^{\frac{x}{h}} \right]$$

The expression within the square bracket is similar in pattern to the definition of e given in section 8.1. Put $n = \dfrac{x}{h}$, then as n tends to infinity so does $\dfrac{1}{h}$ for any positive x, and the expression becomes exactly the same, and $\dfrac{d}{dx}(\ln x) = \dfrac{1}{x} \ln e = \dfrac{1}{x}$.

8.5 The derivative of e^x

The function $y = e^x$ is illustrated in Figure 8.3. Choose any point on this function, say the point (a, e^a), and draw the tangent to the

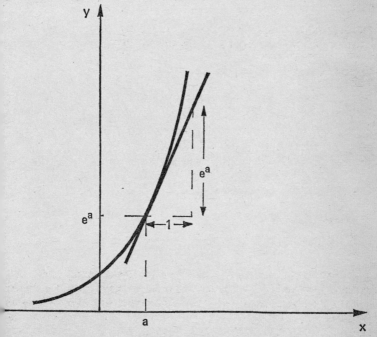

Figure 8.3 The slope of the function $y = e^x$ is always the same value as y

curve at this point. Now find the slope of the tangent at this point by drawing a right-angle triangle with a base of unit length, so that the height of the triangle is the slope of the tangent. It will be found that this slope is also e^a. For example, if $a = 3$, the slope of the tangent will be $e^3 \approx 2\cdot7^3 \approx 20$. The slope of the function at a particular point is the same as the value of the function at that point. In symbols: $\frac{d}{dx}(e^x) = e^x$.

When $y = \ln x$, $x = e^y$ by definition,

$$\text{and } \frac{dy}{dx} = \frac{1}{x} \text{ from section 8.4,}$$

$$\text{and } \frac{dx}{dy} = x \text{ by the inverse function rule,}$$

so when $x = e^y$, $\frac{dx}{dy} = x$.

Reversing the notation we have: when $y = e^x$, $\frac{dx}{dy} = y$, which is to say that $\frac{d}{dx}(e^x) = e^x$.

We have discovered a function whose rate of growth, $\frac{dy}{dx}$, is the same as its stage of growth, y.

8.6 The derivative of a function of a function

An example of a function of a function is: $y = u^{\frac{1}{2}}$, where $u = x^2 + 2x + 3$. Using $f(\;)$ as a general notation for the function relating u to y, and $g(\;)$ for the function relating x to u, we have:

$y = f(u)$, where $u = g(x)$
or $y = f[g(x)]$ ('y equals f of g of x').

To find how y reacts to changes in x, we find how y reacts to changes in u, and how u reacts to changes in x. The two reactions are then geared together so $\frac{dy}{dx} = \frac{dy}{du} \cdot \frac{du}{dx}$.

When $y = u^{\frac{1}{2}}$, $\frac{dy}{du} = \frac{1}{2}u^{-\frac{1}{2}}$, and when $u = x^2 + 2x + 3$, $\frac{du}{dx} = 2x + 2$.

So $\frac{dy}{dx} = \frac{dy}{du} \cdot \frac{du}{dx} = \frac{1}{2}u^{-\frac{1}{2}}(2x + 2) = (x + 1)(x^2 + 2x + 3)^{-\frac{1}{2}}$.

A little practice with the function of a function rule can allow many derivatives to be calculated more quickly than by the methods given so far. For example, when $y = (x + 1)^2$, $\frac{dy}{dx}$ can be found by multiplying out and then taking the derivative $\frac{d}{dx}(x^2 + 2x + 1) =$

$2x + 2$. Alternatively, put $u = x + 1$ so $y = u^2$ and $\frac{dy}{du} = 2u$, giving $\frac{dy}{dx} = \frac{dy}{du} \cdot \frac{du}{dx} = 2u \cdot 1 = 2(x + 1)$.

The rule is used for breaking down expressions into parts, each part having a derivative which is easy to calculate. For example, to find $\frac{dy}{dx}$ when $y = (x^3 + 7)^{\frac{3}{4}}$, put $u = x^3 + 7$ so $y = u^{\frac{3}{4}}$, and

$$\frac{dy}{dx} = \frac{dy}{du} \cdot \frac{du}{dx} = (\tfrac{3}{4}u^{-\frac{1}{4}})(3x^2) = \tfrac{9}{4} x^2(x^3 + 7)^{-\frac{1}{4}}.$$

Similarly, to find $\frac{dz}{dx}$ when $z = \ln y$ and y is a function of x, we have $\frac{dz}{dx} = \frac{dz}{dy} \cdot \frac{dy}{dx}$, and since $\frac{dz}{dy} = \frac{1}{y}$ from section 8.4, we have $\frac{dz}{dx} = \frac{1}{y} \cdot \frac{dy}{dx}$.

8.7 The rate of growth and the stage of growth

The formula giving y as a function of t when y grows exponentially is $y = ae^{rt}$. The way in which y grows over time is $\frac{dy}{dt}$, and this derivative can be found by using the function of a function rule. We know that $\frac{d}{dx}(ae^x) = a\frac{d}{dx}(e^x) = ae^x$, so put $x = rt$ in $y = ae^{rt}$ to obtain: $y = ae^x$, where $x = rt$.

Since $\frac{dy}{dx} = ae^x$ and $\frac{dx}{dt} = r$,

we have $\frac{dy}{dt} = \frac{dy}{dx} \cdot \frac{dx}{dt} = ae^x \cdot r = rae^{rt}$,

or $\frac{dy}{dt} = ry$.

The rate of growth is proportional to the stage of growth. The **proportionate rate of growth** is given by the expression $\frac{1}{y} \cdot \frac{dy}{dt}$, which is r in this example.

The formula $y = ae^{rt}$ is an abbreviation of the statement 'If an amount a grows continuously and exponentially at the rate r, its value after time t will be y.' Compare this with the formula $y = a(1 + r)^t$ which is an abbreviation of the statement 'If an amount a

grows in discrete jumps at the rate r for integer values of t, its value at time t will be y.' The continuous version is used when it is desired to describe a continuous process, as in natural science. It is also useful in theoretical economics because continuous functions are easier to manipulate when making deductions from assumptions. The continuous function will be met in studies of economic growth, technical progress, the accumulation of capital and so on.

We now give an example of exponential decay, which is used in studies involving discounting, depreciation, obsolescence and so on. Let y be a measure of the extent of radioactivity in a substance. The amount of radioactivity declines with age in a process of exponential decay given by the formula $y = ae^{-rt}$, where a and r are parameters, a being the value of y at $t = 0$ and r being the rate of decay. At what time will the radioactivity have declined to half its initial value, i.e. what value of t makes y equal $\frac{a}{2}$? This time is known as the 'half-life' of the radioactivity:

$$\frac{a}{2} = ae^{-rt}$$

$$0{\cdot}5 = e^{-rt}$$

$$\ln 0{\cdot}5 = -rt$$

$$t = -\frac{\ln 0{\cdot}5}{r} = -\frac{2{\cdot}3026 \log 0{\cdot}5}{r} \text{ from section 8.3.}$$

Since $\log 0{\cdot}5$ is negative, the value of t will be positive and will depend on the units of measurement and the parameter r.

8.8 Short-cuts using logarithmic derivation

Logarithmic derivation allows a short-cut to be taken when calculating the elasticity of functions which are linear in logarithms. Consider the log linear demand function $x = ap^{-b}$, where a, b are positive constants. Taking logarithms to the base e gives: $\ln x = \ln a - b \ln p$.

Write $u = \ln x$ and $v = \ln p$, so $\dfrac{du}{dx} = \dfrac{1}{x}$ and $\dfrac{dv}{dp} = \dfrac{1}{p}$.

But $\dfrac{dv}{dx} = \dfrac{dv}{dp} \cdot \dfrac{dp}{dx} = \dfrac{1}{p} \cdot \dfrac{dp}{dx}$,

so $\dfrac{du}{dv} = \dfrac{du}{dx} \cdot \dfrac{dx}{dv} = \dfrac{1}{x} \cdot p\dfrac{dx}{dp} = \dfrac{p}{x} \cdot \dfrac{dx}{dp}$, which is the price elasticity of demand.

Because $u = \ln x$ and $v = \ln p$, we can write:

$$x = ap^{-b}$$
$$\ln x = \ln a - b \ln p$$
$$u = \ln a - bv$$
$$\frac{du}{dv} = -b,\text{ which is the price elasticity of demand.}$$

In general, the elasticity of x in response to change in p is given by $\dfrac{d(\ln x)}{d(\ln p)}$. Sometimes this is easier to manipulate than the more usual $\dfrac{p}{x} \cdot \dfrac{dx}{dp}$.

When logarithmic derivation is combined with the function of a function rule, a short-cut can be used for finding the derivatives both of products of functions and of quotients of functions. If y is a function of x, and z is the particular function of y given by $z = \ln y$, then the function of a function rule gives:

$$\frac{dz}{dx} = \frac{dz}{dy} \cdot \frac{dy}{dx} = \frac{1}{y} \cdot \frac{dy}{dx},\text{ so }\frac{d}{dx}(\ln y) = \frac{1}{y} \cdot \frac{dy}{dx}$$

If $y = u \cdot v$, where $u = u(x)$ and $v = v(x)$:

then $\ln y = \ln (u \cdot v)$

so $\ln y = \ln u + \ln v$

$$\frac{d}{dx}(\ln y) = \frac{d}{dx}(\ln u) + \frac{d}{dx}(\ln v)$$

$$\frac{1}{y} \cdot \frac{dy}{dx} = \frac{1}{u} \cdot \frac{du}{dx} + \frac{1}{v} \cdot \frac{dv}{dx}$$

Since $y = u \cdot v$, we can multiply the left-hand side by y and the right-hand side by $u \cdot v$ to obtain the formula found in Chapter 5:

$$\frac{dy}{dx} = v \cdot \frac{du}{dx} + u \cdot \frac{dv}{dx}$$

If $y = \dfrac{u}{v}$, where $u = u(x)$ and $v = v(x)$:

then $\ln y = \ln u - \ln v$,

and $\dfrac{1}{y} \cdot \dfrac{dy}{dx} = \dfrac{1}{u} \cdot \dfrac{du}{dx} - \dfrac{1}{v} \cdot \dfrac{dv}{dx}$

We can find $\dfrac{dy}{dx}$ by multiplying the left-hand side by y and the right-hand side by $\dfrac{u}{v}$ to obtain the derivative of the quotient of two functions:

$$\frac{dy}{dx} = \frac{u}{v} \cdot \frac{1}{u} \cdot \frac{du}{dx} - \frac{u}{v} \cdot \frac{1}{v} \cdot \frac{dv}{dx} = \frac{1}{v^2}\left(v \cdot \frac{du}{dx} - u \cdot \frac{dv}{dx}\right)$$

8.9 Marginal cost and average cost

In this section the quotient rule is used to prove that the marginal cost function always cuts the average cost functions at their lowest

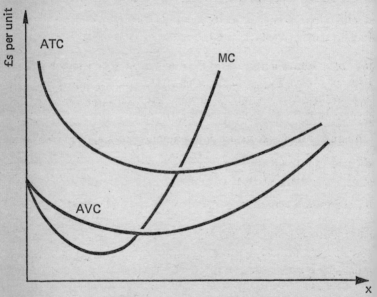

Figure 8.4 Average total, average variable and marginal costs

points. In previous chapters we have always meant average total costs when we referred to average costs. Here we distinguish between **average total costs** and **average variable costs**. Figure 8.4 illustrates typical shapes for the three curves.

Write C for total costs, a function of the quantity produced, x, so $\dfrac{C}{x}$ is average total costs (ATC).

Write V for total variable costs, a function of x, so $\frac{V}{x}$ is average variable costs (AVC).

Write F for fixed costs, which are constant by definition, so $C = V + F$.

Marginal costs (MC) are $\frac{dC}{dx} = \frac{d}{dx}(V + F) = \frac{dV}{dx}$.

Average total costs are at a minimum when $\frac{d}{dx}(\text{ATC}) = 0$, but $\frac{d}{dx}(\text{ATC}) = \frac{d}{dx}\left(\frac{C}{x}\right)$, which is the quotient of two functions of x: C, and x. Apply the quotient rule to obtain:

$$\frac{d}{dx}\left(\frac{C}{x}\right) = \frac{1}{x^2}\left(x \cdot \frac{dC}{dx} - C \cdot \frac{dx}{dx}\right) = \frac{1}{x^2}\left(x \cdot \frac{dC}{dx} - C\right),$$

and this is zero when $x \cdot \frac{dC}{dx} = C$, or when $\frac{dC}{dx} = \frac{C}{x}$, which is MC = ATC. So at that point on the average total cost function where average costs are at a minimum, they have the same value as marginal costs.

Average variable costs are at a minimum when $\frac{d}{dx}(\text{AVC}) = 0$.

$$\frac{d}{dx}(\text{AVC}) = \frac{d}{dx}\left(\frac{V}{x}\right) = \frac{1}{x^2}\left(x \cdot \frac{dV}{dx} - V\right),$$

and this is zero when $x \cdot \frac{dV}{dx} = V$, or $\frac{dV}{dx} = \frac{V}{x}$, which is MC = AVC.

This follows because F is constant, making $\frac{dC}{dx} = \frac{d}{dx}(V + F) = \frac{dV}{dx}$, so there is no distinction between 'marginal total costs' and 'marginal variable costs'.

8.10 Summary

The following is a summary of formulae for derivations:

$$\frac{d}{dx}(\text{constant}) = 0$$

$$\frac{d}{dx}(ax^n + bx^m) = anx^{n-1} + bmx^{m-1}$$

$$\frac{dx}{dy} = \frac{1}{\frac{dy}{dx}}$$

$$\frac{d}{dx}(\ln x) = \frac{1}{x}$$

$$\frac{d}{dx}(e^x) = e^x$$

If z is a function of y, and y is a function of x, then $\frac{dz}{dx} = \frac{dz}{dy} \cdot \frac{dy}{dx}$.

In particular, if $z = \ln y$ and y is a function of x, then $\frac{dz}{dx} = \frac{1}{y} \cdot \frac{dy}{dx}$.

When u and v are each functions of x, then

$$\frac{d}{dx}(u \cdot v) = v \cdot \frac{du}{dx} + u \cdot \frac{dv}{dx}$$

Also if $y = u \cdot v$, then

$$\frac{1}{y} \cdot \frac{dy}{dx} = \frac{1}{u} \cdot \frac{du}{dx} + \frac{1}{v} \cdot \frac{dv}{dx}$$

$$\frac{d}{dx}\left(\frac{u}{v}\right) = \frac{1}{v^2}\left(v \cdot \frac{du}{dx} - u \cdot \frac{dv}{dx}\right)$$

Also if $y = \frac{u}{v}$, then

$$\frac{1}{y} \cdot \frac{dy}{dx} = \frac{1}{u} \cdot \frac{du}{dx} - \frac{1}{v} \cdot \frac{dv}{dx}$$

The elasticity of y in response to changes in x is: $\frac{x}{y} \cdot \frac{dy}{dx} = \frac{d(\ln y)}{d(\ln x)}$.

Drill

1. Use logarithmic derivation to find the elasticities of the following demand functions: $x = \dfrac{9}{p^{\frac{1}{2}}}$, $x = bp^{-k}$, $x = 12 \cdot 09 p^{-2 \cdot 7}$.

2. Use the function of a function rule to find the derivative with respect to x of: $\ln x^{20}$, $\ln 3x$, $\ln 10x$, $\ln(3x + b)$, $\ln \dfrac{x}{3}$, $\ln x^3$.

3. Use the function of a function rule to find the proportionate rate of growth of output over time $\left(\dfrac{1}{Q} \cdot \dfrac{dQ}{dt}\right)$ when output (Q) is the following function of time (t): $Q = Me^{0.02t}$ and M is man-hours which are assumed constant.

4. Output per annum (Q) is related to the size of the labour force (L) in such a way that when $L = 1$, $Q = 100$. Also the elasticity of Q in response to changes in L is 0·7. Devise a formula giving Q as a function of L. Check that $\dfrac{d(\ln Q)}{d(\ln L)} = \dfrac{L}{Q} \cdot \dfrac{dQ}{dL} = 0.7$.

Answers

1. $-\frac{1}{2}$, $-k$, $-2\cdot7$.

2. $\dfrac{20}{x}$, $\dfrac{1}{x}$, $\dfrac{1}{x}$, $\dfrac{3}{3x + b}$, $\dfrac{1}{x}$, $\dfrac{3}{x}$.

3. 0·02.

4. $Q = 100L^{0.7}$.

8.11 A note on difference equations and differential equations

In dynamic economics, **differential equations** can provide many insights into the movements of economic variables. A simple example of a differential equation is $\dfrac{dy}{dt} = ry$. We know from section 8.7 that this can be found by derivation from the expression $y = ae^{rt}$, so $\dfrac{dy}{dt} = ry$ is the same as $\dfrac{dy}{dt} = rae^{rt}$. The process of finding y from $\dfrac{dy}{dt}$ is the reverse of finding the derivative of y with respect to t; it is known as **integration**.

Finding integrals is sometimes simple, provided one is familiar with many examples of derivation. Sometimes, however, it is difficult and calls for the division of labour; one would take a difficult problem of integration to a professional mathematician and ask him to solve it. Sometimes integration is impossible. In the exercises at the end of this chapter, a few of the more frequently met functions which result from integration are stated first and the reader is asked to find the derivatives.

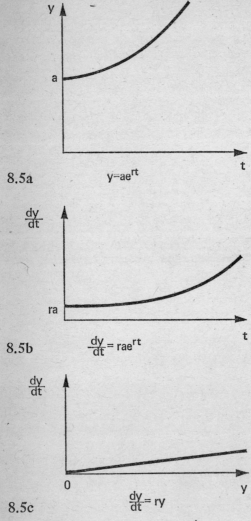

8.5a $y = ae^{rt}$

8.5b $\dfrac{dy}{dt} = rae^{rt}$

8.5c $\dfrac{dy}{dt} = ry$

Figure 8.5 Relations between y, t, and $\dfrac{dy}{dt}$

The differential equation $\frac{dy}{dt} = ry$ or $\frac{dy}{dt} = rae^{rt}$ represents the rate of change of a continuous function. Analogous to this is the rate of change of a discrete function. For example, if $A_t = a(1 + r)^t$, then $A_{t-1} = a(1 + r)^{t-1}$. The difference between these two expressions gives the change that has occurred between time t and time $t - 1$:

$$A_t - A_{t-1} = a(1 + r)^t - a(1 + r)^{t-1}$$
$$= a(1 + r)^{t-1}(1 + r - 1)$$
$$= ra(1 + r)^{t-1} = rA_{t-1}$$

so $A_t - A_{t-1} = rA_{t-1}$

This equation is an example of a **difference equation**. Such equations are formed from discrete functions and are useful in applied work because most economic measurements of change are made as discrete measures. Differential equations are formed from continuous functions and are used in theoretical work because deductions by derivation or integration are often easier than with discrete functions. The analogy between the two becomes clear for the particular simple functions which describe a constant proportionate rate of growth:

Continuous: $\frac{1}{y} \cdot \frac{dy}{dt} = \frac{rae^{rt}}{ae^{rt}} = r$

Discrete: $\frac{A_t - A_{t-1}}{A_{t-1}} = \frac{ra(1 + r)^{t-1}}{a(1 + r)^{t-1}} = r$

Figure 8.5(a) illustrates y as a continuous function of t, part (b) illustrates $\frac{dy}{dt}$ as a function of t, and part (c) illustrates the differential equation relating $\frac{dy}{dt}$ to y on the assumption that $0 < r < 1$.

Exercise 8

1. The rate of growth of an economic variable is observed to be proportional to its stage of growth so that $\frac{dy}{dt} = 0·03y$. Show that if the relation between y and t is $y = ae^{0·03t}$, where a is any constant, the given differential equation follows.

2. Find $\frac{x}{y} \cdot \frac{dy}{dx}$ in terms of x when $y = e^x$, when $y = 1n\ x$, when $x = e^y$, and when $x = 1n\ y$.

3. If total costs are related to quantity produced by the function $C = a + bx - \dfrac{h}{2} x^2 + \dfrac{k}{3} x^3$, find the marginal cost function.

4. If the marginal cost function is $\dfrac{dC}{dx} = 7 - 4x + 9x^2$, what additional information is necessary before the total cost function can be found? Using a symbol for this additional information, give the total cost function.

5. $y = N(1 - e^{-kt})$, where N and k are parameters.

i. Find $\dfrac{dy}{dt}$.

ii. Express e^{-kt} in terms of y and N.

iii. Express $\dfrac{dy}{dt}$ in terms of y, N, and k.

iv. If a new product is advertised by an intensive television campaign among a fixed population of potential customers, and if the product and the advertising are successful, the rate of increase of new customers will be proportional to the number who are not yet customers. Devise a differential equation relating the increase of new customers $\left(\dfrac{dy}{dt} \right)$ to the number of the total relevant population (N) and the number of people who are already customers (y). Sketch curves showing (a) the relations between y and t, (b) between $\dfrac{dy}{dt}$ and t, and (c) between $\dfrac{dy}{dt}$ and y.

Chapter 9

Many Dimensions

9.1 Introduction

Some primitive people use an uncomplicated system of counting with three numbers: one, two, many. We have complicated life with the idea of integers from zero towards infinity in one direction and towards minus infinity in the other direction. Between any two integers there are an infinite number of fractions which are formed by combining the whole numbers in ratios. There are also the irrational numbers which can be defined in words (π is the area of the circle of unit radius) or in symbols (the definition of e) but not in terms of the ratios of integers. Our analytical techniques can manage any value of a variable, or any value for the member of a set. However, our study of relations has so far been kept at the primitive level, the relation between one set and another or between one variable and another.

In this chapter the relations between many sets, or between many variables, are investigated. When the sets with which we are working are obvious we will speak of variables and leave unsaid the sets to which these variables belong. This will allow us to concentrate on the way the functions behave, without excessive notation. In some cases the sets themselves present the obstacles to understanding but here the language of sets will clarify rather than complicate.

9.2 Substitutes and complements

Suppose that we are trying to explain the quantity of feed-wheat demanded by livestock producers. A study of the market shows that barley is a close substitute for this type of wheat because both are cheap sources of starch, and that protein-meal is a complement to wheat since wheat by itself would constitute an unbalanced diet.

Let x_w be the quantity of feed-wheat demanded, p_w be the price of feed-wheat, p_b be the price of barley, and p_m be the price of protein-meal. The general demand relation can be described as:

$$x_w = D(p_w, p_b, p_m)$$

or as a specific example

$$x_w = 9 - \tfrac{1}{2}p_w + \tfrac{1}{3}p_b - \tfrac{1}{5}p_m$$

If we are trying to explain x_w during some period in the past, and if we observe that during this period p_b stays constant at 30 and p_m stays constant at 60, the demand relation becomes one between x_w and p_w only:

$$x_w = 9 - \tfrac{1}{2}p_w + \tfrac{1}{3}(30) - \tfrac{1}{5}(60)$$
so $x_w = 7 - \tfrac{1}{2}p_w$.

To find how x_w reacts to changes in p_w we find $\dfrac{dx_w}{dp_w}$ which is $-\tfrac{1}{2}$.

Provided p_b and p_m stay constant, they can be grouped together with the constant term:

$$x_w = (9 + \tfrac{1}{3}p_b - \tfrac{1}{5}p_m) - \tfrac{1}{2}p_w$$

This procedure allows x_w to be treated as a function of p_w only: $x_w = D(p_w)$ as in Chapter 4. We are assuming that other things remain equal. However, if p_b and p_m vary as well as p_w, the effects on x_w are still not difficult to find: x_w goes up by $\tfrac{1}{3}$ unit for every unit increase in p_b and down by $\tfrac{1}{5}$ unit for every unit increase in p_m. If the values of the independent variables, the three prices, are known, a unique value for the dependent variable x_w can be found. This uniqueness makes x_w a function of all three variables, p_w, p_b, and p_m.

The operation of finding the derivative of x_w with respect to p_w involves the same manipulation when $x_w = D(p_w, p_b, p_m)$ as when $x_w = D(p_w)$, but the notation is changed to $\dfrac{\partial x_w}{\partial p_w}$. The curved d serves as a reminder that x_w does not depend only on p_w but also on other independent variables. The instruction given by the operator $\dfrac{\partial}{\partial p_w}(\quad)$ is 'find the **partial derivative** with respect to p_w'. If there are two or more independent variables, we find the partial derivative with respect to one of them and assume that the others are constants.

If $x_w = 9 - \tfrac{1}{2}p_w + \tfrac{1}{3}p_b - \tfrac{1}{5}p_m$, then $\dfrac{\partial x_w}{\partial p_w} = -\tfrac{1}{2}$, measured in tons of wheat per £ change in the wheat price. Similarly, $\frac{\partial x_w}{\partial p_b} = \frac{1}{3}$, measured in tons of wheat per £ change in the barley price, and $\frac{\partial x_w}{\partial p_m} = -\frac{1}{5}$, measured in tons of wheat per £ change in the protein-meal price.

The directions of change of these partial derivatives are applicable generally.

For the normal demand relation: $\frac{\partial x_w}{\partial p_w} < 0$

For substitutes: $\frac{\partial x_w}{\partial p_b} > 0$

For complements: $\frac{\partial x_w}{\partial p_m} < 0$

Once the demand function is defined to include the prices of several products, the price elasticity of demand becomes ambiguous unless it is qualified by saying which price is being considered. The elasticity of the quantity demanded of a good in response to changes in its own price is known as the **own price elasticity**: $\frac{p_w}{x_w} \cdot \frac{\partial x_w}{\partial p_w}$.

An elasticity in response to changes in another price is known as a **cross elasticity**: $\frac{p_b}{x_w} \cdot \frac{\partial x_w}{\partial p_b}$ and $\frac{p_m}{x_w} \cdot \frac{\partial x_w}{\partial p_m}$. The cross elasticity of demand between substitutes will be positive because of the sign of the derivative. There are a great number of cross elasticities which could be calculated. One of the arts of economics is to judge correctly when the cross elasticities are zero or negligible so that factors can be omitted from the analysis, or when they are appreciable and should be taken into account.

Drill

There are three goods: good One, good Two, and good Three. The quantity demanded of good One depends on its own price and on the prices of goods Two and Three. The demand function is:

$x_1 = D(p_1, p_2, p_3) = kp_1^{-a}p_2^{b}p_3^{-c}$, where k, a, b, c are positive constants.

1. Find the own price elasticity of demand for good One.

2. Find the cross elasticity between x_1 and p_2.

3. Find the elasticity of response of x_1 to changes in p_3.

4. Which good is a substitute for One?

5. Which good is a complement to One?

Note that $\ln x_1 = \ln k - a \ln p_1 + b \ln p_2 - c \ln p_3$.
Revise section 8.8.

Answers

1. $\dfrac{\partial(\ln x_1)}{\partial(\ln p_1)} = -a.$

2. $\dfrac{\partial(\ln x_1)}{\partial(\ln p_2)} = b.$

3. $\dfrac{\partial(\ln x_1)}{\partial(\ln p_3)} = -c.$

4. Two.
5. Three.

_____

9.3 Many variables and many dimensions

It may be helpful at this stage to give a name to a concept which we have been using continuously. When we were discussing the speed of a falling object, we pictured the relation between time and distance in two-dimensional space. The horizontal axis represented the set of times, T, and the vertical axis represented the set of distances, S. The two-dimensional space represented the product set $T \times S$ whose members were the ordered pairs (t, s). These ordered pairs (t, s) could be thought of both as members of the product set and as points in two-dimensional space. Similarly with supply and demand: (p, x) represented members of the product set $P \times X$ and also points in two-dimensional space.

If we were attempting to describe the position of a point in a room we could do so by defining a corner of the room as the origin and then measuring three distances from this origin: the distance north-wards, the distance eastwards and the height of the point. Let E

be the set of distances eastwards, and $x \in E$, N be the set of distances northwards, and $y \in N$, H be the set of distances upwards, and $z \in H$, then the product set $E \times N \times H$ is the set of points in three-dimensional space, and the ordered trio (x, y, z) is a typical member of this product set. Figure 9.1 illustrates.

We can conceive of, but not picture, the products of more than

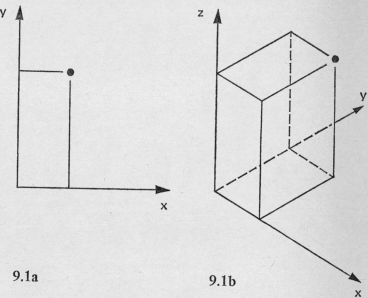

9.1a

9.1b

Figure 9.1 Two and three dimensions

three sets: of n sets, where n is any number. The members of this product set can be thought of as points in n-dimensional space. To avoid running out of letters we will use integer subscripts to label the sets and their members.

Let Q_1 be a set containing members with a particular characteristic, for example Q_1 may be the set of amounts of a particular commodity. A typical member of the set is q_1. Let Q_2 be a set containing members with a different characteristic; $q_2 \in Q_2$ . . . . Let Q_n be a set containing members with a characteristic which is different again; $q_n \in Q_n$. The members of the product set $Q_1 \times Q_2 \times \cdots \times Q_n$ are the ordered groups $(q_1, q_2, \ldots, q_n)$ and these can be conceived of as points in n-dimensional space.

$(t, s), (p, x), (x, y, z)$, and $(q_1, q_2, \ldots, q_n)$ are sometimes called **vectors**. (t, s) is a two-dimensional vector; (x, y, z) is three-dimensional, and $(q_1, q_2, \ldots, q_n)$ is an n-dimensional vector. We can use the term 'n-tuple' to convey a continuation of the series: pair, trio, quartet, $\ldots$, n-tuple. Then an n-dimensional vector is an ordered n-tuple of

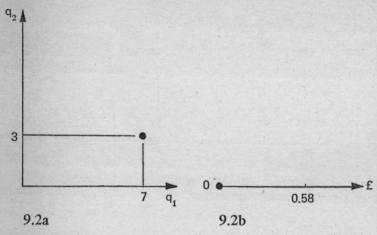

9.2a   9.2b

Figure 9.2 Weights can convert a two-dimensional vector into one dimension

numbers written $(q_1, q_2, \ldots, q_n)$ and sometimes abbreviated to q. In most text-books vectors are printed in heavy type, but underlining is easier to reproduce.

Consider the product set $Q_1 \times Q_2$ of all the things that an ascetic buys in a week. Q_1 is the set of pints of milk, Q_2 is the set of loaves of bread, $q_1 \in Q_1$ and $q_2 \in Q_2$, and this particular person buys only these two commodities. If he buys 7 pints of milk and 3 loaves of bread a week, $(q_1, q_2) = (7, 3)$.

If we are interested in the amount of money the ascetic spends, we can add the items together by *weighting* each item by its price. If milk is £0·04 per pint and bread is £0·10 per loaf his total expenditure is:

$$\sum_{i=1}^{2} p_1 q_1 = p_1 q_1 + p_2 q_2$$
$$= 0{\cdot}04 \times 7 + 0{\cdot}10 \times 3 = £0{\cdot}58$$

Prices have allowed us to combine the (pints, loaves) vector into a number of £s. We have moved from a two-dimensional space of quantities of commodities to a one-dimensional space of £s. Figure 9.2 illustrates.

9.4 Changes in the general level of prices

Consider the commodity space formed from the product set $Q_1 \times Q_2 \times \cdots \times Q_n$ (product in the sense of multiplication rather than output), where Q_1 is apples, Q_2 is bananas, . . ., Q_n is washing powder. $(q_1, q_2, \ldots, q_n)$ is a vector of the amounts of each commodity which the typical family buys, where q_1 is pounds of apples, and so on.

The total expenditure of the family is $\sum\limits_{i=1}^{n} p_1 q_1$, where p_1 is the price per pound of apples, and p_i is the price of Q_i.

If we are interested in changes in the level of these prices over the years we have to add an additional dimension, time, order to date each set of observations. This can be done by adding an additional subscript, thus:

$$\sum_{i=1}^{n} p_{i, \ 1958} \, q_{i, \ 1958}$$

is the expenditure of the family in 1958, being the total of the quantities bought in 1958 weighted by the prices in 1958.

To compare prices in 1970 with prices in 1958 we form an **index** which uses the quantities bought in 1958 as weights to allow the different prices to be added. If we did not use the quantities as weights, a doubling of the price of pepper would seem as significant as a doubling of the price of bread, even though expenditure on pepper would have been only a fraction of the expenditure on bread. The price index is expressed as a percentage. Obviously:

$$\frac{\sum p_{i, \ 1958} \, q_{i, \ 1958}}{\sum p_{i, \ 1958} \, q_{i, \ 1958}} \cdot 100 = 100, \text{ but } \frac{\sum p_{i, \ 1970} \, q_{i, \ 1958}}{\sum p_{i, \ 1958} \, q_{i, \ 1958}} \cdot 100$$

will be greater than 100 if most of the significant prices have been rising. In this example 1958 is the base year. The index compares the cost of a bundle of goods in the base year with the cost of the same bundle of goods in 1970.

Now we do not know that a typical family will be buying the same amounts of these goods in 1970 as they were buying in 1958. Indeed there are two reasons why this may not be so. If the costs of production of good A increased by more than the costs of production of good B, if tastes have changed little, and if goods A and B are substitutes for each other, the typical family will buy more of good B and less of good A because p_B will have increased less than p_A. The extent of the shift from good A to good B will depend on the cross-elasticities of demand: $\frac{p_A}{q_B} \cdot \frac{\partial q_B}{\partial p_A}$ and $\frac{p_B}{q_A} \cdot \frac{\partial q_A}{\partial p_B}$. Those goods whose prices have risen most will be purchased less frequently if the price changes are due more to supply changes than to demand changes. Under these circumstances a base-weighted index will tend to exaggerate the increase in the cost of living. It assumes that people are inflexible in their purchasing patterns. However, substitution has caused a reduced quantity to be bought of those goods whose prices have risen most, and an increased quantity of those goods whose prices have risen least.

On the other hand, tastes may have changed and people may buy more of a good because they like it more than they did. If there has been no change in the conditions of supply of the good (no shift of the supply function), the price will rise (a movement along the supply function). But those goods whose prices have risen most will be those which are purchased in larger quantities than before, because the price rises are due to shifts outward of the demand functions. In this case a base-weighted index will tend to underestimate changes in the cost of living.

An alternative to a base-weighted index is one that uses current weights. The cost of the bundle of goods bought in 1970 is compared with what the same bundle would have cost at 1958 prices. The disadvantages of a current-weighted index are the reverse of a base-weighted one. If prices have risen due to increases in costs of production, the current-weighted index will underestimate the extent of the increase. If price increases are due to changes in demand the current-weighted index will exaggerate the effect.

We can abbreviate the two types of index by calling the base year 0, the current year t, and omitting the i subscript since the goods involved are the same in each case. The indexes are often named after the men who first used them:

Base-weighted price index: $\frac{\sum p_t q_0}{\sum p_0 q_0} \cdot 100$ (Laspeyres)

Current-weighted price index: $\frac{\sum p_t q_t}{\sum p_0 q_t} \cdot 100$ (Paasche)

The Index of Retail Prices is the most suitable of the available indexes to use as an indicator of changes in the cost of living. It is a base-weighted index with 1958 as the base year. As with all summary statistics, the Retail Price Index must be used with caution even for the changes in those prices which affect a typical family. This caution is even more important when considering particular groups in the economy other than the typical family. For example, the prices of those goods which the average old-age pensioner buys have been increasing more rapidly than the Index of Retail Prices. For low-income groups there can be serious consequences if the decrease in their purchasing power is concealed from the rest of the community by the assumption that one index applies to all. There are now special indices weighted by the bundles of goods bought by typical pensioners.

Drill

1. A man is walking up the side of a pyramid where the height in feet (z) is related to the distance east in yards (x) and the distance north in yards (y) by the expression $z = 2x + 7y$. See Figure 9.3(a).

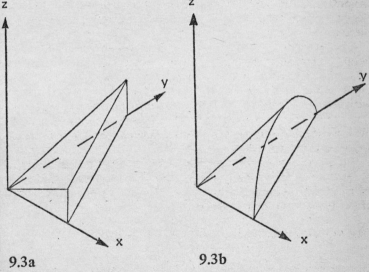

9.3a   9.3b

Figure 9.3 (a) An inclined plane; (b) A curved mound

i. If he starts 10 yards to the east and then walks due north, what is the relation between z and y?

ii. If he starts 30 yards to the north and then walks due east, what is the relation between z and x?

iii. How does height change in response to changes of distance in an easterly direction? In a northerly direction?

iv. How does the slope in a northerly direction change as he proceeds further north? How does the slope in an easterly direction change as he proceeds further east?

v. How does the slope in a northerly direction change as he proceeds in an easterly direction? How does the slope in an easterly direction change as he proceeds in a northerly direction?

2. A man is walking on a mound, as illustrated in Figure 9.3(b). The relation between z, x, and y is described by $z = 3x^{\frac{3}{2}}y^{\frac{1}{4}}$.

i. If he starts 16 yards to the east and walks due north, what is the relation between z and y?

ii. If he starts 81 yards to the north and then walks due east, what is the relation between z and x?

iii. iv and v as for question 1.

Answers

1. i. $z = 2(10) + 7y = 20 + 7y$.

   ii. $z = 2x + 210$.

   iii. $\dfrac{\partial z}{\partial x} = 2$ feet per yard, $\dfrac{\partial z}{\partial y} = 7$ feet per yard.

   iv. $\dfrac{\partial}{\partial y}\left(\dfrac{\partial z}{\partial y}\right) = \dfrac{\partial^2 z}{\partial y^2} = 0$, $\dfrac{\partial}{\partial x}\left(\dfrac{\partial z}{\partial x}\right) = \dfrac{\partial^2 z}{\partial x^2} = 0$.

   v. $\dfrac{\partial}{\partial x}\left(\dfrac{\partial z}{\partial y}\right) = \dfrac{\partial^2 z}{\partial x \partial y} = 0$, $\dfrac{\partial}{\partial y}\left(\dfrac{\partial z}{\partial x}\right) = \dfrac{\partial^2 z}{\partial y \partial x} = 0$.

2. i. $z = 3(16)^{\frac{3}{2}}y^{\frac{1}{4}} = 3(2^4)^{\frac{3}{2}}y^{\frac{1}{4}} = 3 \cdot 2^3 y^{\frac{1}{4}} = 24y^{\frac{1}{4}}$.

   ii. $z = 3x^{\frac{3}{2}}(81)^{\frac{1}{4}} = 9x^{\frac{3}{2}}$.

   iii. $\dfrac{\partial z}{\partial x} = \dfrac{9}{4}x^{-\frac{1}{2}}y^{\frac{1}{4}}$, $\dfrac{\partial z}{\partial y} = \dfrac{3}{4}x^{\frac{3}{2}}y^{-\frac{3}{4}}$.

   iv. $\dfrac{\partial}{\partial y}\left(\dfrac{\partial z}{\partial y}\right) = -\dfrac{9}{16}x^{\frac{3}{2}}y^{-\frac{7}{4}}$, $\dfrac{\partial}{\partial x}\left(\dfrac{\partial z}{\partial x}\right) = -\dfrac{9}{16}x^{-\frac{5}{2}}y^{\frac{1}{4}}$.

   v. $\dfrac{\partial}{\partial x}\left(\dfrac{\partial z}{\partial y}\right) = \dfrac{9}{16}x^{-\frac{1}{2}}y^{-\frac{3}{4}} = \dfrac{\partial}{\partial y}\left(\dfrac{\partial z}{\partial x}\right)$.

9.5 Production functions

A production function is a method of expressing the relation between the output of a productive unit and its inputs. It expresses quantity produced as a function of the factors of production. The actual processes of production are not explained by such a function, nor are they described in great detail. The production function is an aid in understanding why certain decisions are taken, those decisions which affect the market for the product and the markets for the factors of production.

The simplest approach is to assume that output is produced by labour and capital, and that this relation does not vary from one period of time to the next. For long time periods the relation would be more complicated since it would have to take into account technological progress and learning by doing. However, we assume here that output is a function of labour and capital only: $Q = Q(L, K)$. The variable Q is output in physical units such as tons per month. The variable L is the amount of labour employed, such as man-hours per month. The variable K is the amount of capital equipment employed, such as machine-hours per month. The notation $Q(\ )$ is the functional relation: when L and K take particular values, Q has a unique value.

The production function assumes **technical efficiency**: all the inputs are used in such a way that they yield the maximum amount of output in physical units. Of course it is possible that a producer will have capital in his plant but will not use it, or he may be paying labour but have no work for them to do. When this is so, the possibilities for production can be described by the relation $Q \leqslant Q(L, K)$, but this is not a function. By assuming technical efficiency the more precise functional relation $Q = Q(L, K)$ can be used.

There are four groups of rules that a production function should obey if it is to be typical of many productive processes.

The first group follows from the observation that additional workers (or additional machines) usually add to output. The **marginal product** of labour is positive. The marginal product of labour is the reaction of Q to changes in L, assuming other things remain constant. If the production relation can be described mathematically by a smooth function, then the marginal product of labour is the partial derivative of Q with respect to L. So the positive marginal product of labour can be written $\frac{\partial Q}{\partial L} > 0$. A similar empirical result is usually found for capital: $\frac{\partial Q}{\partial K} > 0$.

Secondly, it has been found empirically that if one factor of production is increased while everything else stays constant, the marginal product of that factor diminishes. The reaction of the marginal product of labour to changes in the amount of labour is written $\frac{\partial}{\partial L}\left(\frac{\partial Q}{\partial L}\right)$ or $\frac{\partial^2 Q}{\partial L^2}$, so the diminishing marginal product of labour can be abbreviated to $\frac{\partial^2 Q}{\partial L^2} < 0$. Similarly for capital: $\frac{\partial}{\partial K}\left(\frac{\partial Q}{\partial K}\right) = \frac{\partial^2 Q}{\partial K^2} < 0$.

A third empirical finding is that if one factor increases, the marginal product of the other factor will usually increase. The marginal product of labour reacts in a positive direction to increases in the amount of capital: $\frac{\partial}{\partial K}\left(\frac{\partial Q}{\partial L}\right) > 0$, or $\frac{\partial^2 Q}{\partial K \partial L} > 0$. Similarly, the marginal product of capital increases when the quantity of labour increases: $\frac{\partial}{\partial L}\left(\frac{\partial Q}{\partial K}\right) = \frac{\partial^2 Q}{\partial L \partial K} > 0$. $\Big($Mathematically these last two statements are the same because it can be proved that $\frac{\partial^2 Q}{\partial K \partial L} = \frac{\partial^2 Q}{\partial L \partial K}.\Big)$

Finally, when there is no labour, production is zero. When there is no capital, production is usually negligible. And of course when there is neither labour nor equipment, there is no output. So:

$Q(0, K) = 0$
$Q(L, 0) = 0$
$Q(0, 0) = 0$

A production function which meets the four groups of rules is $Q = 10L^{\frac{3}{4}}K^{\frac{1}{4}}$.

1. The marginal products are positive, since:

$$\frac{\partial Q}{\partial L} = \tfrac{3}{4} \cdot 10L^{-\frac{1}{4}}K^{\frac{1}{4}} > 0 \quad \text{and} \quad \frac{\partial Q}{\partial K} = \tfrac{1}{4} \cdot 10L^{\frac{3}{4}}K^{-\frac{3}{4}} > 0.$$

2. The marginal products diminish, since:

$$\frac{\partial}{\partial L}\left(\frac{\partial Q}{\partial L}\right) = (-\tfrac{1}{4})\tfrac{3}{4} \cdot 10L^{-\frac{5}{4}}K^{\frac{1}{4}} < 0$$

and $\dfrac{\partial}{\partial K}\left(\dfrac{\partial Q}{\partial K}\right) = (-\tfrac{3}{4})\,\tfrac{1}{4}\cdot 10L^{\frac{3}{4}}K^{-\frac{7}{4}} < 0.$

3. As one factor increases, the marginal product of the other factor increases:

$$\dfrac{\partial}{\partial K}\left(\dfrac{\partial Q}{\partial L}\right) = (\tfrac{1}{4})\,\tfrac{3}{4}\cdot 10L^{-\frac{1}{4}}K^{-\frac{3}{4}} > 0$$

and $\dfrac{\partial}{\partial L}\left(\dfrac{\partial Q}{\partial K}\right) = (\tfrac{3}{4})\,\tfrac{1}{4}\cdot 10L^{-\frac{1}{4}}K^{-\frac{3}{4}} > 0$

Note that these two expressions are equal.

4. When $L = 0$, $Q = 10\,(0)^{\frac{3}{4}}K^{\frac{1}{4}} = 0$.
When $K = 0$, $Q = 10L^{\frac{3}{4}}(0)^{\frac{1}{4}} = 0$
and $Q(0, 0) = 10(0)^{\frac{3}{4}}(0)^{\frac{1}{4}} = 0$.

Production functions of the type $Q = aL^b K^c$, where a, b, c are positive parameters, are known as Cobb–Douglas production functions after the two men who first used them.

What happens to the scale of output when the inputs are increased by the same proportion for each input? For example, would output double if all inputs were doubled? In the cases of both the production functions considered below, output would double if inputs were doubled.

If $Q = 9L + 5K$, then $9(2L) + 5(2K) = 2(9L + 5K) = 2Q$.
If $Q = 10L^{\frac{3}{4}}K^{\frac{1}{4}}$, then $10(2L)^{\frac{3}{4}}(2K)^{\frac{1}{4}} = 2^{\frac{3}{4}+\frac{1}{4}}(10L^{\frac{3}{4}}K^{\frac{1}{4}}) = 2Q$.

Both these production functions display **constant returns to scale**. If all inputs are increased by m per cent, output increases by m per cent. Note that a production function can display constant returns to scale and decreasing marginal products to each factor. The first function has constant marginal products, but the second has marginal products which decrease.

Examples of other types of returns to scale can be found by considering the general form of the Cobb–Douglas production function $Q = aL^b K^c$, where a, b, and c are positive parameters. If inputs are doubled: $a(2L)^b(2K)^c = 2^{b+c}(aL^b K^c) = 2^{b+c}Q$.

If $b + c = 1$, there are constant returns to scale.
If $b + c < 1$, there are decreasing returns to scale.
If $b + c > 1$, there are increasing returns to scale.

9.6 The aggregate production function

The distribution of income is a subject which has fascinated economists for generations. Why does about seven-tenths of national output go back to wage and salary earners and about three-tenths go back to the providers of capital? Why are these proportions about the same in the United Kingdom and in the United States? Why do these proportions change so slowly from decade to decade?

One attempt to answer these questions involves the use of 'aggregate' production functions, and one type of function which does provide a few hints is the Cobb–Douglas: $Q = aL^{0.7}K^{0.3}$. The parameter a indicates how efficient the productive process is at converting L and K into Q; it is not the same for each country. Unlike the previous section, Q does not stand for a simple measure of output such as tons of steel or numbers of motor cars. In an aggregate production function Q is the total output of the economy, all the many thousands of different products added together. The weights used to enable so many different things to be added together into one number are the prices. Therefore Q seems to be the value of total output. However, Q in this context is not thought of as a number of £s but as an index of physical outputs; the different outputs are aggregated by weighting them by their prices (unlike the price indexes of section 9.4, which were prices added together by weighting them by physical quantities). Similarly, L is an aggregate index of the amount of labour, found by taking all the different labour units (man-years) and weighting them by their prices (each man's annual earnings from employment, but not his income from capital assets). K is an aggregate index of the input of the services of capital, whether owned by individuals or companies. The capital index presents the most problems because it involves rent, interest, and company profits.

To use the function to explain labour's share of the product, we have to accept the marginal productivity theory of the demand for labour. This states that the real wage rate will equal the marginal product of labour.

If $Q = aL^{0.7}K^{0.3}$, then $\dfrac{\partial Q}{\partial L} = 0.7aL^{-0.3}K^{0.3}$

$$= 0.7a\frac{L^{0.7}}{L}\,K^{0.3}$$

$$= 0.7\frac{Q}{L}$$

The marginal product of labour is seven-tenths of the average product of labour. Total wages will be the wage rate (expressed in aggregate form) $\frac{\partial Q}{\partial L}$ times the size of the labour force L:

$$L\frac{\partial Q}{\partial L} = 0\cdot7Q$$

The total wage is seven-tenths of total output, and this proportion is constant regardless of the size of the labour force or the size of total output.

The share of total output which goes to capital is explained similarly. The price of capital (in aggregate terms) is its marginal product. The amount of output which goes to the owners of capital is the price of capital times the amount of capital.

If $Q = aL^{0\cdot7}K^{0\cdot3}$, then $\frac{\partial Q}{\partial K} = 0\cdot3\,aL^{0\cdot7}K^{-0\cdot7}$

$$= 0\cdot3aL^{0\cdot7}\frac{K^{0\cdot3}}{K}$$

$$= 0\cdot3\frac{Q}{K}$$

$$\text{and } K\frac{\partial Q}{\partial K} = 0\cdot3Q$$

With this production function the total product is completely exhausted after payment has been made to the factors of production:

$$L\frac{\partial Q}{\partial L} + K\frac{\partial Q}{\partial K} = 0\cdot7Q + 0\cdot3Q = Q.$$

Other types of production function might not give this result. It occurs because $0\cdot7 + 0\cdot3 = 1$, but in section 9.5 we saw that the Cobb–Douglas production function $Q = aL^bK^c$, where $b + c = 1$ means that there are constant returns to scale.

Figure 9.4 illustrates the relation between Q and L when K is constant. The function $Q(L, K)$ displays a positive slope because the marginal product of labour is positive, $\frac{\partial Q}{\partial L} > 0$. The slope becomes less steep as L increases because the marginal product of labour diminishes, $\frac{\partial^2 Q}{\partial L^2} < 0$. When OD is the amount of labour, DA will be the amount of output, and $\frac{\partial Q}{\partial L}$ is the slope of the tangent at A:

$\frac{\partial Q}{\partial L} = \frac{BA}{CB} = \frac{BA}{OD}$, but OD is the amount of L, so $L\frac{\partial Q}{\partial L} = BA$, and therefore BA is labour's share of total output.

With the particular production function which we are considering, a Cobb–Douglas with constant returns to scale, that output which does not go to labour goes to capital, so $DB = K\frac{\partial Q}{\partial K}$. BA is seven-tenths of DA and DB is three-tenths of DA.

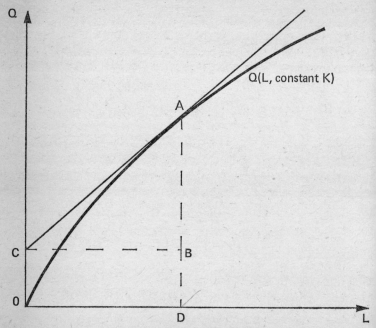

Figure 9.4 Output as a function of labour services

Symmetrical reasoning applies to the relation between Q and K when L is constant. In Figure 9.5(*a*), DB is labour's share and BA is capital's share of the total output DA.

One can imagine an economy where there is plenty of capital and where the demand for the products which require capital has been limited by education or propaganda (depending on one's point of view). Such an economy might have a production function where the marginal product of capital was zero. Figure 9.5(*b*) illustrates

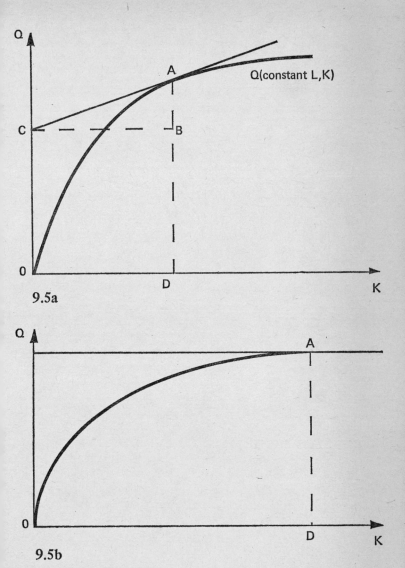

Figure 9.5 (a) Output as a function of capital services; (b) Capital saturation

such a production function. At A, $\frac{\partial Q}{\partial K} = 0$ because the economy is saturated with capital. Here it would be possible to have a situation where $L\frac{\partial Q}{\partial L} = Q$, or $\frac{\partial Q}{\partial L} = \frac{Q}{L}$. The marginal product of labour equals its average product and all the total product is returned to labour. Unfortunately the situation in some countries is almost the reverse of this: the economy has surplus labour and it is the marginal product of labour which can be very small.

This approach to an explanation of the distribution of income between labour and the owners of capital can never be a complete one. In the aggregate production function each unit of output is weighted by its price and then these weighted outputs are added together. But the prices depend upon supply and demand. Demand is a result of both the willingness and the ability to pay for the goods. The ability to pay depends on the distribution of income. So the prices themselves are decided to some extent by labour's share. Of course, the prices depend also on technology, natural resources, and international markets, but to the extent that they do depend on the distribution of income we cannot explain this distribution by using prices as data.

A modification of the Cobb–Douglas function is sometimes used to allow for technical progress. One more variable, t for time, is introduced and the function becomes: $Q = ae^{rt}L^{0.7}K^{0.3}$ where a is the efficiency parameter and r is a parameter of technological change.

Again $\frac{\partial Q}{\partial L} = 0.7\frac{Q}{L}$ and $\frac{\partial Q}{\partial K} = 0.3\frac{Q}{K}$,

but also $\frac{\partial Q}{\partial t} = r\,a\,e^{rt}L^{0.7}K^{0.3} = rQ$.

The proportionate rate of growth of output over time is $\frac{1}{Q}\frac{\partial Q}{\partial t} = r$. At any point of time labour's share of the total product is constant at 0.7. However, since total product is growing at the rate r, so is the amount which goes to labour.

Note that $\frac{\partial Q}{\partial L}$ and $\frac{\partial Q}{\partial K}$ are marginal products, but $\frac{\partial Q}{\partial t}$ is the amount by which Q reacts to changes in time. $\frac{\partial Q}{\partial t}$ is the measure of the effects of technological progress, and $\frac{1}{Q}\frac{\partial Q}{\partial t}$ is assumed to be constant. The similarity of pattern of these three partial derivatives has led to the question 'If the marginal product of time is due to technological progress, then who is technological progress and what does he do with his share of the total product?' The easiest answer to this awkward question is to point out the difference between Q at any moment of time and Q as it changes over time. The partials $\frac{\partial Q}{\partial L}$ and $\frac{\partial Q}{\partial K}$ assume that time stands still; $\frac{\partial Q}{\partial t}$ assumes that L and K are constant.

This section raises many more questions than it answers. How do we aggregate capital? Why does technological change occur and why does it not affect the distribution of income? Why is a production function which displays constant returns to scale a suitable way of describing the production processes in an economy? Nevertheless, aggregate production functions are extremely useful tools for gaining insights into the problems both of the distribution of income and of economic growth. Their drawbacks are well known, but their use has led to many interesting discoveries about the way economic systems work.

Exercise 9

1. In the following production function, Q is output per annum in tons, L is the amount of labour input in man-hours per annum, and K is the capital equipment used in machine-hours per annum.

$Q = 2L + 7K$

   i. Can any output be produced from only one input?
   ii Is the marginal product of labour positive?
   iii. Does the marginal product of capital diminish?

2. In year 0 a firm employed 100 men and used the services of a stock of equipment which was worth £1 000 000 to produce 300 units of output which were sold for £1 000 each. In year 1 the firm employed 98 men and had the use of £1 500 000 worth of equipment to produce 327 units of output which were sold at the same price.

   i. If the firm pays wages which are based on the value of output per man, what was the percentage increase in wages?

   ii. If the firm bases its dividend payment to shareholders on the value of output per £1 of capital equipment, by what percentage did the dividend change?

3. The firm in question 2 has a production function of the form: $Q = 3L^{\frac{3}{4}}K^{\frac{1}{4}}$ where Q is output in units of product per annum, L is the number of workers in man-years per annum, and K is the value of capital equipment in use, measured in units of £10 000.

  i. Calculate Q when $L = 100$ and $K = 100$.

  ii. Calculate Q when $L = 98$ and $K = 150$.

  iii. Find the marginal product of labour in terms of L and K.

  iv. Show that the marginal product of labour diminishes.

  v. How does the marginal product of labour react to changes in the amount of capital?

  vi. If the firm pays a wage based on the marginal product of labour in its own plant, by what percentage did wages change between year 0 and year 1?

Chapter 10

Optimisation

10.1 Introduction

Economics is sometimes called the science of choice, the choices being about the best use of scarce resources. Of course the 'best' use depends on the ends which people desire, but once these ends are decided the problem of means still remains. Optimisation is about the best means to use in order to achieve some agreed ends. The techniques of optimisation may be found in many different contexts. They may be used to explain some aspects of human behaviour, and to predict some of the future actions of particular groups of people. Apart from explanation and prediction, optimisation techniques are also used to suggest how to obtain particular results. Suppose, for example, we have a technique which shows how to maximise profits when certain data are known. We can use this technique in four different ways, as shown by the following illustrations:

Explanatory. The price of X was £p because the sellers were trying to maximise profit.

Predictive. The price of X will be £$(p + 2)$ because the cost conditions will change and this will change the most profitable price.

Prescriptive. If you want to maximise profits from the production and sale of X, you should charge £$(p + 2)$.

Normative. Since I think that profit maximisation encourages initiative and efficiency, you ought to maximise profit, which means that you should charge £$(p + 2)$.

For the purposes of this chapter the use to which the optimisation techniques are put does not matter. We give a few examples to illustrate the technique. Note, however, that profit maximisation is just one type of optimisation. There are some businessmen whose position depends on the quantity of product that their organisation sells and who are interested in sales maximisation. Other organisations may be concerned with minimising the number of deaths, minimising the effects of pollution, maximising the amount of food which can be rushed to a disaster area. Optimisation techniques are widely applicable, but the wider applications turn out to have many analogies with the elementary, if narrow, techniques of profit maximisation.

10.2 Maximising profit for a monopolist

If both total cost and total revenue can be expressed as functions of output, how do we find the output that should be produced and sold to maximise profit?

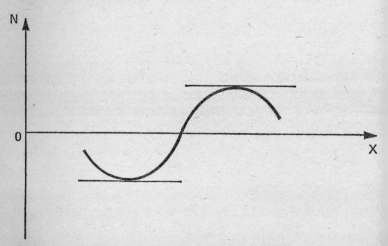

Figure 10.1 Extreme points: a minimum and a maximum

This is the same problem that arose in Chapter 5. Profit, N, is total revenue less total cost, $N = R - C$. Since $R = R(x)$ and $C = C(x)$, it follows that $N = N(x)$. Profit will be at a maximum or a minimum when $\frac{dN}{dx} = 0$, but $\frac{dN}{dx} = \frac{dR}{dx} - \frac{dC}{dx}$, and so $\frac{dN}{dx} = 0$ when $\frac{dR}{dx} = \frac{dC}{dx}$. The first-order conditions are fulfilled when marginal revenue equals marginal cost.

When profit is at a maximum, $\frac{d^2N}{dx^2} < 0$; but $\frac{d^2N}{dx^2} = \frac{d^2R}{dx^2} - \frac{d^2C}{dx^2}$.

Therefore the second-order conditions are fulfilled when $\frac{d^2R}{dx^2} < \frac{d^2C}{dx^2}$.

This problem is simple to solve because there is only one independent variable, the output x. Profit can be expressed in terms of the revenue and cost functions (functions of x) and we assume that these functions are known. We use the techniques of derivation to find the maximum. In Figure 10.1 a typical profit function is illustrated. There are two **extreme points** and $\frac{dN}{dx} = 0$ at each. N is a maximum when $\frac{d^2N}{dx^2} < 0$ and a minimum when $\frac{d^2N}{dx^2} > 0$.

When there are two or more independent variables the problems of finding maxima and minima become more complicated. The complications arise over the second-order conditions.

10.3 Maximising a function of two or more variables

Consider the problem of finding the values of x and y which will maximise z, where x and y are related to z by the function $z = f(x, y)$. To picture the problem in three dimensions we can think of x as the distance eastwards, y as the distance northwards, and z as the height. The function f describes a land surface. Finding the value of x and y which will maximise z is equivalent to finding the distances eastwards and northwards on a two-dimensional map which will describe the position of the highest point of land.

Necessary conditions for a maximum are that $\frac{\partial z}{\partial x} = 0$ and $\frac{\partial z}{\partial y} = 0$, and these are the first-order conditions. One group of second-order conditions is that $\frac{\partial^2 z}{\partial x^2} < 0$ and that $\frac{\partial^2 z}{\partial y^2} < 0$, but these conditions by themselves are not sufficient to ensure a maximum. The problem arises because we cannot confine ourselves to the study of movements north-south and east-west only, as the following examples illustrate.

Imagine two roads, one running due east and the other due north. They cross on a hill-top. To find the distance east at which the crossroads lies we can find the value of x which makes z a maximum by solving for that x which makes $\frac{\partial z}{\partial x} = 0$ and checking that $\frac{\partial^2 z}{\partial x^2} < 0$.

Similarly, the distance north of the hill-top cross-roads is given by that y which makes $\frac{\partial z}{\partial y} = 0$ provided $\frac{\partial^2 z}{\partial y^2} < 0$. Figure 10.2($a$) pictures this cross-roads.

But now imagine the ridge of a mountain range running from the south-west to the north-east. At the lowest part of this ridge there is a pass, and at the highest point of the pass there is a cross-roads where the road running due east meets the road running due north. The

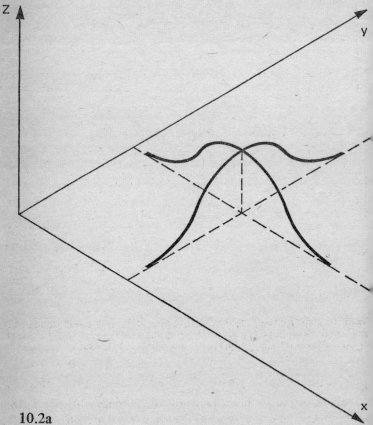

10.2a

cross-roads is the highest point of each road but it is the lowest point of the ridge. Here we have $\frac{\partial z}{\partial x} = \frac{\partial z}{\partial y} = 0$, $\frac{\partial^2 z}{\partial x^2} < 0$, and

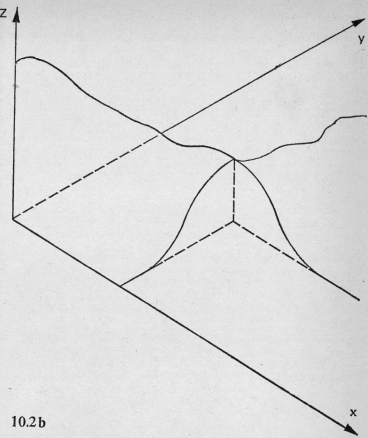

10.2 b

Figure 10.2 (a) A maximum in the north–south and east–west directions, and in all other directions; (b) A maximum in the north–south and east–west directions, but a minimum in the northeast–southwest direction

$\frac{\partial^2 z}{\partial y^2} < 0$, but z is not at a maximum. The conditions are not sufficient

to exclude errors in those functions which behave like mountain passes. Figure 10.2(b) illustrates. The usual name for such a point is **a saddle point**, because it is shaped like a horse-saddle. Problems where maximisation in one direction involves minimisation in another direction are important in economics.

We could extend our analytical techniques so that we could find sufficient conditions for a maximum where there are many variables. However, the purpose of this chapter is to introduce the reader to the economic concepts of optimisation, substitution, and economies of scale. The examples will be chosen so that these concepts can be illustrated without running up against problems of second-order conditions.

(The object of each of the final four chapters of this book is simply to illustrate important techniques rather than to go into these in detail. A more rigorous approach to problems involving many variables can be very complicated unless the elementary tools of matrix algebra are used. Matrix algebra is a set of methods for manipulating tables of numbers. It is simple to learn. The reader who intends studying problems of optimisation, linear programming, and regression analysis in depth is strongly advised to do so via matrix algebra. It is an aid to the understanding of such problems.)

10.4 Maximising profit for a competitive producer

If the production function is known, and the product price and the prices of the services of the factors of production are given, how much of each factor should be employed to maximise profit?

Let Q be the amount of output per annum, and P be the (given) price of the output. Let L be the amount of labour employed per annum, and w be the (given) wage rate. Let K be the amount of capital equipment employed per annum, and h be the (given) hire price of capital equipment. So Q, L, K are variables and P, w, h are parameters. Write the production function in general form $Q = Q(L, K)$.

The problem is to maximise total profit subject to the conditions imposed by the production function. Profit is total revenue minus total cost:

$$N = PQ - (wL + hK)$$

and this expresses profit as a function of the three variables Q, L, K. But the production function gives Q as a function of L and K, so profit can be expressed as a function of L and K only:

$$N = P \cdot Q(L, K) - (wL + hK)$$

In order to find the first order conditions, put both $\dfrac{\partial N}{\partial L}$ and $\dfrac{\partial N}{\partial K}$ equal to zero:

$$\frac{\partial N}{\partial L} = P \cdot \frac{\partial Q}{\partial L} - w = 0$$

$$\frac{\partial N}{\partial K} = P \cdot \frac{\partial Q}{\partial K} - h = 0$$

giving $P \cdot \dfrac{\partial Q}{\partial L} = w$ and $P \cdot \dfrac{\partial Q}{\partial K} = h$.

Now $\dfrac{\partial Q}{\partial L}$ is the marginal product of labour expressed in terms of physical quantities of product, so $P \cdot \dfrac{\partial Q}{\partial L}$ is the value of the marginal product of labour. We have found that one of the first-order con-

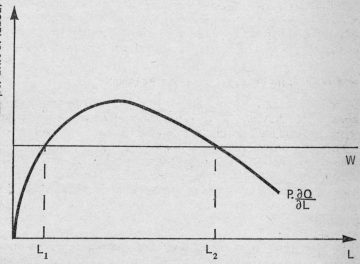

Figure 10.3 A wage equal to the marginal product of labour can lead to profit minimisation

ditions for profit maximisation is that the value of the marginal product of labour must equal the wage rate. The other first-order condition is that the value of the marginal product of capital must equal its hire price.

We can see what the second-order conditions must be by imagining a production function where the marginal product of labour increases at first (as more specialisation becomes possible) and then diminishes (as bottlenecks develop). Figure 10.3 shows the value of the marginal product of labour plotted against the amount of labour. Maximum profit is obtained when $L - L_2$. If $L = L_1$ an increase in the amount of labour will increase the value of total product by more than the increase in the total wage bill.

A similar argument would apply to capital. Therefore the second order conditions are that the marginal products must be diminishing:

$$\frac{\partial^2 Q}{\partial L^2} < 0 \quad \text{and} \quad \frac{\partial^2 Q}{\partial K^2} < 0$$

An example:

P, the price of the product, is £10.
w, the wage rate, is £2 per hour.
h, the hire price of equipment, is £3 per hour.

The production function is:

$$Q = \tfrac{3}{2}L^{\frac{3}{5}}K^{\frac{2}{5}}$$

where Q is output per week, L is man-hours of labour per week, and K is machine-hours of equipment per week.

The profit function is $N = PQ - (wL + hK)$
$$= 10(\tfrac{3}{2}L^{\frac{3}{5}}K^{\frac{2}{5}}) - (2L + 3K)$$

$$\frac{\partial N}{\partial L} = \tfrac{3}{5} \cdot 10 \cdot \tfrac{3}{2}L^{-\frac{2}{5}}K^{\frac{2}{5}} - 2 = 0 \tag{1}$$

$$\frac{\partial N}{\partial K} = \tfrac{1}{5} \cdot 10 \cdot \tfrac{3}{2}L^{\frac{3}{5}}K^{-\frac{3}{5}} - 3 = 0 \tag{2}$$

from (1) $9L^{-\frac{2}{5}}K^{\frac{2}{5}} = 2$
so $\qquad K = [\tfrac{2}{9}L^{\frac{2}{5}}]^5 = (\tfrac{2}{9})^5 L^2$ \hfill (3)
from (2) $3L^{\frac{3}{5}}K^{-\frac{3}{5}} = 3$
so $\qquad L = [K^{\frac{3}{5}}]^{\frac{5}{3}} = K^{\frac{3}{5}} = [(\tfrac{2}{9})^5 L^2]^{\frac{3}{5}}$
$$= (\tfrac{2}{9})^{\frac{20}{3}} L^{\frac{6}{5}}$$

$$L^{-\frac{5}{3}} = (\tfrac{2}{9})^{\frac{20}{3}}$$
$$L^{\frac{5}{3}} = (\tfrac{9}{2})^{\frac{20}{3}}$$
$$L = (\tfrac{9}{2})^4 = 410$$
and from (3) $K = (\tfrac{2}{9})^5 (410)^2 \approx 91$

The output for maximum profit will be $Q = \tfrac{3}{2}(410)^{\frac{3}{5}}(91)^{\frac{2}{5}} \approx 137$. The profit will be $N = 10 \times 137 - (2 \times 410 + 3 \times 91) = £277$ per week.

10.5 The objective function

If a businessman employs only two factors of production, labour at £2 per hour and capital equipment at £3 per hour, his costs C are given by the function $C = 2L + 3K$, where L and K are the amounts of labour and capital employed. Suppose he has decided to produce a particular quantity of product and he knows that he can produce this by a variety of methods, each method using L and K in different proportions. Under these circumstances he will choose the method which minimises the costs of production. His objective is to minimise cost, and $C = 2L + 3K$ is known as the **objective function**.

The function can be pictured in three dimensions as an upward sloping plane. Any increase in L or K will cause an increase in C. Figure 10.4(a) illustrates.

If $C = 6$, then $2L + 3K = 6$, and we could picture this as a line in two dimensions with L and K on the axes. If L is measured along the horizontal axis, the line has a slope of $-\frac{2}{3}$. This slope can be readily found by inspection if the equation is rearranged to $K = 2 - \frac{2}{3}L$. If $C = 12$, the equation becomes $K = 4 - \frac{2}{3}L$. The function involving three variables can be pictured as a family of lines of equal slope in two dimensions, each line giving combinations of L and K which will result in equal costs. Figure 10.4(b) illustrates. We shall use this approach in section 10.6.

Another sort of objective function could occur when a businessman has certain resources available which he can use to produce two goods, whose quantities are given by Q_1 and Q_2. His objective may be to maximise the revenue R from the sale of the two goods. If the price of Q_1 is £5 and of Q_2 £7, then his objective is to maximise $R = 5Q_1 + 7Q_2$. This function can be pictured as a plane in the three dimensions of Q_1, Q_2, and R, or it can be pictured as a family of lines of equal slope in the two dimensions of Q_1 and Q_2, each line showing the combinations of Q_1 and Q_2 which will yield an equal revenue.

Although each of the above functions can be thought of as planes, they are called **linear functions**, because any function where all the variables are raised to the power unity is known as a linear function. In one case the objective was to minimise a linear function of costs. In the other case the objective was to maximise a linear function of revenues.

In this chapter and the next we shall make three important assumptions about objectives. First, we shall assume that the objectives are agreed. The problems which arise when people try to decide how to use scarce resources by applying conflicting objectives are studied in Welfare Economics, but within any single economic unit it is usually a reasonable assumption that objectives are agreed. Second, we shall assume that the weights on the objective function can be given in numerical form. (The weights on the cost function $C = 2L + 3K$ are 2 and 3; on the revenue function $R = 5Q_1 + 7Q_2$, they are 5 and 7.) There are organisations where it is extremely

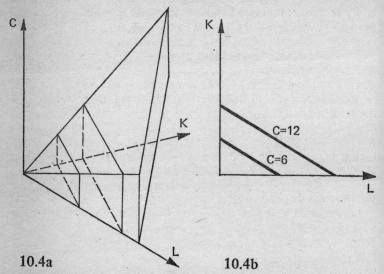

10.4a   10.4b

Figure 10.4 (a) Cost as a plane in three dimensions; (b) Cost as a family of lines in two dimensions

difficult to weight the objective function in this way, for example a hospital whose resources are limited but whose managers are understandably reticent to say which healing activities are more important, and to be so precise about it as to use a numerical objective function.

The third assumption is that the objective function is linear. This will be the case in a cost function if the market for the factors of production is competitive, so the prices of the factors do not change as the quantities purchased vary. A revenue function will be linear if the markets for the products are competitive. Often the objective function is less clear-cut than simply 'revenue to be maximised'. Sometimes the objective is to maximise something intangible like utility, where the objective function is not linear. However, we can make the inquiries we want to make by confining ourselves to linear functions, bearing in mind that we could complicate the mathematics by using non-linear objective functions if the problems called for these.

10.6 A cost minimising problem

If the production function is known, if the required level of output is given and if the prices of the factors of production are known, how do we find the amount of each factor which should be employed in order to minimise the cost of producing the required level of output?

We can separate this problem into two parts. What is the range of choices open to us? Which one should we choose? The range of choices is given by the required level of output and the known production function. If we require 100 units of output and the production function is:

$$Q = L^{\frac{2}{3}}K^{\frac{1}{3}}$$

then L and K must be combined in such a way that:

$$L^{\frac{2}{3}}K^{\frac{1}{3}} = 100$$

If Q is fixed, we can assume that there are only two variables, L and K. Once L is known, K can be found because K can be expressed as a function of L:

$$K^{\frac{1}{3}} = 100L^{-\frac{2}{3}}, \text{ so } K = 100^5L^{-3}$$

Given that 100 units of product are to be produced in a technically efficient way, we can find how K can be varied when L is varied:

$$\frac{dK}{dL} = (-3)100^5L^{-4}$$

and the units of measurement of this expression are machine-hours per unit change in man-hours. The expression is negative, so an increase in L allows a decrease in K; L can be *substituted* for K, and K can be substituted for L. Note also that:

$$\frac{d^2K}{dL^2} = (-3)(-4)100^5L^{-5}$$

which is positive, so the rate at which K can be substituted for L becomes greater and greater as L increases.

In Figure 10.5(*a*) the continuous curve illustrates the relation between L and K when Q is held constant. This curve is an 'equal-quantity' curve or **isoquant**. It shows the combinations of L and K which, when used with technical efficiency, will produce a particular level of Q. In Figure 10.5(*b*) the production function itself is illustrated as a surface in three dimensions. Drawing an isoquant in the two-dimensional L, K space is similar to a contour line on a geo-

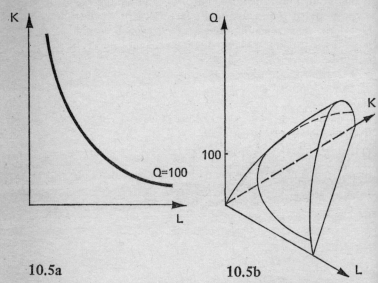

10.5a   10.5b

Figure 10.5 (*a*) An isoquant; (*b*) The production possibility surface

grapher's map; the isoquant marks those points in the L, K plane at which the 'height' of Q is 100.

Now that we have found the range of choices open to us, we still have to decide which combination of L and K is the cheapest. This depends on the prices of L and K. If the wage for labour is £2 and the hire price of capital is £3, we are trying to minimise the cost C, where $C = 2L + 3K$. We have to choose the cheapest from the range of choices, or to put this another way we have to:

minimise $C = 2L + 3K$
subject to $K = 100^5L^{-3}$

There are three ways in which we can do this. The first method is a mechanical one. Simply substitute for K in the cost function so that cost is expressed as a function of L only. Then find the level of L which gives the minimum cost by derivation:

$$C = 2L + 3 \times 100^5 L^{-3}$$
$$\frac{\partial C}{\partial L} = 2 - 3 \times 3 \times 100^5 L^{-4} = 0$$
$$9 \times 100^5 L^{-4} = 2$$
$$L = \left(\frac{9 \times 100^5}{2}\right)^{\frac{1}{4}}$$

Once L is known K can be found from the formula $K = 100^5 L^{-3}$.

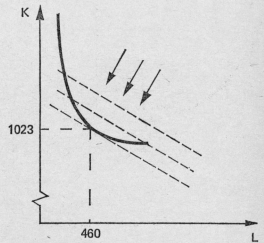

Figure 10.6 Cost minimisation; the tangency solution

The second method involves graphical techniques. We can plot two projections onto the L, K space: the projection of the isoquant $Q = 100$ (as from Figure 10.5(b) to Figure 10.5(a)) and the projections of the equal-cost lines (as in section 10.5). The isoquant and the equal-cost lines are shown together in Figure 10.6. The problem is to choose that equal-cost line which gives the lowest cost but still provides a combination of L and K which is sufficient to produce 100 units of output. By drawing parallel equal-cost lines nearer and nearer to the origin we find that the lowest one is that which just touches the isoquant; it is tangential to the isoquant. A lower cost gives a combination of L and K which is insufficient to produce the required output. A higher cost is economically inefficient. We can find the values of L and K at the point of tangency by reading them from the graph.

The third method is similar in concept to the graphical approach. Since the lowest cost is where the equal-cost line is tangential to the isoquant, we find that point on the isoquant which has the same slope as the equal-cost lines. Each of the family of lines represented by $2L + 3K$ has a slope of $-\frac{2}{3}$. The isoquant $K = 100^5 L^{-3}$ has a slope of $\frac{dK}{dL}$. By finding that the value of L which makes $\frac{dK}{dL} = -\frac{2}{3}$ we can find the least cost blend of factors of production:

$$\frac{dK}{dL} = (-3)100^5 L^{-4} = -\frac{2}{3}$$
$$L = \left(\frac{9 \times 100^5}{2}\right)^{\frac{1}{4}} \approx 460$$

The three methods give the same result.

The second-order conditions for a minimisation problem of this type can be seen from studying Figure 10.6. The isoquant bulges in towards the origin and this ensures that the point of tangency is where the lowest equal-cost line just touches the isoquant. The isoquant is **convex to the origin** since $\frac{dK}{dL} < 0$ and also $\frac{d^2K}{dL^2} < 0$. In practical terms this means that the greater is the amount of labour, the easier it is to substitute equipment for labour, and the more difficult it is to substitute still more labour for equipment. This is usually the case.

If the second-order conditions did not apply we could have an isoquant which is concave to the origin, where $\frac{dK}{dL} < 0$ and $\frac{d^2K}{dL^2} > 0$, as shown in Figure 10.7. In practical terms this means that if a producer has chosen a combination of labour and equipment where labour is used as much as possible, a very large amount of equipment would be needed to replace a small amount of labour; this is unlikely to occur in practice. The cost minimisation technique would not work with such an isoquant because the tangency solution is not the least cost solution. In Figure 10.7 the least cost solution is where capital only is used, but a production process which uses no labour is very unlikely.

In this section we have taken the production function and then found a formula relating L to K when Q is held constant at a known level. There is a more general mathematical technique which allows us to keep all the information contained in the production function when finding how K can be substituted for L. Consider the case where the marginal product of labour is known and we wish to find the amount of additional output which would result from a small addition to the labour force. Call the increase in labour ΔL, and the additional output which we wish to find ΔQ. Figure 10.8 shows the production function in the L, Q space. The marginal product of labour,

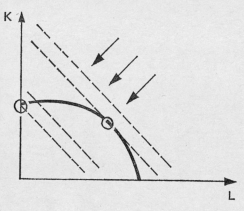

Figure 10.7 A tangency solution leading to maximum costs, but a corner solution leading to minimum costs because there is no advantage from specialisation

$\frac{\partial Q}{\partial L}$, is the slope of the tangent to the production function at the point decided by the value of L before the additional labour is added, the point where $L = \bar{L}$ on the diagram. The height of the triangle whose base is ΔL is given by $\frac{\partial Q}{\partial L}\Delta L$, since 'base equals slope times height'.

Although ΔQ is not the same as $\frac{\partial Q}{\partial L}\Delta L$, it will be approximately the same provided ΔL is small.

So ΔQ due to changes in $L \approx \frac{\partial Q}{\partial L}\Delta L$

Similarly ΔQ due to changes in $K \approx \dfrac{\partial Q}{\partial K}\Delta K$

Therefore ΔQ due to changes in both L and $K \approx \dfrac{\partial Q}{\partial L}\Delta L + \dfrac{\partial Q}{\partial K}\Delta K$

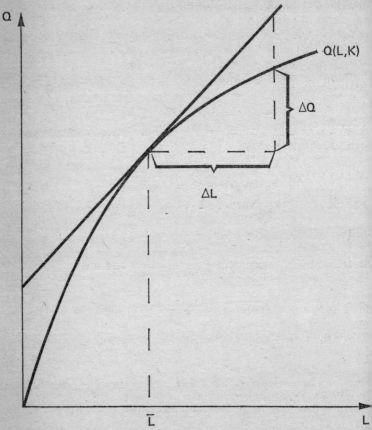

Figure 10.8 Using the tangent to approximate small changes

Now provided ΔL and ΔK are 'sufficiently small' we can use the following equality, known as the **total differential** of the production function:

$$dQ = \frac{\partial Q}{\partial L}dL + \frac{\partial Q}{\partial K}dK$$

where dQ stands for the change in Q due to changes in both L and K, and dL and dK stand for 'sufficiently small' changes in L and K to allow the equality to hold.

When Q is held constant, dQ is zero and changes in L and K must exactly compensate each other. So when $dQ = 0$, we have:

$$\frac{\partial Q}{\partial L}dL + \frac{\partial Q}{\partial K}dK = 0$$

and $\dfrac{dK}{dL} = -\dfrac{\frac{\partial Q}{\partial L}}{\frac{\partial Q}{\partial K}}$

This expression is known as the **marginal rate of substitution** of capital for labour (MRS).

$$\text{MRS} = \text{minus} \; \frac{\text{the marginal product of labour}}{\text{the marginal product of capital}}$$

For the production function $Q = L^{\frac{3}{5}}K^{\frac{2}{5}}$,

$$\text{MRS} = -\frac{\frac{3}{5}L^{-\frac{2}{5}}K^{\frac{2}{5}}}{\frac{2}{5}L^{\frac{3}{5}}K^{-\frac{3}{5}}} = -3\frac{K}{L}$$

In the particular case where $Q = 100$, we found that $K = 100^5 L^{-3}$, so for this case, but only this case:

$$\text{MRS (when } Q = 100) = -3\frac{100^5 L^{-3}}{L} = -3 \; 100^5 L^{-4}$$

This is the same result that we found when we assumed that K was a function of L only, and then found $\dfrac{dK}{dL}$. The marginal rate of substitution is a more general approach to this type of problem because it applies to all values of Q.

For the economist there are three relevant stages in the examination of a productive process:

The production possibilities: $Q \leqslant Q(L, K)$

Technical efficiency: $Q = Q(L, K)$

Economic efficiency: $\dfrac{\frac{\partial Q}{\partial L}}{\frac{\partial Q}{\partial K}} = \dfrac{\text{wage of labour}}{\text{price of capital}}$

The total cost function which was used in previous chapters relates total cost C to output x, $C = C(x)$, and refers to economically efficient ways of producing each level of output. If cost is greater than it need be, $C \geqslant C(x)$, this may be due either to economic or to technical inefficiency. Since Q as defined by the production function assumes technical efficiency, but x as used in the cost function assumes both technical and economic efficiency, two different symbols, Q and x, seem preferable so that the concepts are not confused.

10.7 Maximising revenue

Consider an organisation which has a budget of £B per annum and is instructed to produce and sell two different products, good One and good Two, in the most profitable blend. Assume that the budget is spent on buying the services of the factors of production and combining these factors in a way that is both technically and economically efficient. The budget allows a range of combinations of One and Two to be produced such that the range can be described by the function: $B = \sqrt{Q_1{}^2 + 9Q_2{}^2}$, $Q_1 \geqslant 0$ and $Q_2 \geqslant 0$, where Q_1 is the number of units of good One produced per annum, and Q_2 is the number of units of good Two produced per annum.

From the description of the economic problem, B is causing some combination of goods One and Two to be produced, whereas the mathematical description of the problem makes B a function of Q_1 and Q_2. The assumption of efficiency allows us to do this: once Q_1 and Q_2 are known, there is a unique value for B.

How much of good One and good Two should be produced if the budget is fixed at £10, the price of good One is £5 and of good Two £7?

If the budget is £10, Q_1 and Q_2 must be such that $\sqrt{Q_1{}^2 + 9Q_2{}^2} = 10$. Manipulation of this expression allows the relation between Q_1 and Q_2 to be found on the assumption of a fixed budget. This relation gives the range of possible choices:

$$Q_1{}^2 + 9Q_2{}^2 = 100$$
$$Q_2{}^2 = \frac{100 - Q_1{}^2}{9}$$
$$Q_2 = \tfrac{1}{3}(100 - Q_1{}^2)^{\frac{1}{2}}$$

This is illustrated in Figure 10.9(a). The original function where B is not fixed is shown in Figure 10.9(b).

The revenue R depends on the prices and quantities of goods One and Two: $R = 5Q_1 + 7Q_2$. The problem is to find those values of Q_1 and Q_2 which will:

maximise $R = 5Q_1 + 7Q_2$
subject to $Q_2 = \frac{1}{3}(100 - Q_1^2)^{\frac{1}{2}}$

The approach is similar to that taken in section 10.6, except that in this case the problem is one of maximisation. Either we can express

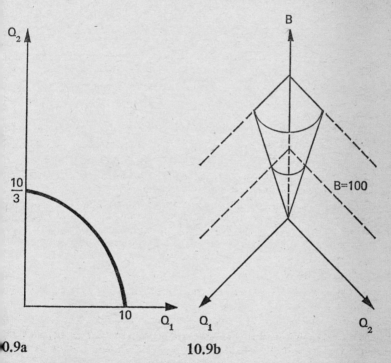

Figure 10.9 (a) The production possibility frontier when resources are fixed; (b) Production possibilities when resources vary

R as a function of Q_1 only and then find that value of Q_1 which makes R a maximum, or we can find that point on the curve relating Q_2 to Q_1 where the slope is equal to the slope of the family of equal-revenue lines. The slope of the equal-revenue lines is $-\frac{5}{7}$, so we find Q_1 and Q_2 such that:

$\dfrac{dQ_2}{dQ_1} = -\tfrac{5}{7}$, as shown in Figure 10.10

so by using the function of a function rule, we have:

$$\frac{dQ_2}{dQ_1} = \tfrac{1}{2} \cdot \tfrac{1}{3}(100 - Q_1^2)^{-\frac{1}{2}}(-2Q_1) = -\tfrac{5}{7}$$

$$\frac{Q_1}{3}(100 - Q_1^2)^{-\frac{1}{2}} = \tfrac{5}{7}$$

$$100 - Q_1^2 = \frac{49Q_1^2}{225}$$

$$Q_1 \approx 9 \cdot 06$$

and $Q_2 = \tfrac{1}{3}(100 - 9 \cdot 06^2)^{\frac{1}{2}} \approx 1 \cdot 45$

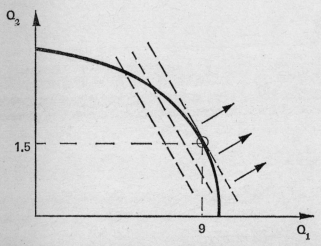

Figure 10.10 Maximising the value of output; the tangency solution

In section 10.6 a formula was given for finding how one factor could be substituted for another by manipulating the production function. In the present problem we are concerned with the way in which a budget can be transferred from one use to another so that different blends of outputs can be produced. We are interested in how one output can be substituted for another rather than in how one factor can be substituted for another. Sometimes this is called the marginal rate of transferability between outputs, but more usually it is labelled the marginal rate of substitution between outputs. The formula is analogous to that for the MRS between factors of production:

$$\text{MRS between outputs} = -\frac{\dfrac{\partial B}{\partial Q_1}}{\dfrac{\partial B}{\partial Q_2}}$$

This follows since $B = B(Q_1, Q_2)$, so the total differential is:

$$dB = \frac{\partial B}{\partial Q_1}dQ_1 + \frac{\partial B}{\partial Q_2}dQ_2$$

When B is held constant, dB is zero, so:

$$\frac{\partial B}{\partial Q_1}dQ_1 + \frac{\partial B}{\partial Q_2}dQ_2 = 0, \text{ and hence}$$

$$\frac{dQ_2}{dQ_1} = -\frac{\dfrac{\partial B}{\partial Q_1}}{\dfrac{\partial B}{\partial Q_2}}$$

For the particular function $B = \sqrt{Q_1^2 + 9Q_2^2}$ we use the function of a function rule to find:

$$\frac{\partial B}{\partial Q_1} = \tfrac{1}{2}(2Q_1)(Q_1^2 + 9Q_2^2)^{-\frac{1}{2}} = Q_1(Q_1^2 + 9Q_2^2)^{-\frac{1}{2}}$$

$$\frac{\partial B}{\partial Q_2} = \tfrac{1}{2}(18Q_2)(Q_1^2 + 9Q_2^2)^{-\frac{1}{2}} = 9Q_2(Q_1^2 + 9Q_2^2)^{-\frac{1}{2}}$$

and the MRS between Q_1 and Q_2 is $-\dfrac{\dfrac{\partial B}{\partial Q_1}}{\dfrac{\partial B}{\partial Q_2}} = -\dfrac{Q_1}{9Q_2}$

In the particular case when $B = 10$ we found that $Q_2 = \tfrac{1}{3}(100 - Q_1^2)^{\frac{1}{2}}$, so the MRS (when B is 10) $= -\dfrac{Q_1}{9Q_2} = -\dfrac{Q_1}{3}(100 - Q_1^2)^{-\frac{1}{2}}$ which is the same result as that obtained from finding $\dfrac{dQ_2}{dQ_1}$ on the assumption that B was constant at 10.

Functions such as this are useful in aggregative economics for clarifying thinking about comparisons between goods now (putting Q_1 as aggregate consumption) and goods in the future (putting Q_2 as aggregate investment). They can also be used to compare the choices between output produced by the market sector and output produced by the public sector. If all outputs are aggregated into just two categories, Q_1 and Q_2, and if all inputs are aggregated into B, then B decides the limit of what it is possible to produce. The function $B = B(Q_1, Q_2)$, where $Q_1 \geqslant 0$ and $Q_2 \geqslant 0$, defines the **production possibility frontier**. The set of combinations of Q_1 and Q_2 which it is possible to produce, including inefficient production and inefficient use of resources, is $B(Q_1, Q_2) \leqslant B$, which is the **set of production possibilities**.

When an economy's production is aggregated into just two categories there will be no simple market price appearing for each of these two categories. However, society's decision-makers will have some rough idea of the relative weight to put on each, even though these weights are only relative and not absolute. Provided that we think in terms of ratios, and we remember that we are dealing with aggregations and approximations, we can say that society is producing efficiently when it is on its production possibility frontier and when:

$$\text{MRS} = -\frac{\dfrac{\partial B}{\partial Q_1}}{\dfrac{\partial B}{\partial Q_2}} = -\frac{w_1}{w_2},$$

where $\dfrac{w_1}{w_2}$ represents the relative weights given by society to the two types of output.

10.8 Economies of scale

The second-order conditions for the maximising problem of the previous section are particularly important under modern methods of production. In the example, the production possibility frontier bulges out from the origin; it is concave to the origin, as shown in Figure 10.10. The tangency solution is an optimal solution because $\dfrac{dQ_2}{dQ_1} < 0$ and $\dfrac{d^2Q_2}{dQ_1^2} < 0$, this latter inequality being a second-order condition. With capital intensive methods, high research costs and mass markets this second-order condition is sometimes not met. An organisation may have a command over resources which we can represent by £B, and it may have a choice of producing various combinations of good Three and good Four. It may find that it is more profitable to concentrate on the production of only one good rather than a combination of the two because the methods of production involve economies of scale.

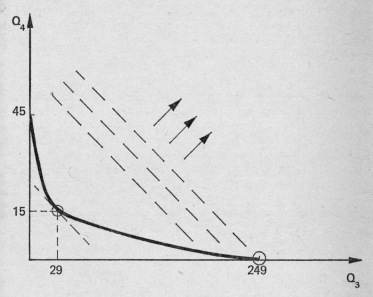

Figure 10.11 A tangency solution leading to a minimum value of output, but a corner solution leading to a maximum value because of economies of scale

As a numerical example, consider the case where the relation between B, representing the resources, and Q_3 and Q_4, representing the levels of output of goods Three and Four, is given by the function $B = (Q_3 + 7)^{\frac{1}{4}}(Q_4 + 9)^{\frac{1}{4}}$.

We will consider the particular case of the production frontier that results when B is 12, as illustrated in Figure 10.11. (Since B represents costs as well as resources, the profits will turn out to be rather more realistic if we take the units of measurement for B to be units of £10 000.) When $(Q_3 + 7)^{\frac{1}{4}}(Q_4 + 9)^{\frac{1}{4}} = 12$, manipulation of this expression allows Q_4 to be expressed as a function of Q_3:

$$Q_4 = 144(Q_3 + 7)^{-\frac{1}{2}} - 9$$

giving $\dfrac{dQ_4}{dQ_3} = -\frac{1}{2}\, 144(Q_3 + 7)^{-\frac{3}{2}} < 0$

but $\dfrac{d^2 Q_4}{dQ_3{}^2} = (-\frac{3}{2})(-\frac{1}{2})\, 144(Q_3 + 7)^{-\frac{5}{2}} > 0$

The second-order conditions for maximisation are not met. Under these circumstances the tangency solution will result in the minimum revenue rather than the maximum.

Let the price of good Three be £1000 per unit and of good Four £3000 per unit. The revenue function is $R = 1000Q_3 + 3000Q_4$. The problem is to:

maximise $R = 1000Q_3 + 3000Q_4$
subject to $Q_4 = 144(Q_3 + 7)^{-\frac{1}{2}} - 9$

Since the slope of each of the equal-revenue lines is $-\frac{1}{3}$, the tangency solution occurs when:

$$\frac{dQ_4}{dQ_3} = -\frac{1}{2}.\, 144(Q_3 + 7)^{-\frac{3}{2}} = -\frac{1}{3}$$

which when solved gives $Q_3 = 29$ and $Q_4 = 15$, so the revenue is $R = 1000(29) + 3000(15) = 81\,000$. Compare this revenue with that which results from producing good Three only. When $Q_4 = 0$, $Q_3 = 249$ and so revenue is £249 000.

FURTHER READING

Allen, R. G. D., *Mathematical Analysis for Economists*, London, Macmillan, 1962, pp. 298–341.

Huang, David S., *Introduction to the Use of Mathematics in Economic Analysis*, New York, John Wiley, 1964, pp. 73–103.

Chapter 11

Linear Programming

11.1 A problem of maximisation

This section deals with a common type of maximisation problem where substitution of one factor for another is not possible. In many situations the resources available to a decision-maker cannot easily be varied. He will have only a certain amount of labour available, and for many productive processes he cannot maintain a skilled and contented team of workers if he hires and fires men too frequently. He cannot change his equipment because of the difficulty of finding funds. The land and buildings available are particularly difficult to vary. In the short run the resources available to him are fixed. If he finds he has too much labour and too little equipment, a period of several months might elapse before he could reduce the one and increase the other. Expanding land and buildings could take several years. Linear programming is a technique which is particularly useful for tackling problems during the short run when resources are fixed.

In the simplified examples which follow, the solutions are found by graphical or numerical methods. One great advantage of linear programming, however, is that complicated calculations can be done in a few seconds by a computer. We illustrate the concepts by solving a problem involving two products and three resources, but a large computer can manage problems with up to 900 products and many thousands of different resources.

Consider the simple problem of a farmer who knows how to grow potatoes and barley. He has 100 acres of land and he wants to know how many acres of each crop to grow for maximum profit. We need three sets of information before we can answer this question.

First, what is the 'net revenue' per acre from each crop? 'Net revenue' per acre means revenue per acre less variable costs per acre, but variable costs are used here in a more restricted sense than they were used in previous chapters. We are now treating labour and equipment as fixed resources. When resources are fixed their costs are not relevant to decisions about the blend of outputs. The farmer has to meet the fixed costs anyway, unless he closes down the farm.

Second, what resources could limit his expansion and how much of these resources does he have available?

Third, how many units of each of these resources are needed to produce one unit of output? The answers to these questions are found to be:

First, the 'net revenue' per acre for potatoes is £7 and for barley £10. Write x for the number of acres of potatoes, y for the number of acres of barley, and z for the total 'net revenue'. Then $z = 7x + 10y$. The farmer's objective is to maximise z, and so $z = 7x + 10y$ is the objective function. The numbers 7 and 10 are the weights on the objective function. (Here the weights are the net revenues per acre. In section 10.7 the objective function was a total revenue function and the weights were the prices of the outputs.)

Second, the resources that could limit expansion are found to be labour, equipment, and land. There are 980 man-days of labour available, 400 machine-days, and 100 acres of land. Since the production cycle lasts for one year, all measurements are understood to include 'per annum'.

Third, 11 man-days are required to produce 1 acre of potatoes and 2 man-days for an acre of barley. 3 machine-days are needed for an acre of potatoes and 5 for an acre of barley. Obviously 1 acre of land is needed to produce an acre of potatoes and the same for an acre of barley. The information in these last two paragraphs is summarised in Table 11.1.

Table 11.1

	Requirements for an acre of:		Amount available
	potatoes	barley	
labour	11	2	980 man-days
equipment	3	5	400 machine-days
land	1	1	100 acres

Consider the labour requirements. Since 11 man-days are needed for an acre of potatoes but only 980 are available, the most potatoes that could be produced would be $\frac{980}{11} \approx 89$ acres, and then there would be no labour available for growing barley. If barley only were grown, the labour would restrict the total acreage to $\frac{980}{2} = 490$ acres.

Assuming for the moment that labour is the only resource limiting expansion, we can state the possibilities as $11x + 2y \leqslant 980$. Of course we cannot 'ungrow' either crop although we could decide to grow nothing, so we have the additional restrictions: $x \geqslant 0$ and $y \geqslant 0$.

The range of possible combinations of x and y allowed by the avail-

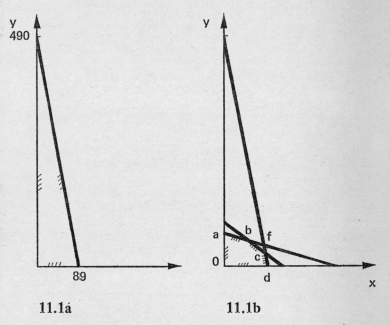

11.1a   11.1b

Figure 11.1 (a) One resource constraint and the non-negative constraints; (b) The set of production possibilities

able labour is illustrated in Figure 11.1(a). The lines represented by the **equalities** $11x + 2y = 980$, $x = 0$, and $y = 0$ define the frontiers of production. When these are made **inequalities** all the possibilities of production are defined, and represented by the whole area of the triangle including its borders.

Similar reasoning applies to the equipment and land. Equipment restricts production by the inequality $3x + 5y \leqslant 400$, and land by the inequality $x + y \leqslant 100$. There are five constraints on production, as shown in Figure 11.1(b). Points to the west of *oa* are impossible because there are no such things as negative potatoes.

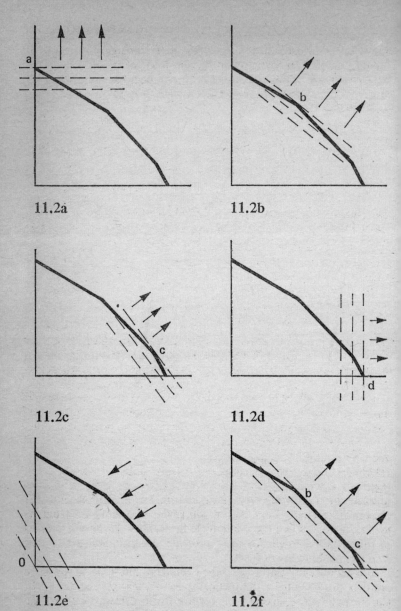

11.2a

11.2b

11.2c

11.2d

0

11.2e

11.2f

Figure 11.2 Different objective functions lead to different optimum levels of outputs

Points to the north-east of *ab* are impossible because of insufficient equipment, of *bc* because of insufficient land, of *cd* because of insufficient labour. Points south of *od* are impossible because barley cannot be 'ungrown'. If we let S represent the set of production possibilities, then:

$$S = \{(x, y) : 11x + 2y \leqslant 980,$$
$$3x + 5y \leqslant 400,$$
$$x + y \leqslant 100,$$
$$x \geqslant 0,$$
$$y \geqslant 0\}$$

The problem facing the farmer is to choose those values of x and y which will maximise z subject to the conditions imposed by S. The linear programming problem is usually set out thus:

maximise $z = 7x + 10y$
subject to $11x + 2y \leqslant 980,$
$3x + 5y \leqslant 400,$
$x + y \leqslant 100,$
$x \geqslant 0, y \geqslant 0$

This simple problem can be solved graphically by pushing out the objective function until it reaches the boundary of the set of production possibilities. In Figure 11.2(*b*) (ignoring the other diagrams in this figure for the moment) point *b* gives the combination of x and y which will yield the maximum z. An accurate graph would show that x is 50 and y is 50. The farmer should grow 50 acres of potatoes and 50 acres of barley, and this is not the result which one would have expected from studying the 'net revenues' or the production possibilities in isolation.

Different objective functions would give different solutions. In Figure 11.2, six examples of objective functions are given. If the 'net revenue' from potatoes were nil and from barley £10 per acre, the objective function would be horizontal and the point *a* would be the optimum: barley only would be grown. Table 11.2 gives examples of different 'net revenues' per acre and the points which would result as the optimum.

If both crops make a loss the optimal solution is to produce nothing, and the objective function leads to a loss-minimising problem rather than a maximising problem (the arrows point to the origin rather than away from it). If the objective function has the same slope as one of the constraints, a range of combinations of x

Table 11.2

'Net revenue' potatoes	barley	Objective function $z =$	Optimal blend at
0	10	$10y$	a
7	10	$7x + 10y$	b
11	10	$11x + 10y$	c
7	0	$7x$	d
−1	−2	$-x - 2y$	0
10	10	$10x + 10y$	b to c

and y will all give optimal solutions; here anywhere between and including points b and c will be equally profitable.

We investigate these different objective functions in order to illustrate two important features of linear programming. First, the optimal blend of x and y always lies on the boundary of the set of production possibilities. Second, there are no better combinations than those at the vertices. Even when there is a range of equally good combinations, none of them are better than the points defining the vertices at either end of the range. This means that we need consider only a limited number of choices: we need choose only from the vertices o, a, b, c, and d. The infinite number of possibilities in the set S has been reduced to five.

These vertices are the points where some of the constraints cross. To find the values of x and y at these points, we solve the equations formed from the relevant constraints. Note that some of the constraints cross at points which are outside the set of production possibilities, the point f in Figure 11.1(b) for example; so care must be taken to ensure that only the relevant constraints are considered. Impossible solutions must be ignored. A solution that is possible is known as a **feasible** solution.

Table 11.3 shows the vertex being considered, the equations which must be solved in order to find the levels of x and y at this vertex, the solution to the equations and the value of z which results from these levels of x and y. Inspection shows that z is at a maximum when $x = 50$ and $y = 50$.

Each of these vertices can be interpreted as a **programme**. For example, b is the programme to grow 50 acres of potatoes and 50 acres of barley. The origin, o, is the programme to do nothing. **Linear programming** is the technique of finding the optimal feasible programme.

If the farmer had asked us to decide the optimal blend of three crops instead of only two, we would have had three equations in three unknowns for each vertex, and we would find it more difficult to check that each solution was feasible, that it was within the set of production possibilities. For more than three crops the calculations could involve many days and plenty of risk of mistakes in the arithmetic. However, the solution of large numbers of simultaneous

Table 11.3

Vertex	Constraints	x	y	$z = 7x + 10y$
a	$x = 0$ $3x + 5y = 400$	0	80	800
b	$3x + 5y = 400$ $x + y = 100$	50	50	850
c	$x + y = 100$ $11x + 2y = 980$	86·6	13·4	740
d	$11x + 2y = 980$ $y = 0$	89	0	623
e	$x = 0$ $y = 0$	0	0	0

equations is done rapidly by a computer. Many simple rules are given to the machine to ensure that each solution is feasible. The machine usually starts with the programme 'do nothing' and then moves step by step towards the optimal feasible programme. The rules ensure that the machine moves towards the optimum by the fewest steps. For example, it would calculate the value of z at o, at a, at b, check that b is best and then print out the result. It would not move from o, to d, to c, to b because this route involves more calculations. When there are many thousands of feasible solutions, as there are in a large linear programming problem, this ability to move always in the direction of the optimal solution is an important saving in time.

(Do not confuse linear programming with computer programming. A linear programme is a feasible solution. A computer programme is a set of rules fed into a machine. Hence the expression 'linear programming programme' for the set of instructions which tells a machine how to solve a linear programming problem.)

11.2 A problem of minimisation

A farmer has a group of livestock which will not thrive unless they receive at least 9 units of starch, 6 units of protein, and 12 units of vitamins. He can obtain two foods: food U which is rather like oats, and food V which is rather like beans. Food U contains 5 units of starch per ton, 2 units of protein per ton, and 3 units of vitamins per ton. Each ton of food V contains 3 units of starch, 3 units of protein, and 10 units of vitamins. The cost of food U is £12 per ton and of food V £11 per ton. What is the cheapest way of obtaining the necessary nutrients from the two foods?

First, the objective function is defined. In this case the objective is to minimise costs. Write u for the number of tons of food U, v for the number of tons of food V, and C for the total cost of the two foods. Then $C = 12u + 11v$.

Second, state the various requirements and third, find how many units of each requirement are met by one ton of each food. Table 11.4 sets out the data.

Table 11.4

| | Number of units of requirement met by one ton of: | | Total requirement |
	U	V	
starch	5	3	9
protein	2	3	6
vitamins	3	10	12

This set of requirements can be labelled R, where:

$$R = \{(u, v) : 5u + 3v \geqslant 9,$$
$$2u + 3v \geqslant 6,$$
$$3u + 10v \geqslant 12,$$
$$u \geqslant 0,$$
$$v \geqslant 0\}$$

Note that these inequalities are all 'greater than or equal to', whereas in the maximising problem of the previous section the resource constraints were 'less than or equal to'. The result is that the requirement set is not completely enclosed. The set is illustrated in Figure 11.3(a). Note that there is an infinite area to the north-east where the requirements will be met.

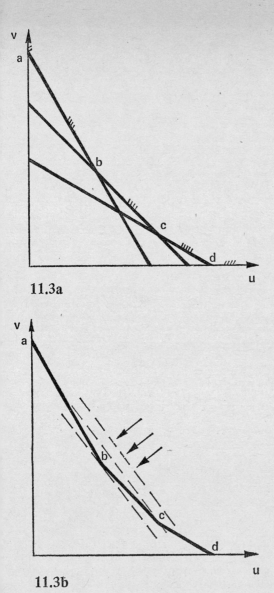

v
a

b

c

d

u

11.3a

v
a

b

c

d

u

11.3b

Figure 11.3 (*a*) The set of requirements; (*b*) Minimising the cost of meeting the requirements

The problem facing the farmer is to choose that combination of U and V which minimises C subject to the constraints imposed by R. The linear programming problem can be stated as:

$$\text{minimise } C = 12u + 11v$$
$$\text{subject to } 5u + 3v \geqslant 9$$
$$2u + 3v \geqslant 6$$
$$3u + 10v \geqslant 12$$
$$u \geqslant 0, v \geqslant 0$$

The problem can be solved graphically by pushing the family of cost lines as far as possible towards the origin, as shown in Figure 11.3(b). Alternatively the vertices which form feasible solutions can be found algebraically and the least costly combination can then be found by inspection. Table 11.5 illustrates.

Table 11.5

Vertex	Constraints	Levels of u	v	$C = 12u + 11v$
a	$u = 0$	0	3	33
	$5u + 3v = 9$			
b	$5u + 3v = 9$	1	1·3	26·7
	$2u + 3v = 6$			
c	$2u + 3v = 6$	2·2	0·5	32·2
	$3u + 10v = 12$			
d	$3u + 10v = 12$	4	0	48
	$v = 0$			

The farmer can meet his stock's requirements for nutrients most cheaply by feeding one ton of food U and 1·3 tons of food V.

11.3 Summary

Simple optimisation problems can be converted into either maximisation or minimisation problems. If substitution between inputs or between outputs is easy, the real situation can be interpreted by using smooth continuous functions. Provided the second-order conditions are met, the solution can be found by derivation. If substitution is difficult, as often happens in the short run, the problem may be interpreted as a linear programming problem. Provided only feasible solutions are considered, the solution can be found algebraically.

Generally, approaches using continuous smooth functions are useful to clarify the concepts involved in any problem. For long-run problems they can yield numerical solutions provided the number of variables is small. When large numbers of variables are involved, linear programming with electronic aids is easiest. Further study of linear programming can lead to an understanding of many apparent puzzles of economic behaviour, and some economists would consider it to be a more fruitful method of understanding concepts than derivatives; it is not just a technique for the economic engineer.

The most important part of any optimisation problem is the objective function. What is a correct description of the objectives of one decision-maker in the short run may be incorrect over a longer period of time. Two people rarely have the same objectives. Marshall McLuhan says 'The specialist is one who moves by small error-free steps towards the grand fallacy.' The solution to an optimisation problem involves hard work to find the data and some inspiration to make sure that the objectives are correct. Neglect of data will result in no solution; an uninspired approach to objectives will result in a wrong solution.

Chapter 12

Statistics

12.1 Introduction

Consider a linear function relating $x \in X$ to $y \in Y$. This function will be of the form $y = a + bx$, and if we have two particular observations of the ordered pairs (x, y) we can find the values of the parameters a and b. For example, if the two observations are $(3, 2)$ and $(6, -7)$, then:

$$2 = a + 3b$$
$$-7 = a + 6b$$

and the solution to these two equations gives $a = 11$ and $b = -3$, so the explicit function is $y = 11 - 3x$.

Precise relations of this sort are common in introductory texts to the natural and social sciences, but in the natural sciences the student can himself illustrate them by performing experiments. The elementary study of the natural sciences conveys a feeling of precision because it involves at least one of the following: very large numbers of 'actors' (the number of molecules in a cubic centimetre of gas is many millions of times the population of the world); experiments in laboratory conditions which allow other variables to be held constant (experiments in the social sciences are rarely possible and those that are done are often too disastrous to be repeated); carefully recorded experiments that can be checked (in the social sciences, if an important problem is solved the solution is applied, so the problem disappears); no interaction between the observer and the observed. These conveniences disappear when the frontiers of natural science are reached. Phenomena are studied in small numbers, outside the laboratory, under conditions which are difficult to repeat, and the actions of the observer do affect the phenomena being studied. Discovery in natural science is no easier than in social science. The difficulty with social science is at the start, because the student does not have the advantage of these convenient simplifications in his elementary field work. As soon as social scientists start observing, the precision of the neat functional relations disappears. Human behaviour is not tidy.

The previous chapters of this book were concerned with various techniques to show how deductions can be made from assumptions. To do this we assumed that relations are precise, either as functions or as inequalities. In these last two chapters we introduce the reader to some techniques designed to handle observations which do not fit exactly into precise relations.

12.2 A problem of description

A librarian wonders how many feet of spare shelving will be used up each week if book purchases continue at their present rate of 50 books per week. She decides to base her calculations on the width of books in the present collection, assuming that future book sizes

Table 12.1

(1) X_i	(2) X_i	(3) $X_i - \bar{X}$	(4) $|X_i - \bar{X}|$	(5) $(X_i - \bar{X})^2$
15	7	−5·5	5·5	30·25
19	9	−3·5	3·5	12·25
21	10	−2·5	2·5	6·25
10	10	−2·5	2·5	6·25
14	10	−2·5	2·5	6·25
12	11	−1·5	1·5	2·25
12	11	−1·5	1·5	2·25
9	11	−1·5	1·5	2·25
11	11	−1·5	1·5	2·25
7	11	−1·5	1·5	2·25
11	12	−0·5	0·5	0·25
13	12	−0·5	0·5	0·25
17	13	0·5	0·5	0·25
10	13	0·5	0·5	0·25
11	13	0·5	0·5	0·25
13	14	1·5	1·5	2·25
11	15	2·5	2·5	6·25
10	17	4·5	4·5	20·25
13	19	6·5	6·5	42·25
11	21	8·5	8·5	72·25
250	250	0·0	50·0	216·00

will keep to the pattern of the present collection. Since the shelving contains supports at foot intervals, she is more interested in the number of books which can be shelved in a foot length than in the width of the books. (The two measures are not the same; the latter measure would be useful only if fractions of books could be shelved.) The collection contains many thousands of feet of shelving, so to save time she selects 20 different feet scattered at random throughout the collection and counts the number of books in each foot ('at random' means that each foot of shelving is equally likely to be selected). The result is given in column (1) of Table 12.1.

12.3 The mean, the mode, and the median

In order to summarise this information, she takes the average of the 20 observations. The 20 lengths of shelving contain 250 books, or 12·5 books per foot on average. This is the **arithmetic mean** of the 20 observations.

The usual notation for the arithmetic mean is $\bar{X}$ ('X bar'). The rule for calculating it can be stated by labelling the first observation X_1 (which is 15 in the first column), the second X_2 (which is 19), . . . and the twentieth X_{20} (which is 11), so:

$$\bar{X} = \tfrac{1}{20} \sum_{i=1}^{i=20} X_i$$

For n observations the mean is $\bar{X} = \dfrac{1}{n} \sum X_i$, where the summation sign is assumed to sum from $i = 1$ to $i = n$.

Since the arithmetic mean is 12·5 books per foot, the librarian will be about right in assuming that 50 books will require 4 feet of shelving. However, for many problems 'about right' is not good enough. Approximations are always useful, but we may want to know how approximate a calculation is. If it is too rough the result may be inefficiency or in some problems, loss of life.

If the observations are arranged in order of magnitude, as in column (2) of Table 12.1, the most frequently occurring value is seen to be '11'. This number is the **mode** of the set of numbers. A 'typical' section of shelving contains 11 books. The mode is sometimes a useful measure with which to work. For example, if we were trying out a new fashion in shoes but we wanted to manufacture only one size, the size that would be most likely to sell would be the most common size, the modal size.

Yet another method of using one number to describe a list of numbers is to choose that number which has half the observations greater in value and half less. The **median** is the middle value of a series of numbers when these numbers are arranged in order of magnitude. In column (2) there are twenty numbers; the tenth is '11' and the eleventh is '12', so the median lies between 11 and 12. By convention, when there is an even number of observations so that the median falls between two of them, the arithmetic mean of these two is taken as the median. In this case the median is $\dfrac{11 + 12}{2} = 11 \cdot 5$.

The median is helpful when the inequalities in a list of numbers are being studied. For example, if we were introducing a new income tax but we wanted to tax only half of all income-receivers in order to reduce the costs of administration, we would tax all those incomes above the median income.

Inspection of the numbers in column (2) shows that they tend to bunch in the range 10 to 13. The further away from this range, the less likely is the number to occur. We can measure this central tendency in three ways:

Mean   12·5
Mode   11
Median 11·5

Which measure is best depends on the problem in hand. For the librarian's problem the mean is best because she wishes to take into account the possibility of very small or very large books. Neither the mode nor the median would change in value if the largest number of books in a foot of shelving (the last entry in column 2) were doubled, nor if the smallest number (the first entry) were halved; whereas the mean would change.

12.4 The deviation from the mean

The mean is used as a summary of the information contained in the list of observations, the list itself being too detailed to remember and unsuitable as a basis for prediction. However, by summarising in this way considerable information is sacrificed. In column (2) the mean is 12·5, but the observations range from 7 to 21. And yet if we stated both the mean and the range we would still not convey the way in which the observations bunch around the mean. (For example, 12 observations of '7' and 8 observations of '21' would also have a range from 7 to 21 and almost the same mean, and yet there is no central tendency here at all.)

In column (3) of Table 12.1 the deviation of each observation from the mean is given. Always these deviations will sum to zero because of the definition of the mean.

By definition $\bar{X} = \frac{1}{n}\sum X_i$, so $\sum X_i = n\bar{X}$.

The sum of the deviations is $\sum(X_i - \bar{X}) = \sum X_i - \sum \bar{X}$.

The second term on the right-hand side of this expression is n of $\bar{X}$s added together, so $\sum(X_i - \bar{X}) = \sum X_i - \sum \bar{X} = n\bar{X} - n\bar{X} = 0$.

One method of describing the deviations from the mean of a list of numbers is to sum the absolute values of these deviations. The notation for the absolute value of a particular deviation is $|X_i - \bar{X}|$ and the sum is $\sum|X_i - \bar{X}|$ as shown in column (4). This measure will be larger the more observations there are, so to avoid its dependence on the number of observations we divide by n. In other words we find the mean-of-the-absolute-values of the deviations from the mean-of-the-observations. This measure is known as the **mean deviation**:

$$\frac{\sum|X_i - \bar{X}|}{n} = \frac{50}{20} = 2 \cdot 5$$

A much better method of describing the spread of a group of observations about their mean is by squaring each deviation $(X_i - \bar{X})^2$ and then summing these squares $\sum(X_i - \bar{X})^2$. This approach has two immediate advantages. It avoids having to juggle with the signs of the deviations since all squares are positive. It also puts more weight onto the larger deviations, and since these are the ones that bother us most in devising a summary of information (they are the most untidy), it is these that we want to emphasise most. The larger the number of observations the larger will be the value of $\sum(X_i - \bar{X})^2$, so to adjust for this we divide by n to obtain an expression known as the **variance**. If we agree to call the group of data X, then var (X) is a shorthand for the variance of X:

$$\text{var}(X) = \frac{\sum(X_i - \bar{X})^2}{n} = \frac{216}{20} = 10 \cdot 8$$

The variance is used in calculating many summary measures, as we shall see in later sections. For describing directly the extent of the spread of a group of observations it is confusing because its units are squared. In our example we found that the mean was 12·5 books per foot, but the variance is in units of 'books squared per foot'. When the square root of the variance is taken, the units of measurement become the same as those used for the mean. This measure is known as the **standard deviation**, which we shall abbreviate to SD (X): SD $(X) = \sqrt{\text{var }(X)} = \sqrt{10\cdot8} = 3\cdot28$. The 20 observations of X can be summarised into the two measures, mean and standard deviation: $\bar{X} = 12\cdot5$, SD $(X) = 3\cdot28$.

Table 12.2

X_i	$X_i - \bar{X}$	$(X_i - \bar{X})^2$
7	−5·6	31·36
7	−5·6	31·36
7	−5·6	31·36
7	−5·6	31·36
7	−5·6	31·36
7	−5·6	31·36
7	−5·6	31·36
7	−5·6	31·36
7	−5·6	31·36
7	−5·6	31·36
7	−5·6	31·36
7	−5·6	31·36
21	8·4	70·56
21	8·4	70·56
21	8·4	70·56
21	8·4	70·56
21	8·4	70·56
21	8·4	70·56
21	8·4	70·56
21	8·4	70·56

$X_i = 252$ 0   940·80
$\bar{X} = 12\cdot6$ var $(X) = 47\cdot04$
           SD $(X) = 6\cdot86$

Compare the above with the summary measures that result from 20 observations which have no central tendency, as in Table 12.2. Here the range is exactly the same as for the previous group of figures, the mean is almost the same, but the standard deviation is more than half the size of the mean.

Usually, the smaller is the ratio $\dfrac{\text{SD}\,(X)}{\bar{X}}$, the greater is the tendency for the observations to bunch about the mean. (However, this only applies when X takes non-negative values. If X could take both positive and negative values, then $\bar{X}$ could be very small or even zero, resulting in huge values for the ratio even though the observations were bunched tightly about the mean.) Referring back to column (2) of Table 12.1, we note that 15 of the 20 observations fall within the range of one standard deviation either side of the mean: $12\cdot5 \pm 3\cdot28$, which is from $8\cdot82$ to $15\cdot78$.

If we were to measure the height of 100 or more men, or the I.Q. of 100 or more children, or the length of time that 100 or more light-bulbs will burn continuously, we would find the same tendency for the observations to cluster about the mean value. If this clustering occurs, and if we have a large number of observations, we will usually find that: about 68 per cent of the observations fall within $\bar{X} \pm \text{SD}\,(X)$, about 95 per cent of the observations fall within $\bar{X} \pm 2\text{SD}\,(X)$, and only about 3 in 1000 observations fall outside the range $\bar{X} \pm 3\text{SD}\,(X)$.

Drill

1. Find the mode, the median, the mean, the variance, and the standard deviation of the following list of numbers: 7, 8, 9, 9, 9, 10, 11, 11, 12, 14.

2. Show that $\displaystyle\sum_{i=1}^{3} (X_i - a) = \sum_{i=1}^{3} X_i - 3a$.

3. Show that $\displaystyle\sum_{i=1}^{3} bX_i = b\sum_{i=1}^{3} X_i$.

4. Show that $\sum(X_i - \bar{X}) = \sum X_i - n\bar{X} = 0$.

5. Show that $\dfrac{1}{n}\bar{X}\sum X_i = \bar{X}^2 = \left(\dfrac{\sum X_i}{n}\right)^2$.

6. Show that $\sum(X_i - \bar{X})^2 = \sum X_i{}^2 - 2\bar{X}\sum X_i + n\bar{X}^2$.

7. Show the equivalence of these two expressions for the variance

(for large numbers of observations, the one on the right is easier to calculate):

$$\frac{\sum(X_i - \bar{X})^2}{n} = \frac{\sum X_i^2}{n} - \left(\frac{\sum X_i}{n}\right)^2$$

Answers

1. Mode = 9, median = 9·5, mean = 10, var (X) = 3·8, SD (X) = 1.95.

12.5 Samples and populations

If 50 books are to be bought, they will be selected from the total world population of books, a population of many millions. To

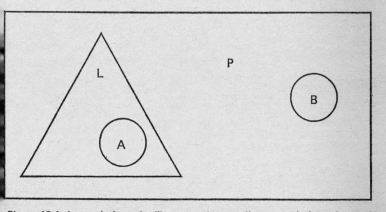

Figure 12.1 A sample from the library used to predict a sample from the total population

estimate how many books will go into a foot length of shelving, the librarian selected a sample of 20 different feet dotted about the existing library which contains many thousands of feet of shelving. The sets and subsets involved in this process are illustrated in Figure 12.1. P is the world book population and L is the particular library, so L is a subset of P. A is the sample of 20 sections of shelves from the library, so A is a subset of L. B is the selection of 50 books to be bought next week, so B is a subset of P. A is being used to predict the mean and standard deviation of B.

If we knew the mean and standard deviation of all the books-per-foot in the library as a whole, we would have a more accurate idea of what to expect from B. Suppose that we know from the records that there are 120 000 books and 10 000 feet of full shelving, so the

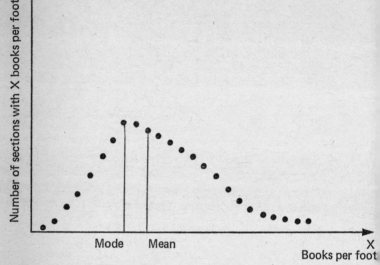

Figure 12.2 A frequency distribution

average number of books per foot is 12 for the library as a whole, compared with 12·5 for the sample. We still do not know the standard deviation of books per foot for the library as a whole, but we do know that for the sample of 20 the sample standard deviation is 3·16.

By using the sample mean (12·5), the sample mode (11), the population mean (12), and some common-sense, we can build up a picture of the pattern of book sizes in the library. It is impossible for a section of shelving to contain less than zero books, but it is possible for a section to contain more than 22 books. Therefore if we were to count all the sections in the library we would expect to obtain a pattern as in Figure 12.2 which extends further to the right of the mode than to the left.

When a pattern is skewed away from the mode towards the right it is called **positively skewed**. Whenever the mean is greater than the mode (provided there is only one mode) the pattern will be positively skewed. This is because the mean takes into account the size of the extreme values whereas the mode does not. An important example of a positively skewed pattern is the distribution of income; most people have an income which is below the average because the few people with very high incomes pull the average to a higher value than the mode.

In Figure 12.3 the example of the library is presented in a different manner. Here the measurements refer to the width of the books, so the pattern goes the opposite way to Figure 12.2 because many books per foot implies books of small width. The pattern of Figure 12.3 has a tail extending to the left; it is **negatively skewed**.

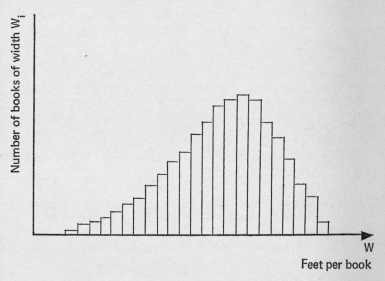

Figure 12.3 A histogram

This figure presents a problem in defining the widths W. We could be very precise and measure the widths to the nearest thousandth of a foot, but if we are too precise we may find that there is only one observation, or no observation at all, for each width. For example, if we try to find out how many books are exactly 0·085 feet wide we may find that none are, even though the mean of all books in the library is 12 books per foot, which implies that the average width is 0·085 feet. 'Books per foot' was defined as the number of books that could be fitted between supports placed at one foot intervals, so it takes integer values only: X takes only discrete values. The widths in 'feet per book' must also be defined so that they take only discrete values. There are a number of ways in which this can be done. For example, there can be 20 values of W, each covering a range of 0·05 feet (this would cover all the books in most libraries since few books are more than 1 foot wide). So each W_i can be defined:

$$0 < W_1 \leqslant 0·05 \text{ feet}$$
$$0·05 < W_2 \leqslant 0·10 \text{ feet}$$
. . . .
$$0·95 < W_{20} \leqslant 1·00 \text{ feet}$$

The definitions using 'less than' and 'less than or equal to' avoid any ambiguities between W_1 and W_2, between W_2 and W_3, etc. The number of books which will fall into each range can be counted and the pattern pictured on a chart such as Figure 12.3. In this figure the area of each rectangle is proportionate to the number of books within each range. Provided the rectangles are of equal width, the heights will be proportionate to the number of books within each range. Charts which use the areas of rectangles to describe observed patterns, as in Figure 12.3, are known as **histograms**.

12.6 Probability

The term 'probability' is used to describe a numerical indicator of the likeliness of an event. A probability of zero means the event is impossible. A probability of one means the event is certain. The probability of a penny showing a head when tossed is 0·5, and the probability of a penny showing a tail is 0·5; $0·5 + 0·5 = 1$, because the penny is certain to show either a head or a tail (ignoring the possibility of the penny landing on its edge, and assuming that the penny is 'fair').

If two pennies are tossed there are apparently three possibilities: two heads, two tails, and one of each. However, the probabilities of each possibility are not $\frac{1}{3}$, $\frac{1}{3}$, $\frac{1}{3}$. There are actually four possible events:

The first penny may show H and the second H: HH
The first penny may show H and the second T: HT
The first penny may show T and the second H: TH

The first penny may show T and the second T: TT

Each event is equally likely, so the chance of one-head-and-one-tail is twice as likely as either two heads or two tails. The probability of no heads is ¼, of one head ½, and of two heads ¼. The probability of each number of heads is pictured in Figure 12.4.

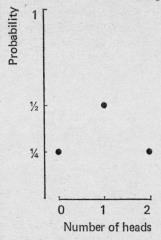

Figure 12.4 The probabilities of heads when two pennies are tossed

Number of heads

Each time we toss two pennies we do not know how they are going to turn up. However, if we toss two pennies 100 times we will expect roughly 25 two-tails, 50 one-head-and-one-tail, and 25 two-heads. Although each event is random, the outcome of a large number of events follows a particular pattern; not precisely, but the larger the number of events the nearer will the result come to that predicted from working out the probabilities. Suppose that we have thrown two pennies 99 times and have found 25 two-tails, 50 one-head-and-one-tail, and 24 two-heads. It does not follow that the next throw will be a two-head. The events are not connected to each other. Each event is independent. (This is the way the market for insurance works. No individual knows when an accident will occur to him. But when many thousands of people insure against accidents, the insurance company can calculate from past evidence the proportion of people who will suffer from an accident even though it does not know which individuals will suffer. In this way risks can be shared via the insurance premiums and the organisation of the insurance company. What is uncertainty for the individual is probability for the insurance company.)

If three pennies are tossed, the probability of a particular outcome can be calculated as follows:

HHH   THH
HHT   THT
HTH   TTH
HTT   TTT

Each event is equally likely, so the probability of no heads is $\frac{1}{8}$, of one head $\frac{3}{8}$, of two heads $\frac{3}{8}$, and of three heads $\frac{1}{8}$. Figure 12.5 illus-

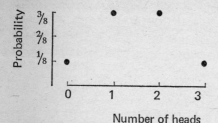

Figure 12.5 The probabilities of heads when three pennies are tossed

trates the case for three pennies, and Figure 12.6 illustrates the probabilities of the various outcomes when four pennies are tossed. Readers familiar with the binomial theorem will have noticed how the probabilities follow the same pattern as the coefficients in the

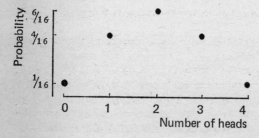

Figure 12.6 The probabilities of heads when four pennies are tossed

expansion of $(a + b)^n$. For one penny, the probability of no head is $\frac{1}{1+1}$ and of one head it is also $\frac{1}{1+1}$. Likewise $(a + b)^1 = 1 \cdot a + 1 \cdot b$. For two pennies prob(no head) = $\frac{1}{1+2+1}$, prob(one head) $=\dfrac{2}{1+2+1}$, prob(two heads) $=\dfrac{1}{1+2+1}$. Likewise $(a+b)^2 = 1 \cdot a^2 + 2 \cdot ab + 1 \cdot b^2$. Probabilities and coefficients follow the pattern of numbers known as Pascal's triangle:

```
    1 1
   1 2 1
  1 3 3 1
 1 4 6 4 1
```

The binomial theorem allows calculation of any probabilities when the possible outcomes involve only two alternatives for each item at risk, as with tossing pennies. For example, if 100 pennies were

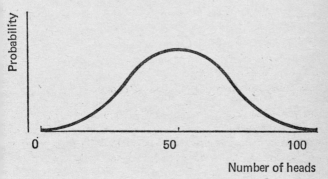

Figure 12.7 The probabilities of heads when a hundred pennies are tossed

tossed the pattern of probabilities for each outcome is like the bell-shape illustrated in Figure 12.7.

Although Figure 12.7 shows a smooth continuous curve, it is really 101 points giving the probabilities of 0 head, 1 head, 2 heads, ... 100 heads. The number of heads is a discrete variable: it takes integer values only. How do we picture the probability of a particular X occurring when X is a continuous variable? If X is continuous we have to develop a new approach because there are now an infinite number of possible values for X, and therefore the chance of any particular value occurring is infinitesimally small. We can overcome this by considering ranges of values of X instead of precise values. We can then plot a curve such that the area under the curve gives the probability that X will fall within a given range.

In Figure 12.8, X measures the height of men in feet. The probability that a man's height will fall within the range 5 feet to 5·5 feet is given by the shaded area. The curve defines the areas of probability. The total area under the curve must be unity. Such a curve is known as a **probability distribution**. The particular bell-shape shown here is known as a **normal curve**. The vertical axis is labelled $f(X)$, a

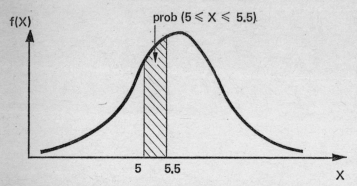

Figure 12.8 A continuous probability distribution

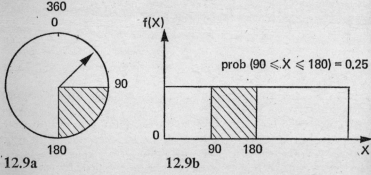

Figure 12.9 A rectangular continuous probability distribution

notation for the continuous function that encloses the area. For an example of a probability distribution which is not a normal probability distribution, consider a pointer fixed in the centre of a circular dial which is marked out in degrees from 0° to 360°. If the pointer is spun, the probability of it coming to rest in a particular range is given by the area under the 'curve' really the straight line in Figure

12.9(*b*). Such a curve is known as a **rectangular** probability distribution.

Probability distributions may be of any shape: rectangular, many-peaked, single-peaked. Of the single-peaked distributions (those with one obvious mode) they may be positively or negatively skewed, or they may be symmetrical. Of the single-peaked symmetrical distributions, the most important is the normal distribution. All probability distributions have an area under the curve equal to unity.

A normal distribution is defined once the mean and the standard deviation are known. Writing m for the mean and s for the standard deviation, the formula for the normal curve is:

$$f(X) = \frac{1}{s\sqrt{2\pi}} e^{-\frac{(X-m)^2}{2s^2}}, \text{ where the expression 'upstairs' is the index of } e.$$

The drill on page 243 is an exercise in manipulating this expression. Figure 12.10 illustrates the normal curve, which is at its maximum where $X = m$. The points of inflexion of the curve are where $X = m - s$ and $X = m + s$. (A point of inflexion is where the second derivative is zero, so the first derivative changes sign at that point.) The area under the curve between $X = m - s$ and $X = m + s$ is 0·68, so:

$$\text{prob}(m - s \leqslant X \leqslant m + s) = 0\cdot68,$$
also $\text{prob}(m - 2s \leqslant X \leqslant m + 2s) = 0\cdot95,$
and $\text{prob}(m - 3s \leqslant X \leqslant m + 3s) = 0\cdot997.$

Compare these figures with those given at the end of section 12.4.

12.7 Summary

This chapter introduced some of the statistical ideas involved in describing or predicting the behaviour of one variable. For example, we know from observation that most men are of about average height: few men are very tall and few are very short. The heights of men turn out to be normally distributed. Although we cannot guess what will be the height of the next man we meet, we can put a probability on any range of heights within which he may fall. Also, if we choose at random any 100 men we can be fairly certain that their heights will be normally distributed.

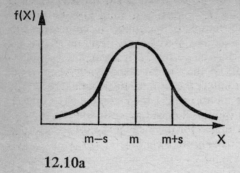

12.10a

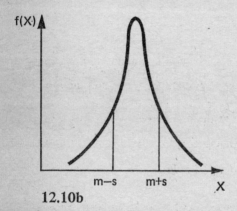

12.10b

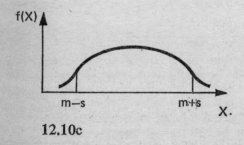

12.10c

Figure 12.10 Normal probability distributions; (*b*) Small standard deviation;
(*c*) Large standard deviation

Not all distributions are normal. Some are positively skewed, some negatively skewed; some are rectangular, and there are other types. However, the normal distribution is important in statistical techniques. Whenever large numbers of individual measurements are involved and each measurement appears to be at random, there is often some central tendency exhibited by the pattern of measurements taken as a whole. By plotting the frequencies with which each of the discrete values of a variable occurs, or each of the ranges of a variable, a picture of the distribution can be formed from a histogram. Often the distribution is symmetrical and bell-shaped. Numerical calculations of the mean and standard deviation provide a convenient way of describing a list of numbers; they may also provide a way of building up a probability distribution.

Drill

1. Note that e^{ax} can also be written exp (ax), and be^{ax} can be written b exp (ax). Use the function of a function rule to find the following:

  i. If $y = $ exp (aX), what is $\dfrac{dy}{dX}$?

  ii. If $y = b$ exp (aX), what is $\dfrac{dy}{dX}$?

  iii. If $y = b$ exp $(-\tfrac{1}{2}X^2)$, what is $\dfrac{dy}{dX}$?

  iv. If $z = \dfrac{-(X - m)^2}{2s^2}$, where s and m are parameters, what is $\dfrac{dz}{dX}$?

2. The formula for the normal curve is:

$$y = \frac{1}{s\sqrt{2\pi}} \exp\left[\frac{-(X - m)^2}{2s^2}\right]$$

where m is the arithmetic mean and s is the standard deviation.

  i. Find $\dfrac{dy}{dX}$. Hence show that y is a maximum where $X = m$. Does

this imply that the mean is the same value of X as the mode? Show that the maximum height of y is inversely proportional to s.

  ii. Use the function of a function rule and the product rule to find

$\frac{d^2y}{dX^2}$. Hence show that the points of inflexion of the normal curve are where $X = m - s$ and $X = m + s$.

Answers

1. i. $a \, e^{aX} = a \exp(aX)$.
   ii. $ab \exp(aX)$.
   iii. $-bX \exp(-\frac{1}{2}X^2)$.
   iv. $\frac{-(X - m)}{s^2}$.

2. i. $\frac{dy}{dX} = \frac{1}{s\sqrt{2\pi}}\left(\frac{-(X - m)}{s^2}\right) \exp\left[\frac{-(X - m)^2}{2s^2}\right]$

and this is zero when $X = m$. From the original expression,

when $X = m$, $y = \frac{1}{s\sqrt{2\pi}} \exp[0] = \frac{1}{s\sqrt{2\pi}}$

so the maximum value of y varies inversely with s.

ii. $\frac{d^2y}{dX^2} = \frac{1}{s\sqrt{2\pi}}\left(\frac{-1}{s^2}\right) \exp\left[\frac{-(X - m)^2}{2s^2}\right]$

$+ \frac{1}{s\sqrt{2\pi}}\left(\frac{-(X - m)}{s^2}\right)\left(\frac{-(X - m)}{s^2}\right) \exp\left[\frac{-(X - m)^2}{2s^2}\right]$

and this is zero when

$$-\frac{1}{s^2} + \frac{(X - m)^2}{s^4} = 0$$
$$(X - m)^2 = s^2$$
$$X - m = \pm s$$
$$X = m \pm s$$

READING

Huff, Darrell, *How to Take a Chance*, London, Pelican, 1965.

Land, Frank, *Language of Mathematics*, Chapter 14.

Kalton, G., *Introduction to Statistical Ideas*, London, Chapman and Hall, 1966, pp. 1–25.

Gregory, A. H., Hartley, J. R., and Lewis, D. G., *Basic Statistics* London, Methuen, 1969, Chapters 1–5.

Chapter 13

Estimating Parameters

13.1 Correlation

When observations are made in pairs (X_i, Y_i), the set of these observations can be plotted on a graph to form a **scatter diagram**. Examples of scatter diagrams are given in Figure 13.1. The observations may have been made in pairs simply for descriptive purposes (plotting g.n.p. against calendar years, for example). However, we may have a feeling that a change in the value of Y is associated with a change in the value of X (plotting total costs against quantity produced, for example). The standard rule of research is that differences are explained by other differences. So if we suspect that changes in Y are associated with changes in X, we want some measure of this association.

One such measure of the degree of association between two variables is the **correlation coefficient,** abbreviated as 'r'. However, this measures only the extent of a linear relation. Figure 13.1 shows the way in which r is used to describe the different patterns in a scatter diagram. A perfect linear relation, with Y increasing as X increases, will result in $r = 1$ as shown in Figure 13.1(*a*). A perfect negative linear relation will result in $r = -1$ as shown in part (*b*). Approximate relations will be between these two figures, but the nearer is r to the two extremes of $+1$ or -1, the more definite is the relationship. If there is no linear relation at all the result will be $r = 0$. Note that r can be near to zero either because there is no relation or because there is a very definite relation which is non-linear.

To calculate the correlation coefficient, first calculate the mean of X and the mean of Y. Then for each observation multiply together the deviations from the means $(X_i - \bar{X})(Y_i - \bar{Y})$. This part of the calculation will decide the sign of r. In Figure 13.2, M is the point $(\bar{X}, \bar{Y})$. Points to the north-east of M will have $(X_i - \bar{X})(Y_i - \bar{Y})$ positive. Points to the south-west of M will also yield a positive value to this product since both $(X_i - \bar{X})$ and $(Y_i - \bar{Y})$ will be negative. Points to the north-west and south-east of M will give a negative value to the product. The sum of the products, $\sum(X_i - \bar{X})(Y_i - \bar{Y})$,

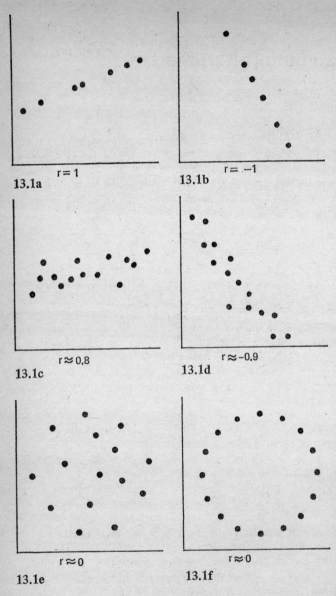

Figure 13.1 Different values of the correlation coefficient

shows whether the overall tendency is positive or negative. However, the absolute value of this sum is dependent on the number of observations, so we divide by n to obtain the expression known as the **covariance** of X and Y:

$$\text{cov}\,(X, Y) = \frac{1}{n}\sum(X_i - \bar{X})(Y_i - \bar{Y})$$

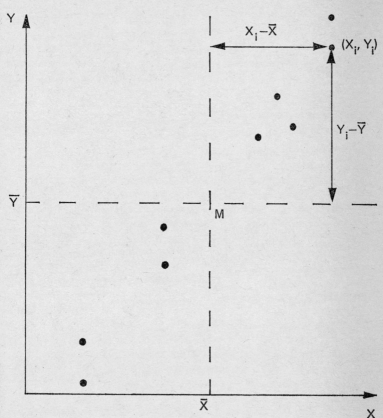

Figure 13.2 The deviations of a point from the two means

The covariance is used in the calculation of several statistical measures. Note that the variance is a special case of the covariance since $\text{cov}\,(X, X) = \text{var}\,(X)$.

The units of measurement of $\text{cov}\,(X, Y)$ will be the product of the units for X and the units for Y, but comparisons from one set of data to another are best made with a dimensionless expression. This can be obtained by dividing the covariance by the standard deviations of both X and Y, and this yields the correlation coefficient, r:

$$r = \frac{\text{cov}(X, Y)}{\text{SD}(X).\text{SD}(Y)} = \frac{\sum(X_i - \bar{X})(Y_i - \bar{Y})}{\sqrt{\sum(X_i - \bar{X})^2\sum(Y_i - \bar{Y})^2}}$$

In the right-hand expression, n is cancelled out.

A great deal of amusement can be obtained from confusing correlation with cause. The more storks in Holland, the higher is the birth-rate. The higher is the rate of interest, the greater is the amount of investment. The higher the price, the more is demanded. Etcetera.

13.2 A problem of estimation

Consider the simple linear function $y = bx$. If y is revenue, b is the known price, and x is the quantity sold, the function gives the revenue of a price-taker once the quantity sold is known. Now consider the case where b is not known, but a particular pair of observed values for x and y are known. We are also sure from observing the market that the seller is a price-taker, so price is a parameter. We will change the notation to $Y = bX$ as a reminder that X and Y are known but b is still to be found. If X is 40 units and Y is £80, then b must be £2 per unit. We can check that this price is correct by studying the quantities sold and revenues received by other firms selling in this market. If we had never been involved in economic research before, we would expect that a firm selling 20 units would have a revenue of £40 and a firm selling 60 units would have a revenue of £120. Alas, the world is seldom like this. More likely, we shall have three pairs of observations from the three firms which do not lie on a straight line. The observations can be correct, and the firms can indeed be price-takers so the simple formula is correct. How then do we estimate the price?

One way to approach this problem is to assume that the observed revenues are not really 'true' revenues but are affected by a host of other factors: differences in transport costs, discounts, dates of payment and many other matters. No single one of these factors would make much difference to the accuracy of the relation $Y = bX$. All these other factors disturb the main relation which we are trying to estimate, but there are a great many of such factors, too many to allow them to be taken into account.

We can imagine what would happen if we were to find a large number of firms each of which sold the quantity X_1 (see Figure 13.3). Under these circumstances we could calculate an average of all the Y observations that correspond to the single X observation of X_1. We could then find many firms each of which sold the quantity X_2, and calculate the average of all the Y observations that correspond to X_2.

We have already made two assumptions. The first is based on

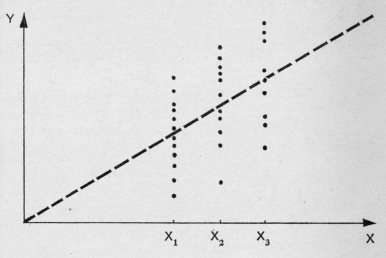

Figure 13.3 Many values of Y for each value of X

economics: if all the firms are price-takers, then revenue is a linear function of quantity sold and the line goes through the origin. The second assumption is based on experience of a wide range of phenomena: if there are many factors influencing a variable (Y) apart from the main factor (X), and if these factors are just as likely to pull the value of Y one way as the other, then the average value of those Y's which correspond to a given X is the value which is most likely to abstract from all the other factors except X. (What we are doing here is using the techniques of the previous chapter to make assumptions about the behaviour of Y when X is held constant. We are assuming that for each X there is a probability distribution of possible values of Y. Figure 13.4 illustrates.) Now if $Y = bX$ is an accurate description of the underlying relationship, and if the average of those Ys corresponding to each X is the most likely value to result when all other influences are ignored except X, then the straight line must connect together these averages of the Y's. Of course, this will happen only if we have many observations of Y for each value of X, so that

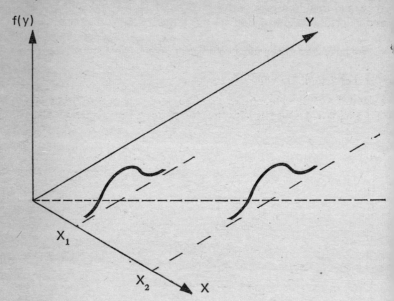

Figure 13.4 A probability distribution of Y values for each value of X

we can be sure that the average Y really does represent the value of Y which lies on the line $Y = bX$.

Drill

A survey is conducted of 11 firms in an industry whose product is sold in a competitive market. The 11 pairs of observations (quantity sold, revenue received) are as follows: (3, 16), (3, 17), (3, 18), (3, 19), (3, 20), (4, 22), (4, 26), (5, 28), (5, 29), (5, 31), (5, 32).

1. What is the average value of revenue received for all those firms who sold 3 units during the period? For those who sold 4 units? For those who sold 5 units?

2. What is the most likely value for the price, if all the other factors affecting revenue are ignored?

Answers
1. 18, 24, 30.
2. 6.

13.3 Estimating the slope

Even if it were possible to get many observations of Y for each value of X, we could never be sure that the pattern taken by these obser-

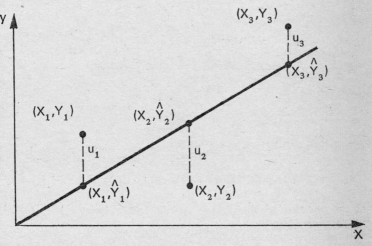

Figure 13.5 u_i is the difference between the observed Y_i and the estimated Y_i

vations was an accurate reflection of the probabilities involved. In practice, we have to make do with those observations that are available. Usually, for each X_i we will have only one observation for Y_i. So we find the line that fits the observations in the neatest way; we remember that it may be misleading, but we console ourselves with the thought that it is better than nothing, provided we do remember that it is only an approximation. (An intermediate text in statistics would show us how to put a probability on the chance that the line is correct.)

Suppose we have three observed pairs (X_1, Y_1), (X_2, Y_2), (X_3, Y_3) as pictured in Figure 13.5. We want to find a line that fits these points as well as possible. We will give a name to the Y value of the point on the estimated line where X is X_i, calling it $\hat{Y}_i$ ('Y_i hat'). If we had a large number of observations of Y corresponding to a value for X of X_i, then $\hat{Y}_i$ would be the average value of Y corresponding to X_i. Since we have only one observation of Y for each X_i, $\hat{Y}_i$ is a reasoned guess. Then $\hat{Y} = \hat{b}X$ is the estimated relation, where $\hat{b}$ is the estimate of b. The estimated average values for the revenues which should correspond to the quantities sold X_1, X_2, X_3 are: $\hat{Y}_1 = \hat{b}X_1$, $\hat{Y}_2 = \hat{b}X_2$, $\hat{Y}_3 = \hat{b}X_3$.

The difference between the best guess at the average values of the revenues $\hat{Y}_i$ and the observed revenues Y_i, we will call u_i, so $u_i = Y_i - \hat{Y}_i$. These u_i are the **residuals** of the observed points from the estimated line. The residuals may be positive or negative. The relations between the observed values of X and the observed values of Y are given by the definitions:

$$Y_1 = \hat{b}X_1 + u_1$$
$$Y_2 = \hat{b}X_2 + u_2$$
$$Y_3 = \hat{b}X_3 + u_3$$

In general, the ith residual is $u_i = Y_i - \hat{b}X_i$.
Note that we cannot find the u_i until we have found $\hat{b}$.

The best estimate for b, which we are calling $\hat{b}$, is that value for the slope which makes the estimated line pass most tidily through the observed points, the measures of untidiness being the sizes of the residuals u_i. This effect of the residuals can be found by summing their squares. Squaring has the advantage of putting most emphasis on the largest residuals, and of putting equal emphasis on positive and negative residuals. The sum of the squares of the residuals is $\sum u_i^2$, and this can be expressed in terms of the unknown $\hat{b}$ and the known observations X_i and Y_i:

$$u_1^2 = (Y_1 - \hat{b}X_1)^2 = Y_1^2 - 2\hat{b}X_1Y_1 + \hat{b}^2X_1^2$$
$$u_2^2 = (Y_2 - \hat{b}X_2)^2 = Y_2^2 - 2\hat{b}X_2Y_2 + \hat{b}^2X_2^2$$
$$u_3^2 = (Y_3 - \hat{b}X_3)^2 = Y_3^2 - 2\hat{b}X_3Y_3 + \hat{b}^2X_3^2$$
$$\sum u_i^2 = \sum(Y_i - \hat{b}X_i)^2 = \sum Y_i^2 - 2\hat{b}\sum X_iY_i + \hat{b}^2\sum X_i^2$$

The value of $\hat{b}$ which minimises the sum of the squares of the residuals can be found by taking the derivative of $\sum u_i^2$ with respect to $\hat{b}$, and putting it equal to zero:

$$\frac{d}{db}(\sum u_i^2) = -2\sum X_i Y_i + 2\hat{b}\sum X_i^2 = 0$$

and therefore $\hat{b} = \dfrac{\sum X_i Y_i}{\sum X_i^2}$

This expression may be a little difficult to grasp because the notation is the reverse of what we have been using in previous chapters: $\hat{b}$ is a variable, but the X_i and Y_i are constants. The following numerical illustration shows that the concepts are familiar.

We observe that three firms have quantities sold (X_i) and revenues received (Y_i) as given in the first and third columns of Table 13.1:

Table 13.1

X_i	X_i^2	Y_i	Y_i^2	$X_i Y_i$
20	400	45	2 025	900
40	1 600	72	5 184	2 880
60	3 600	125	15 625	7 500
	5 600		22 834	10 280

The relation between $\hat{b}$ and the sum of the squares of the residuals is illustrated in Figure 13.6 and given by the following equation:

$$\sum u_i^2 = \sum Y_i^2 - 2\hat{b}\sum X_i Y_i + \hat{b}^2\sum X_i^2$$
$$= 22\ 834 - 2(10\ 280)\hat{b} + 5600\hat{b}^2$$
$$\frac{d}{db}(\sum u_i^2) = -2(10\ 280) + 2(5600)\hat{b} = 0$$
$$\hat{b} = \frac{\sum X_i Y_i}{\sum X_i^2} = \frac{10\ 280}{5600} = 1\cdot84$$

This $\hat{b}$ is only an estimate based on a sample of three firms. Suppose the complete description of all the firms in the industry corresponded to the scatter of points in Figure 13.7. Repeated sampling would lead to a set of estimated lines. For example, if the sample consisted of the boxed points, then the line would be $\hat{Y} = \hat{b}_1 X$; if the sample consisted of the circled points, then the line would be $\hat{Y} = \hat{b}_2 X$. Neither of these lines is the 'true' line. However, from a very large number of such estimated lines there would emerge an 'average' line which would be the 'true' line $\hat{Y} = bX$.

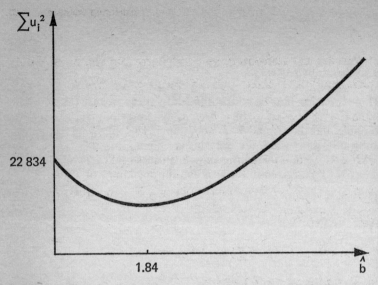

Figure 13.6 The minimum of the sum of the squares of the residuals

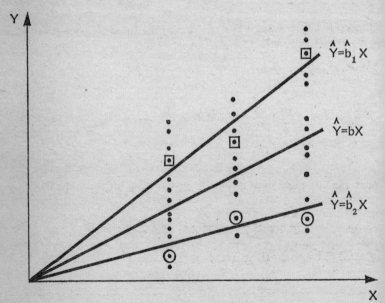

Figure 13.7 Estimated relationships and the 'true' line

Drill

1. Remove the summation sign and factor out the following expressions: $\sum_{i=1}^{3} bX_i$; $\sum_{i=1}^{2} (a - bX_i)$; $\sum_{i=1}^{3} (bX_i)^2$; $\sum_{i=1}^{2} (a - bX_i)^2$.

2. If $y = (a - bX)^2$, what is $\frac{\partial y}{\partial a}$? What is $\frac{\partial y}{\partial b}$?

3. If $S = \sum_{i=1}^{2} (a - bX_i)$, what is $\frac{\partial S}{\partial a}$? What is $\frac{\partial S}{\partial b}$?

4. If $u = (Y - a - bX)$, use the function of a function rule to find $\frac{\partial}{\partial a}(u^2)$ and $\frac{\partial}{\partial b}(u^2)$.

5. Show that $n\bar{X}\bar{Y} = \bar{X}\sum Y_i = \bar{Y}\sum X_i$.

6. Show that $n\bar{X}^2 = \bar{X}\sum X_i$.

Answers

1. $bX_1 + bX_2 + bX_3 = b(X_1 + X_2 + X_3)$.
   $a_1 bX_1 + a - bX_2 = 2a - b(X_1 + X_2)$.
   $bX_1^2 + bX_2^2 + bX_3^2 = b(X_1^2 + X_2^2 + X_3^2)$.
   $a^2 - 2abX_1 + b^2X_1^2 + a^2 - 2abX_2 + b^2X_2^2$
   $\qquad = 2a^2 - 2ab(X_1 + X_2) + b^2(X_1^2 + X_2^2)$.

2. $\frac{\partial y}{\partial a} = 2(a - bX)$, $\frac{\partial y}{\partial b} = -2X(a - bX)$.

3. $\frac{\partial S}{\partial a} = 2$, $\frac{\partial S}{\partial b} = -(X_1 + X_2)$.

4. $\frac{\partial}{\partial a}(u^2) = -2(Y - a - bX)$, $\frac{\partial}{\partial b}(u^2) = -2X(Y - a - bX)$.

5. $n\bar{X}\,\bar{Y} = n\left(\frac{\sum X_i}{n}\right)\left(\frac{\sum Y_i}{n}\right) = \bar{X}\sum Y_i = \bar{Y}\sum X_i$.

6. $n\left(\frac{\sum X_i}{n}\right)^2 = \frac{(\sum X_i)^2}{n} = \bar{X}\sum X_i$.

13.4 Linear regression

According to the dictionary, regression is the act of working back in thought from one thing to another. The technique of linear regression works back from a set of pairs of observations to a linear relation which may be, but is not necessarily, the main reason for the observations having the pattern which they do have. The first problem is to find the straight line which best fits the observations. We are looking for the values of a and b which make the line $Y = a + bX$ pass through the set of observations in the neatest way. (In the previous section the problem was simplified by assuming $a = 0$, as it would be when revenue Y is a function of quantity sold X.)

The second problem is to devise some measure which tells how well the line fits the data. The line may be the best fit possible, but how good is best?

The third problem is to find how reliable is the resulting estimated line when it is used for prediction or explanation. The pairs of observations (X_i, Y_i) are only a sample of the events that might have happened. Statistical theory provides various measures to find the likelihood that the sample really is a good indicator of what might have happened. These measures are based on assumptions about the world. One assumption is that the residuals, the u_i of the previous section, are normally distributed (unless there is reason to think otherwise, in which case there are various modifications which can be used). Statistical theory uses the mechanical methods of algebra and derivatives to estimate the parameters a and b of $Y = a + bX$. It then uses probability theory to provide a set of warnings about the dangers of placing too much reliance on these estimates. However, the main assumption is that the averages of all the Ys which could correspond to a given set of values of X really do lie on a straight line. As in the previous section we are calculating an estimated value for b, but in this section we are also calculating a value for a. We have used hats ' ' to denote when we are finding only an estimated value for a parameter. In this section the hats are omitted from a and b in order to simplify the notation, but remember that the resulting values for the parameters are only estimates. We shall concentrate mainly on the methods of estimation and the calculation of a measure of 'goodness of fit', with only an intuitive approach to the reliance of the resulting calculations.

Let $\hat{Y}_i$ be the value of Y corresponding to X_i as given by the estimated line, so $\hat{Y}_i = a + bX_i$. \hfill (1)

Let u_i be defined as the residual of the observation of Y from the estimated line, so $u_i = Y_i - \hat{Y}_i$,

giving $\qquad\qquad Y_i = \hat{Y}_i + u_i \qquad\qquad\qquad\qquad (2)$

and $\qquad\qquad Y_i = a + bX_i + u_i$ by substituting (1) into (2).

The objective is to find the values of a and b which minimise the sum of the squares of the residuals:

$$u_i = Y_i - a - bX_i$$
$$\sum u_i{}^2 = \sum(Y_i - a - bX_i)^2$$

where the sum is from $i = 1$ to $i = n$ if there are n pairs of observations.

To find the minimum, take the partial derivatives of this expression with respect to both a and b, and put these partials equal to zero:

$$\frac{\partial}{\partial a}(\sum u_i{}^2) = -2\sum(Y_i - a - bX_i) = 0 \qquad\qquad (3)$$

$$\frac{\partial}{\partial b}(\sum u_i{}^2) = -2\sum X_i(Y_i - a - bX_i) = 0 \qquad\qquad (4)$$

From (3) $\sum(Y_i - a - bX_i) = 0$

$$\sum Y_i - na - b\sum X_i = 0$$
$$\frac{\sum Y_i}{n} - a - b\frac{\sum X_i}{n} = 0$$
$$\bar{Y} - a - b\bar{X} = 0$$
$$a = \bar{Y} - b\bar{X} \qquad\qquad (5)$$

From (4) $\sum X_i(Y_i - a - bX_i) = 0$

$$\sum X_iY_i - a\sum X_i - b\sum X_i{}^2 = 0$$

From (5) $\sum X_iY_i - (\bar{Y} - b\bar{X})\sum X_i - b\sum X_i{}^2 = 0$

$$\sum X_iY_i - \bar{Y}\sum X_i + b\bar{X}\sum X_i - b\sum X_i{}^2 = 0$$
$$b(\bar{X}\sum X_i - \sum X_i{}^2) = \bar{Y}\sum X_i - \sum X_iY_i$$
$$b = \frac{\bar{Y}\sum X_i - \sum X_iY_i}{\bar{X}\sum X_i - \sum X_i{}^2} \qquad\qquad (6)$$

Equations (5) and (6) express a and b in terms of the observations. Note that (5) can be written $\bar{Y} = a + b\bar{X}$, so the regression line will always pass through the point $(\bar{X}, \bar{Y})$.

If equations (5) and (6) are used to calculate the estimated values of a and b, the means $\bar{X}$ and $\bar{Y}$ have to be calculated first. For very large quantities of data this can be inconvenient. Equations (7) and (8) below are often easier ones with which to work. These two equations are known as the 'normal equations' because they are used most often (not because they have something to do with the normal distribution). They are found in an earlier stage of the above calculations:

$$\sum Y_i = na + b\sum X_i \qquad (7)$$
$$\sum X_i Y_i = a\sum X_i + b\sum X_i^2 \qquad (8)$$

The most methodical way of setting out the data is by tabulating it in columns headed in the following order: X_i, X_i^2, Y_i, $X_i Y_i$. Once the sums of the columns have been found, a and b can be found by solving simultaneously the normal equations.

There are algebraic patterns which repeat themselves within these and other formulae. Some of these are worth knowing because they often appear in text-books as alternative methods of calculating the regression coefficient b. For example, we can show that:

$$b = \frac{\text{cov}(X, Y)}{\text{var}(X)} \qquad (9)$$

This is because:

$$\frac{\text{cov}(X, Y)}{\text{var}(X)} = \frac{\sum(X_i - \bar{X})(Y_i - \bar{Y})}{\sum(X_i - \bar{X})^2}$$

$$= \frac{\sum(X_i Y_i - X_i \bar{Y} - \bar{X} Y_i + \bar{X}\bar{Y})}{\sum(X_i^2 - 2\bar{X} X_i + \bar{X}^2)}$$

$$= \frac{\sum X_i Y_i - \bar{Y}\sum X_i - \bar{X}\sum Y_i \geqslant n\bar{X}\bar{Y}}{\sum X_i^2 - 2\bar{X}\sum X_i + n\bar{X}^2}$$

$$= \frac{\sum X_i Y_i - \bar{Y}\sum X_i - \bar{X}\sum Y_i + \bar{X}\sum Y_i}{\sum X_i^2 - 2\bar{X}\sum X_i + \bar{X}\sum X_i}$$

$$= \frac{\sum X_i Y_i - \bar{Y}\sum X_i}{\sum X_i^2 - \bar{X}\sum X_i}$$

$$= b \quad \text{from equation (6)}$$

By working with covariances, variances, and standard deviations, we can find the relationship between b and r:

Since $b = \dfrac{\text{cov }(X, Y)}{\text{var }(X)} = \dfrac{\text{cov }(X, Y)}{\text{SD }(X) \cdot \text{SD }(X)}$,

and since $r = \dfrac{\text{cov }(X, Y)}{\text{SD }(X) \cdot \text{SD }(Y)}$

we have $b = r\,\dfrac{\text{SD }(Y)}{\text{SD }(X)}$ (10)

The regression coefficient b gives the reaction of $\hat{Y}$ to changes in X, that is $\dfrac{d\hat{Y}}{dX} = b$. For a given value of var (X), the value of b is

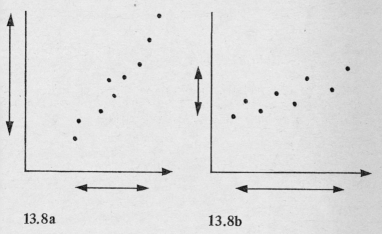

13.8a   13.8b

Figure 13.8 If r is the same, the slope varies with the ratio of the two standard deviations; (*a*) A large value for b; (*b*) A small value for b

greater the larger is the value of cov (X, Y), and cov (X, Y) also decides whether the sign of b is positive or negative. This follows from equation (9).

From equation (10) it follows that when r is constant, the value of b is greater the larger is the value of SD (Y), but is smaller the larger is the value of SD (X). Intuitively this is reasonable, as Figure 13.8 illustrates. If r is constant, the slope of the line is greatest if the observations have a small 'spread' in a horizontal direction but a large 'spread' in a vertical direction as shown in Figure 13.8(*a*).

13.5 The coefficient of determination

If we hypothesise that an appreciable part of the changes in Y can be explained by changes in X, some measure must be found to show what proportion is so explained, so that we can decide whether or not to reject the hypothesis. First we decide on some base from which

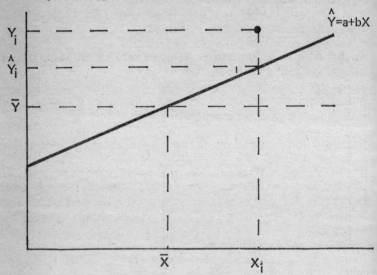

Figure 13.9 Observed Y_i, estimated $\hat{Y}_i$, and the mean $\bar{Y}$

to measure the changes in Y, and the most convenient is the mean $\bar{Y}$. Each observation varies from $\bar{Y}$ by the amount $(Y_i - \bar{Y})$ for the observation corresponding to X_i. An indicator of the total variation in the observations is the sum of the squares of the individual variations $\sum(Y_i - \bar{Y})^2$. Figure 13.9 illustrates. A justification for choosing the sum-of-the-squares of the deviations-from-the-mean will be given later in the section.

The equation $\hat{Y} = a + bX$ will predict a value $\hat{Y}_i$ corresponding to X_i, so that each prediction varies from $\bar{Y}$ by the amount $(\hat{Y}_i - \bar{Y})$ and an indicator of the total predicted variation is $\sum(\hat{Y}_i - \bar{Y})^2$. We can now form a measure of the proportion of change explained by the regression equation:

$$\frac{\text{'explained' variation}}{\text{total variation}} = \frac{\sum(\hat{Y}_i - \bar{Y})^2}{\sum(Y_i - \bar{Y})^2} = R^2$$

This expression is usually referred to as R^2, although its full title is the **coefficient of determination**. The quotation marks on 'explained' are there because the regression equation need not explain anything. For example, if Y_i is the observed proportion of Londoners wearing overcoats on a particular day, and X_i is the temperature in Montreal on that day, the R^2 could be high even though Londoners do not wear overcoats because it is cold in Canada; it just happens that both cities are in the northern hemisphere.

The unexplained variation on one observation is $Y_i - \hat{Y}_i$, which we defined as u_i, so the corresponding indicator of total unexplained variation is $\sum u_i^2$. Finding that a and that b which minimise the total unexplained variation $\sum u_i^2$ can be looked at as an attempt to minimise uncertainty.

An analogy which may be helpful follows from writing:

total variation = 'explained' variation + unexplained variation.

The left-hand side of the equation can be considered to be a message as received by the observer from the observations. The right-hand side can be looked at as the information which the message is trying to convey, the 'explanation', plus some 'noise' which is hiding the message.

For any particular observation Y_i, the total deviation from the mean is $Y_i - \bar{Y}$. Of this total deviation, $\hat{Y}_i - \bar{Y}$ is what would be predicted from the observation X_i, since $\hat{Y}_i = a + bX_i$. This leaves $Y_i - \hat{Y}_i$ still unexplained. We have the obvious statement:

$$(Y_i - \bar{Y}) = (Y_i - \hat{Y}_i) \qquad\qquad + (\hat{Y}_i - \bar{Y})$$

total deviation = unexplained deviation + 'explained' deviation

Algebraic manipulation of this identity will show the justification for the definition of R^2.

Square both sides to obtain:

$$(Y_i - \bar{Y})^2 = (Y_i - \hat{Y}_i)^2 + 2(Y_i - \hat{Y}_i)(\hat{Y}_i - \bar{Y}) + (\hat{Y}_i - \bar{Y})^2$$

Now sum this from $i = 1$ to $i = n$:

$$\sum(Y_i - \bar{Y})^2 = \sum(Y_i - \hat{Y}_i)^2 + 2\sum(Y_i - \hat{Y}_i)(\hat{Y}_i - \bar{Y}) + \sum(\hat{Y}_i - \bar{Y})^2$$

The second term on the right-hand side disappears because:

$$\hat{Y}_i = a + bX_i \quad \text{by definition}$$
$$a = \bar{Y} - b\bar{X} \quad \text{from equation (5)}$$

so
$$\hat{Y}_i = \bar{Y} - b\bar{X} + bX_i = \bar{Y} + b(X_i - \bar{X})$$

giving
$$Y_i - \hat{Y}_i = (Y_i - \bar{Y}) - b(X_i - \bar{X})$$

and
$$\hat{Y}_i - \bar{Y} = b(X_i - \bar{X})$$

so
$$(Y_i - \hat{Y}_i)(\hat{Y}_i - \bar{Y}) = b(X_i - \bar{X})(Y_i - \bar{Y}) - b^2(X_i - \bar{X})^2$$
$$\sum(Y_i - \hat{Y}_i)(\hat{Y}_i - \bar{Y}) = b\sum(X_i - \bar{X})(Y_i - \bar{Y}) - b^2\sum(X_i - \bar{X})^2$$

However, $b = \dfrac{\sum(X_i - \bar{X})(Y_i - \bar{Y})}{\sum(X_i - \bar{X})^2}$ from equation (9)

so
$$\sum(X_i - \bar{X})(Y_i - \bar{Y}) = b\sum(X_i - \bar{X})^2$$
and
$$\sum(Y_i - \hat{Y}_i)(\hat{Y}_i - \bar{Y}) = b^2\sum(X_i - \bar{X})^2 - b^2\sum(X_i - \bar{X})^2 = 0$$

Therefore
$$\sum(Y_i - \bar{Y})^2 = \sum(Y_i - \hat{Y}_i)^2 + \sum(\hat{Y}_i - \bar{Y})^2$$
or
$$\sum(Y_i - \bar{Y})^2 = \sum u_i^2 + \sum(\hat{Y}_i - \bar{Y})^2$$

A little algebra will show that the mean of the $\hat{Y}_i$ is the same as the mean of the Y_i so both can be written $\bar{Y}$. Also the mean of the u_i is zero because of the 'least squares' method of estimation, so $\bar{u} = 0$. The algebra can be rewritten as:

$$\frac{1}{n}\sum(Y_i - \bar{Y})^2 = \frac{1}{n}\sum(u_i - \bar{u})^2 + \frac{1}{n}\sum(\hat{Y}_i - \bar{Y})^2$$

which is var (Y) = var (u) + var $(\hat{Y})$

so total variance = unexplained variance + 'explained' variance

Var (u) can now be looked at as an indicator of the amount of 'noise' which is disguising the explanation. A discussion of the use of var (u) can be found in the books recommended for further reading at the end of this chapter.

The abbreviation for the coefficient of determination is R^2, but that for the correlation coefficient is r. Comparing the definitions we have:

$$R^2 = \frac{\sum(\hat{Y}_i - \bar{Y})^2}{\sum(Y_i - \bar{Y})^2} \quad \text{and} \quad r = \frac{\sum(X_i - \bar{X})(Y_i - \bar{Y})}{\sqrt{\sum(X_i - \bar{X})^2\sum(Y_i - \bar{Y})^2}}$$

By substituting $a + bX_i$ for $\hat{Y}_i$, and then using equations (5) and (6) to eliminate a and b, long and tedious manipulation would reveal that r squared equals R^2. However, the use of the two measures is sufficiently different to justify the use of different cases of letter to emphasise this. R^2 measures the goodness of fit, on the assumption that the Y_i may vary about the average of all the observations which could arise in correspondence with a given X_t. The correlation coefficient r measures whether there is a linear relation between X and Y on the assumption that both the X_i and the Y_i observations may be varying in a random way.

Since R^2 measures the proportion of the total variation in Y which is 'explained' by the regression equation, R^2 will be a number between zero and unity. If the line fits the observations perfectly, then $R^2 = 1$. If R^2 is less than 0·5, there is little strength in the explanation, although if we were merely checking to see if X has some sort of effect on Y then $R^2 = 0·5$ could be looked upon as a hint. If we were looking for a strong relation, then an R^2 greater than 0·9 would be encouraging. But the reliance we place on R^2 depends on the number of observations. Obviously if we have only two pairs of observations, R^2 will always be unity and so the measure is trivial. On the other hand, if there are thirty or more observations then a high R^2 would be significant.

13.5 Using the regression equation

This section contains several warnings against putting too much reliance on the regression equation. However, it is as well to remember how very informative approximations are. Regression equations are misleading only when they are treated as if they are precise functional relations.

There are two ways in which regression equations can be used; testing hypotheses and making predictions. Suppose that we are testing the hypothesis that the revenue of firms selling in a particular market comes mainly from the quantity sold and not from such factors as quality premiums, short transport hauls and so on. In this case we want most of the 'explaining' of revenue Y to be due to X, that is, we want a high R^2. Figure 13.10 shows two cases where Y is explained well by X, but the curvilinear relation will not give a high R^2. A high R^2 confirms the hypothesis only if the market is competitive enough to give an approximately linear relation between revenue and quantity sold.

Now hypothesise that the market is competitive so the firms are price-takers. Figure 13.11 shows two scatter diagrams, both of which support the hypothesis. There is a marked linear trend in both, but Figure 13.11(a) will show a much higher R^2. From Figure 13.11(b) it looks as though there are many other factors influencing revenue apart from quantity sold, so the R^2 will be low although the hypothesis is not refuted. Thus R^2 is sometimes a useful indicator but sometimes it is not.

When using a regression equation to predict a value of Y from a

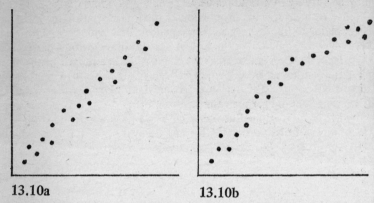

13.10a   **13.10b**

Figure 13.10 (*a*) A good linear fit so a high R^2; (*b*) A good curvilinear fit but a low R^2

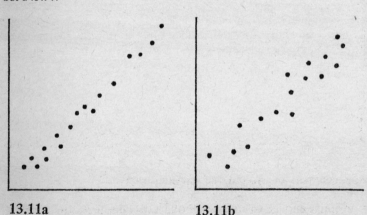

13.11a   **13.11b**

Figure 13.11 A competitive market; (*a*) Where price 'explains' revenue well; (*b*) Where other factors disturb the influence of price on revenue

value of X, there are three matters to be taken into account. The first is the value of R^2. The higher this is the more likely is the prediction to be correct because it means that factors other than X have a small influence on Y. The second matter is the size of the sample. The third matter which is important when using a regression equation for prediction is the range of the observed values of X from which the equation was calculated. In Figure 13.12 the lowest and highest observed values of X are labelled X_1 and X_n respectively.

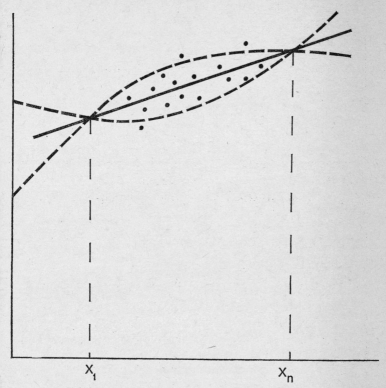

Figure 13.12 Interpolation and extrapolation

When predicting the value of Y which would result from a particular value of X, the prediction is more likely to be accurate if the X occurs within the range X_1 to X_n. Outside this range the regression equation may be inaccurate because the underlying relationship may be one which is approximately linear for small ranges but markedly curved for larger ranges.

If a value of Y_i is predicted by using a value of X_i where $X_1 < X_i < X_n$, this is known as **interpolation**. If Y_i is to be predicted from a value of X_i which is less than X_1 or greater than X_n, this is known as **extrapolation**. Predictions by interpolation are more reliable than predictions by extrapolation.

13.7 Other relations

Many relations which are not linear can be converted to linear relations by taking logarithms of one or other or both of the observed variables. If a particular type of relationship is suspected, it can be handled after conversion in the ways described in this chapter.

If an exponential relation is suspected, such as $V = ae^{bX}$, take natural logarithms to obtain $\ln V = \ln a + bX$. Then put $\ln V = Y$ to obtain $Y = \text{constant} + bX$. Thus Y is regressed on X, but in this case Y is $\ln V$.

Similarly, for two variables U and V, where it is suspected that $V = aU^b$. Take common logarithms to obtain $\log V = \log a + b \log U$. Put $\log V = Y$ and $\log U = X$, giving $Y = \text{constant} + bX$.

For relations involving more than two variables, or for relations between two variables which involve turning points (such as quadratics and cubics), the technique known as multiple regression must be used to obtain the parameters of equations such as:

$$Z = a + bX + cY \quad \text{and} \quad Z = a + bX + cX^2.$$

Multiple regression is easier to do after a study of elementary matrix algebra, but many of the basic principles are the same as those given in this chapter.

Drill and summary of formulae

Regression analysis involving two variables is best performed on data involving thirty or more pairs of observations. If there are fewer than thirty, the advice of a statistician (or study of an intermediate text-book) is usually necessary to interpret the results. The example that follows is given so that the operations involved in making the calculations can be understood without too much effort:

X_i	Y_i
1	20
2	23
3	23
4	24
5	30

The following twenty-one questions cover all the formulae given in this chapter. Calculate the numerical values using the five pairs of observations above. The reader should reassure himself that when there are two different formulae for the same statistic, the numerical results are the same.

1. Find the arithmetic mean of X: $\bar{X} = \frac{1}{n}\sum X_i$.

2. Find the variance of X: $\text{var}(X) = \frac{1}{n}\sum(X_i - \bar{X})^2$.

3. Find the standard deviation of X: $\text{SD}(X) = \sqrt{\text{var}(X)}$.

4. Find $\bar{Y}$, var (Y) and SD (Y).

5. Check that $\sum(X_i - \bar{X}) = 0$ and that $\sum(Y_i - \bar{Y}) = 0$.

6. Find the covariance of X and Y: $\text{cov}(X, Y) = \frac{1}{n}\sum(X_i - \bar{X})(Y_i - \bar{Y})$.

7. Find the regression coefficient when Y is regressed on X:

$$b = \frac{\text{cov}(X, Y)}{\text{var}(X)}$$

Check that this formula gives the same result as:

$$b = \frac{\bar{Y}\sum X_i - \sum X_i Y_i}{\bar{X}\sum X_i - \sum X_i^2}$$

8. Find the constant term in the regression equation: $a = \bar{Y} - b\bar{X}$. Check these results by using the 'normal equations' to find a and b:

$$\sum Y_i = na + b\sum X_i$$
$$\sum X_i Y_i = a\sum X_i + b\sum X_i^2$$

9. Write the regression equation and give the predicted values of Y for each observation of X: $\hat{Y}_i = a + bX_i$.

10. Find the values of the residuals: $u_i = Y_i - \hat{Y}_i$.

11. Check that the mean of $\hat{Y}$ equals the mean of Y.

Mathematics for Modern Economics

12. Check that the mean of u is zero.

13. Find the variance of u: $\operatorname{var}(u) = \frac{1}{n}\sum u_i^2 = \frac{1}{n}\sum(Y_i - \hat{Y}_i)^2$.

14. Find the correlation coefficient: $r = \dfrac{\operatorname{cov}(X, Y)}{\operatorname{SD}(X) . \operatorname{SD}(Y)}$.

15. Find the coefficient of determination: $R^2 = \dfrac{\sum(\hat{Y}_i - \bar{Y})^2}{\sum(Y_i - \bar{Y})^2}$.

16. Check that r^2 from (14) equals R^2 from (15).

17. Find the variance of $\hat{Y}$: $\operatorname{var}(\hat{Y}) = \frac{1}{n}\sum(\hat{Y}_i - \bar{Y})^2$.

18. Check that $\operatorname{var}(Y) = \operatorname{var}(\hat{Y}) + \operatorname{var}(u)$.

19. Check that $\operatorname{var}(\hat{Y}) = R^2 \operatorname{var}(Y)$.

20. What percentage of the change in Y is 'explained' by changes in X?

21. Can much reliance be placed on predictions from this regression equation?

Answers

X_i	$X_i - \bar{X}$	$(X_i - \bar{X})^2$	Y_i	$Y_i - \bar{Y}$	$(Y_i - \bar{Y})^2$	$(X_i - \bar{X})(Y_i - \bar{Y})$
1	-2	4	20	-4	16	8
2	-1	1	23	-1	1	1
3	0	0	23	-1	1	0
4	1	1	24	0	0	0
5	2	4	30	6	36	12
15	0	10	120	0	54	21

1. 3.
2. 2.
3. $\sqrt{2}$.
4. $\bar{Y} = 24$, $\operatorname{var}(Y) = 10{\cdot}8$, $\operatorname{SD}(Y) = \sqrt{10{\cdot}8}$.
6. $\operatorname{cov}(X, Y) = 4{\cdot}2$.

7. $b = 2 \cdot 1$.
8. $a = 17 \cdot 7$.
9. $\hat{Y} = 17 \cdot 7 + 2 \cdot 1X$; $\hat{Y}_1 = 19 \cdot 8$, $\hat{Y}_2 = 21 \cdot 9$, $\hat{Y}_3 = 24$, $\hat{Y}_4 = 26 \cdot 1$, $\hat{Y}_5 = 28 \cdot 2$.
10. $u_1 = 0 \cdot 2$, $u_2 = 1 \cdot 1$, $u_3 = -1 \cdot 0$, $u_4 = -2 \cdot 1$, $u_5 = 1 \cdot 8$.
13. var $(u) = 1 \cdot 98$.
14. $r = 0 \cdot 90$.
15. $R^2 = 0 \cdot 81$.
17. var $(\hat{Y}) = 8 \cdot 82$.
20. 81 per cent.
21. No, there are too few observations.

READING

Gregory, A. H., Hartley, J. R., and Lewis, D. G., *Basic Statistics*, Chapters 8 and 9.

FURTHER READING

Kane, Edward J., *Economic Statistics and Econometrics*, New York, Harper and Row, 1968.

Yamane, Taro, *Statistics*, New York, Harper and Row, second edition, 1967.

Further Reading

The titles which follow under the headings *Analysis* and *Statistics* are based on a personal view. Few economists would select exactly the same list of eight books for the student who has just finished an introductory course, but most would agree that these titles are worth reading. The titles under each heading are given in order of difficulty. (For introductory texts see the other titles in the Fontana series).

ANALYSIS

Baumol, William J., *Economic Theory and Operations Analysis*, second edition, Prentice-Hall, 1965.
This popular university text-book gives a clear introduction to most of that part of economics which is useful for solving optimisation problems. Chapters 5 and 6 on Linear Programming are particularly important. Chapters 13 to 16 provide a concise account of traditional microeconomics and should add to the appreciation of Walsh's text.

Walsh, Vivian Charles, *Introduction to Contemporary Micro-economics*, New York, McGraw-Hill, 1970.
This hilarious book uses the logic of sets to suggest how to break out of the strait-jacket in which present welfare economics is placed by its assumptions. Although the examples are drawn from over-developed economies, the approach is also applicable to the less developed.

Chiang, Alpha C., *Fundamental Methods in Mathematical Economics*, New York, McGraw-Hill, 1967.
This presents most of the mathematical techniques needed by an economist. The approach is easy to understand with plenty of economic illustrations. Dynamics and matrix methods are included.

Allen, R. G. D., *Macro-Economic Theory*, London, Macmillan, 1967.
Although this is an advanced text, Chapters 1 to 5 are not difficult

and are worth reading alongside Chiang. Most macroeconomic texts are seriously misleading in the conclusions they draw about the aggregate effects of many individual decisions. Even in this one, Chapters 6 to 9, on 'Keynes and the Classics' should be approached cautiously and preferably with the help of a guide who is familiar with the important developments in this field since 1967. Chapters 10 to 20 will be found easier if Chiang is mastered first.

STATISTICS

Huff, Darrell, *How to Take a Chance*, Pelican, 1965.
This book is amusing and brief, but very enlightening.

Kane, Edward J., *Economic Statistics and Econometrics—An Introduction to Quantitative Economics*, New York, Harper and Row, 1968.
This is a very good introduction to the statistical techniques necessary for the economist. It covers more than most introductory texts but explains the methods and assumptions with unusual clarity.

Streisser, Erich W., *Pitfalls of Econometric Forecasting*, Research Monograph 23, London, Institute of Economic Affairs, 1970.
An econometrician provides warnings against bad econometrics. This should be read after Chiang and Kane.

GENERAL

The following is a list of titles which the present author found helpful when writing this book and which may be of interest to teachers.

Abbott, P., *Teach Yourself Algebra*, London, English Universities Press, 1942.

Allen, R. G. D., *Mathematical Analysis for Economists*, London, Macmillan, 1938.

Allen, R. G. D., *Basic Mathematics*, London, Macmillan, 1962.

Laurie Carr, J., *Investment Economics*, London, Routledge and Kegan Paul, 1969.

Fletcher, T. J., *Some Lessons in Mathematics*, Cambridge, 1964.

Glicksman, Abraham M., *Linear Programming and the Theory of Games*, New York, John Wiley and Son, 1963.

Green, J. A., *Sets and Groups*, London, Routledge and Kegan Paul, 1965.

Gregory, A. H., Hartley, J. R., and Lewis, D. G., *Basic Statistics*, London, Methuen, 1969.

Henry, S. G. B., *Elementary Mathematical Economics*, London, Routledge and Kegan Paul, 1969.

Hilton, P. J., *Differential Calculus*, London, Routledge and Kegan Paul, 1958.

Huang, David S., *Introduction to the Use of Mathematics in Economic Analysis*, New York, John Wiley and Sons, 1964.

Kalton, G., *Introduction to Statistical Ideas*, London, Chapman and Hall, 1966.

Land, Frank, *The Language of Mathematics*, London, John Murray, 1960.

Land, F. W. (editor), *New Approaches to Mathematics Teaching*, London, Macmillan, 1963.

Evans Munroe, M., *The Language of Mathematics*, Ann Arbor, University of Michigan, 1963.

Rosenthal, Evelyn B., *Understanding the New Mathematics*, London, Souvenir Press, 1965.

Sawyer, W. W., *Mathematician's Delight*, Penguin, 1943.

Yamane, Taro, *Statistics*, second edition, New York, Harper and Row, 1967.

Answers to Exercises

Exercise 1

1. i. calories; ii. calories and £s; iii. tons.
2. $a \in S - D$; $b \in S - D$; $c \in D - S$; $d \in S \cap D$.
3. Opinions will differ on what is relevant, but here is one classification scheme:

    i. $X = \{b, d, f, g, h\}$; $Y = \{a, c, d, e\}$; $X \cap Y = \{d\}$; $X \cup Y = \{a, b, c, d, e, f, g, h\}$; $X - Y = \{b, f, g, h\}$; $Y - X = \{a, c, e\}$.

    ii. 5; 4; 1; 8; 4; 3.

    iii. 1.

Exercise 2

1. i. Yes.

    ii. $x = 500 - \frac{1}{5}p$.

    iii. No because when $p = 0$, $x = 500$ only.

    iv. Perhaps £1850 to £2150.

    v. $p = 2500 - 5x$.

    vi. $R = p \cdot x = 2500x - 5x^2$.

    vii. Revenue per annum $= 12(2500x - 5x^2)$.

2. A: O, C: 2·5 per cent, E: 20 per cent, G: 50 per cent.
3. A: O, C: O, E: 20 per cent, G: 80 per cent.

Exercise 3

2. 1000.
3. $U = aN^{-b}$, where $a = 10\,000$ and $b = 0.3979$.
For the 100th heap, $U = £1601$.

4. $a = \{(t, s) : s = t\}$

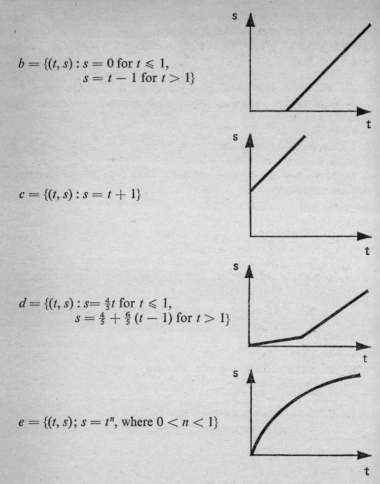

$b = \{(t, s) : s = 0$ for $t \leqslant 1,$
$\quad\quad\quad s = t - 1$ for $t > 1\}$

$c = \{(t, s) : s = t + 1\}$

$d = \{(t, s) : s = \frac{4}{5}t$ for $t \leqslant 1,$
$\quad\quad\quad s = \frac{4}{5} + \frac{6}{5}(t - 1)$ for $t > 1\}$

$e = \{(t, s) ; s = t^n,$ where $0 < n < 1\}$

Exercise 4

1. i. a : positive, b : negative, c : negative, d : positive.
2. The set M is empty, $M = \emptyset$, because the lowest price at which suppliers are prepared to supply is higher than the highest price at which consumers will demand. There are many goods which technically could be produced but could not be sold at a price which would cover costs.

3. i. £18 per week, 4 million men.

ii. £16·29 per week, 3·43 million men.

iii. $2 \times 3·43 - 7 \times 0·57 = £2·87$ million per week.

4. i. Definition.

ii. Causal.

iii. Definition. These are two ways of saying the same thing.

iv. Equilibrium condition.

v. Definition.

vi. Causal.

5. i. Function.

ii. Multiplication.

iii. Multiplication.

iv. Ordered pair.

v. An aside.

vi. Function.

vii. Multiplication.

6. i. Addition.

ii. Multiplication.

iii. Intersection of two sets.

iv. Times ten plus seven.

v. Multiplication.

Exercise 5

1. i. $R = 100 x - \frac{1}{5}x^2$.

ii. $R(11) - R(10) = 95·8$, $R(10) - R(9) = 96·2$.

iii. $\frac{dR}{dx} = 100 - \frac{2}{5}x$.

iv. $100 - \frac{2}{5}(10) = 96$.

3. i. Yes, because there are no fixed costs.

ii. $\frac{C}{x} = ax^2 - bx + c$.

iii. $\frac{d}{dx}\left(\frac{C}{x}\right) = 2ax - b = 0$, when $x = \frac{b}{2a}$.

iv. $\frac{dC}{dx} = 3ax^2 - 2bx + c$.

v. $x = 0$ and $x = \frac{b}{2a}$.

4. i. $p = 20$, $x = 10$.

ii. $R = 40x - 2x^2$, $\frac{R}{x} = p = 40 - 2x$.

   iii. $x = 6$, $p = 28$.
   iv. $x = 6{\cdot}83$, $p = 26{\cdot}34$.
5. i. 500 tons; £5500.

   ii. 833·3 tons; an infinite amount; perhaps the linear total cost function is a useful approximation for a very short range of x, but a farmer usually has steeply rising marginal costs.

Exercise 6

1. Since $\dfrac{dR}{dx} = p\left(1 + \dfrac{1}{e_d}\right)$, $\dfrac{dR}{dx} < 0$, when $e_d = -0{\cdot}9$, so the monopolist could earn more by selling less.
2. i. £10, £7, £0·10, £0·01.

   ii. $\dfrac{dR}{dx} = \dfrac{490}{(x + 7)^2}.$

   iii. $e_d = -\left(\dfrac{x + 7}{x}\right).$

3. i. 553 million; infinite.

   ii. £2.

4. i. zero.

   ii. -11.

   iii. Infinitely elastic: the horizontal demand curve of a price-taker.

Exercise 7

1. Exports: $10 + 20 + \cdots + 120$
            $= 10(1 + 2 + \cdots + 12) = 10 \cdot \tfrac{12}{2}(12 + 1) = 780.$
Trade Gap = £390 million.
2. i. Since $2Y = Y(1 + r)^{15}$, $r = 0{\cdot}047 = 4{\cdot}7$ per cent.

   ii. Yes, $(1{\cdot}076)^{10} = 2{\cdot}08$.

4. If $100(\tfrac{2}{3})^t = 1$, then $t = 11{\cdot}36$, so he must leave on the eleventh day.

Exercise 8

2. x; $\dfrac{1}{\ln x}$; $\dfrac{1}{\ln x}$; x.

3. $\dfrac{dC}{dx} = b - hx + kx^2.$

4. Write F for fixed costs, so $C = F + 7x - 2x^2 + 3x^3$.

5. i. $\dfrac{dy}{dt} = kNe^{-kt}$

   ii. $e^{-kt} = \dfrac{N-y}{N}$.

   iii. $\dfrac{dy}{dt} = k(N-y)$.

   iv. $\dfrac{dy}{dt} = k(N-y)$.

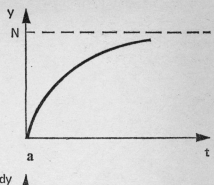

a

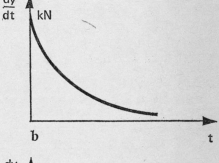

b

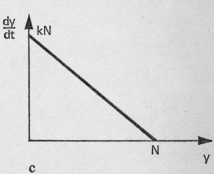

c

Exercise 9

1. i. Yes.
  ii. Yes.
  iii. No.

2. i. 11·1 per cent.
  ii. minus 27·3 per cent.

3. i. 300.

   ii. 327.

   iii. $\dfrac{\partial Q}{\partial L} = \dfrac{9}{4} L^{-\frac{1}{4}} K^{\frac{1}{4}}$.

   iv. $\dfrac{\partial^2 Q}{\partial L^2} = -\dfrac{9}{16} L^{-\frac{5}{4}} K^{\frac{1}{4}} < 0$.

   v. $\dfrac{\partial}{\partial K} \left(\dfrac{\partial Q}{\partial L} \right) = \dfrac{9}{16} L^{-\frac{1}{4}} K^{-\frac{3}{4}} > 0$.

   vi. 11·2 per cent.

Index to Mathematical Terms

References given in heavy type refer to definitions of key terms and concepts

Index to Economic Applications

Fontana Books

Fontana is at present best known (outside the field of popular fiction) for its extensive lists of books on history, philosophy, and theology.

Now, however, the list is expanding rapidly to include most main subjects. New series, sometimes extensive series, of books are being specially commissioned in most main subjects—in literature, politics, economics, education, geography, sociology, psychology, and others. At the same time, the number of paperback reprints of books already published in hardcover editions is being increased.

Further information on Fontana's present list and future plans can be obtained from:

The Non-Fiction Editor,
Fontana Books,
14 St. James's Place,
London, S.W.1.

Fontana Modern Masters

General Editor: Frank Kermode

This series provides authoritative and critical introductions to the most influential and seminal minds of our time. Books already published include:

Camus   Conor Cruise O'Brien
Chomsky   John Lyons
Fanon   David Caute
Freud   Richard Wollheim
Guevara   Andrew Sinclair
Joyce   John Gross
Lévi-Strauss   Edmund Leach
Lukács   George Lichtheim
Marcuse   Alasdair MacIntyre
McLuhan   Jonathan Miller
Orwell   Raymond Williams
Reich   Charles Rycroft
Wittgenstein   David Pears
Yeats   Denis Donoghue

'We have here, in fact, the beginnings of what promises to be an important publishing enterprise. This series is just what is needed by the so-called "general reader" in search of a guide to intellectual currents that clash so confusingly in a confused world.'

The Times Literary Supplement

Many more are in preparation including:

Fuller   Allan Temko
Eliot   Stephen Spender
Gandhi   George Woodcock
Lawrence   Frank Kermode
Lenin   Robert Conquest
Mailer   Richard Poirier
Russell   A. J. Ayer
Sherrington   Jonathan Miller
Trotsky   Philip Rahv
Weber   Donald MacRae

Fontana Social Science

Fontana's first unique social science series is the Fontana Introduction to Modern Economics. Other introductory series, on sociology and geography, are in preparation. Other books available include:

The Sociology of Modern Britain
Edited by Eric Butterworth and David Weir

People and Cities   Stephen Verney

The Acquisitive Society   R. H. Tawney

Memories, Dreams, Reflections   C. J. Jung

African Genesis   Robert Ardrey

The Territorial Imperative   Robert Ardrey

Lectures on Economic Principles   Sir Dennis Robertson

Strike at Pilkingtons   Tony Lane and Kenneth Roberts